FREE RADICALS

in Inorganic Chemistry

Papers presented at the

Symposium on Inorganic Free Radicals and

Free Radicals in Inorganic Chemistry

Division of Inorganic Chemistry

142nd Meeting of the American Chemical Society

Atlantic City, N. J., September 10–12, 1962

CHARLES B. COLBURN, *Symposium Chairman*

Number 36

ADVANCES IN CHEMISTRY SERIES

American Chemical Society

Washington, D. C.

1962

Library of Congress Catalog Card 62-19579

PRINTED IN THE UNITED STATES OF AMERICA

ADVANCES IN CHEMISTRY SERIES

Robert F. Gould, Editor

AMERICAN CHEMICAL SOCIETY APPLIED PUBLICATIONS

CONTENTS

INTRODUCTION

Until recently most of us considered the term "free radical" as applicable to two different types of molecules. One group consisted of the large, thermodynamically stable organic species which owe their existence to resonance stabilization. The other group consisted of molecules which existed as transitory fragments of molecules produced under energy-rich conditions.

In inorganic chemistry, free radicals were mostly of the second type—radicals such as NH, NH_2, OH, and various atoms which are both thermodynamically unstable and so reactive that the interest in them was esoteric rather than chemical. Opposed to these were a very few radicals (NO, NO_2, O_2) whose apparent stability and relative unreactivity sometimes made it difficult for one to remember that they did actually possess unpaired electrons.

Recently a number of inorganic free radicals have been discovered whose reactivity and stability place them in an intermediate area where interest in them is basically chemical but whose reactivity and stability make it easy to visualize them as free radicals. Three such free radicals come immediately to mind: NF_2, SF_5, and SO_3F. There are, of course, numerous other examples.

The time thus appears ripe for a general discussion of inorganic free radicals, their preparation, their detection, their properties, and their reactions—hence this symposium, "Inorganic Free Radicals and Free Radicals in Inorganic Chemistry."

As Professor Rice points out in his opening survey paper, many of "the more spectacular recent advances in our understanding of free radicals have come through the use of the tools and techniques taken from the domain of the physicist." In keeping with the facts, approximately one half of our symposium papers are by physicists and/or physical chemists. At least six of the papers (Robinson, Cochran, MacKenzie, Symons, Weil, and Johnson) discuss the use of electron-spin resonance in the study of inorganic free radicals. Of course spectroscopic studies were used very early in the study of free radicals, and Basco's paper in this collection summarizes some of the most recent work in the field of the spectroscopy of inorganic free radicals. Lossing has done extensive work on the use of the mass spectrometer in the investigation of organic free radicals. Inorganic free radicals, to date, have not lent themselves as willingly to mass spectrometric investigation; however, Foner and Hudson's contribution to our collection shows that beautiful work can be done with inorganic free radicals using mass spectrometric techniques.

One of the more recent, extremely interesting, and less well known physical means of investigation of inorganic free radicals is the use of the magnetron to determine the electron affinity of atoms and free radicals. Page, who has been responsible for much of this work, illustrates its use with inorganic radicals. The remaining papers in our symposium (Rice, Uri, Wilmarth, Addison, Johnson, Freeman, Gowenlock, Grosse, and Drago) fall in with Professor Rice's suggestion that "It seems worthwhile to explore whether or not the methods of classical chemistry with suitable modifications can be developed further to increase our knowledge of transformations involving free radicals." I am happy to report that it is obvious from reading these papers that indeed this can be done successfully. I believe

1

Johnson's paper is particularly demonstrative of the fact that a combination of classical chemical techniques with modern techniques will give to the chemist the information he wants with the greatest expediency.

The purpose of our symposium has not been to exhaust the subject of inorganic free radicals but rather to give an early status report on what we believe will be an extremely active field of chemical investigation over the next few years. We have tried to survey the general methods for investigating free radicals and then to discuss in detail some of the reactions and properties of one of the best known inorganic free radicals, NO_2, and one of the most recently discovered inorganic free radicals, NF_2. I believe it to be of particular value to our purposes to have the comparative studies of the interaction of the inorganic free radicals with inorganic materials (Addison, NO_2; Johnson, NF_2) together with the interaction of one of these inorganic free radicals with organic materials (Freeman, NF_2).

We hope this symposium will serve to arouse new interest in the investigation of inorganic free radicals and the role of free radicals in inorganic chemistry as a whole. If it does, our labors will be more than repaid.

I would like to express my appreciation to the U.S. Army Research Office, Durham, N.C., and to the chief scientist, Dr. John W. Dawson, for their active support of this symposium.

CHARLES B. COLBURN

Redstone Arsenal Research Division
Rohm & Haas Co.
Huntsville, Ala.

Review of the Properties and Reactions of Some Inorganic Free Radicals

F. O. RICE

Department of Chemistry, Georgetown University, Washington 7, D. C.

The chemical properties and reactions of free radicals are more particularly emphasized, even though the more spectacular recent advances in our understanding of free radicals have come through the use of tools and techniques taken from the domain of the physicist. It seems worthwhile to explore whether or not the methods of classical chemistry with suitable modifications can be developed further to increase our knowledge of transformations involving free radicals. The stabilization of various radicals and the type of reactions characteristic of divalent radicals are discussed.

This review emphasizes more particularly the chemical properties and reactions of free radicals, even though the more spectacular recent advances in our understanding of free radicals have come through the use of tools and techniques taken from the domain of the physicist. It seems worthwhile to explore whether or not the methods of classical chemistry with suitable modifications can be developed further to increase our knowledge of transformations involving free radicals.

In general, a univalent free radical is not easily disposed of; if it reacts with surrounding molecules it will itself disappear but will generate another free radical. The only way a univalent free radical can disappear is to collide with another univalent free radical and either combine with it or disproportionate. This result is a necessary consequence of the fact that, with almost negligibly few exceptions, chemical molecules contain an even number of electrons.

It is clear, too, that the generation of a univalent free radical in a chemical system will start a whole chain of reactions that will end only by collision of two radicals. We can understand this by realizing that the initial act, generating the free radical, since it breaks a bond, must require a high activation energy. The subsequent reactions, while they involve breaking bonds, involve also the concomitant making of bonds and have a relatively small activation energy; it is evident therefore that the conditions that initially produce the free radicals will cause the chain reactions to proceed with relatively high speed. The study of these material chains cleared up many problems, notably the inhibition of chemical reactions, that plagued chemists during the early part of the nineteenth century. During that period, attempts were made to develop the concept of energy chains, but these attempts failed because they could not explain the specificity of chemical transformations. It is possible that the curious interchange of resonance light between atoms may lead to some developments of an energy chain.

Nitric Oxide

Perhaps the best known of the inorganic free radicals is the substance nitric oxide, one of the very few "odd" molecules that are known to exist. Its method of preparation is a typical one. Briefly, an equilibrium or stationary state is established at elevated temperatures and then the temperature is suddenly reduced to a low enough point so that the equilibrium is frozen. It is then possible to study the chemical behavior of the particles at leisure. Among free radicals, nitric oxide is peculiar in that it behaves as a stable molecule at ambient temperatures. Its stability (18) may be interpreted as resulting from resonance between the structures $+N-O^-$ and $-N-O^+$. In the liquid and solid states, combination occurs and nitric oxide exists entirely or almost entirely as the dimer. It seems probable that trapping NO in a matrix would be a useful way of studying the effectiveness of this method of stabilizing radicals.

To prepare nitric oxide a mixture of nitrogen and oxygen may be heated to about 3000° C., at which temperature air contains about 4% of NO at equilibrium; by rapid cooling to room temperature one can obtain 2 to 3% of NO in the air. Ordinarily, in order to stabilize free radicals it is necessary to cool the reaction mixtures to liquid nitrogen or even liquid helium temperatures.

The preparation of NO by the oxidation of ammonia over a platinum catalyst suggests that other radicals would be formed in this way.

Methods of Stabilizing Radicals

Free radicals of short life may be produced by heating a substance at low pressures in a flowing system to a high temperature, whereby a portion of the substance is decomposed. The products are rapidly brought in contact with a surface that is cooled to liquid nitrogen or even liquid helium temperatures. This simple method is adequate to prepare active species, as shown by Rice and Freamo's experiments (24) on the preparation of a blue material by the thermal decomposition of hydrazoic acid. Doubtless there were numerous attempts to do this sort of experiment—for example, Staudinger and Kreis (30) report in some detail unsuccessful attempts to prepare S_2. They used a "hot-cold" quartz tube which contained sulfur at one end and was evacuated and sealed. When the end of the tube containing the sulfur was heated, it distilled to the other end, which was cooled to liquid nitrogen temperatures, but only ordinary yellow sulfur was obtained. However, Dewar and his coworkers (5) actually prepared CS using this technique. Apparently CS in the gas phase has the stability of a normal molecule, but there is a heterogeneous reaction at surfaces, causing polymerization (7, 10).

We have to ask what happens when a radical or molecule approaches a surface cooled to liquid nitrogen temperatures or lower. Some of the particles undoubtedly bounce off and there is almost certainly some lateral movement of those that stick on the first collision. The problem of immobilizing radicals on their first collision is critical to the solution of the problem of obtaining them in high concentration. This is discussed in the imaginative experiments of Windsor, who attempted to prepare spin-aligned hydrogen atoms (1).

Very soon after the publication of the work of Rice and Freamo there appeared independently the suggestion that the stabilization of free radicals produced would be facilitated by the addition of some inert material which would dilute the substrate passing through the furnace. Many papers have been published on this technique, which is commonly known as the matrix isolation method (*16, 33*). However, the substances commonly used to form the matrix are molecular solids, so that the forces between the molecules are very weak and consequently radicals can be preserved only at temperatures near the boiling point of liquid nitrogen or even lower. If one could incorporate radicals into a diamond-type lattice, it might be possible to stabilize radicals sufficiently to keep them at room temperature.

Another possibility would be to incorporate radicals into an ionic lattice in which the strong forces existing between the particles could be expected to prevent diffusion. In some experiments along these lines (*27*), in which hydrazoic acid was mixed with vapors of alkali halides, the mixture being passed through a furnace at 800° to 900° C. and a pressure of a few tenths of a millimeter, difficulties were encountered due to formation of *f*-centers. If the alkali metal and the halogen are not present in exactly stoichiometric proportions, there are "holes" in the lattice, producing negative or positive charges and color formation, so it is not certain whether colors are due to radicals or *f*-centers. Because of these difficulties the work was discontinued. Chilton and Porter (*3*) have published a research note on the stabilization of free radicals in salt matrices, but their method of preparation would seem to indicate that they simply had microcrystals of a substrate embedded in the salt matrix.

An ideal matrix would consist of a nonpolar molecular solid to minimize interaction between the free radical species and the matrix molecule. To study a free radical by physical methods it is desirable to have the conditions as nearly as possible those existing in a dilute gas.

Another possible method of stabilizing free radicals would be to imprison them in clathrate compounds (*14, 23*). A clathrate is a homogeneous solid consisting of a host and a guest molecule; the guest is imprisoned in closed cavities or cages formed by the host molecules. If it were possible to find a suitable stable host molecule that would form cages in the matrix on freezing from the dilute gas phase, it should be possible to carry with the vapor free radicals which should then be stabilized in their cages.

An ingenious method of stabilizing free radicals is that of making a "fluff" of an unsaturated polymer such as polystyrene (*11*). In this way radicals are "anchored" on the surface at the site of a double bond.

Sulfur

At ordinary temperatures the stable solid form of sulfur consists of an S_8 ring (*32*). In the molten form at temperatures above about 160° liquid sulfur consists largely of long chains, which on sudden cooling to room temperature give the amorphous form of $S\mu$. In the vapor state the S_8 rings break down and it seems to be fairly well established that at temperatures over 500° C. and pressures of a few tenths of a millimeter sulfur vapor exists to the extent of over 99% as S_2. Rice and Sparrow (*28*) found that this may be frozen out on a liquid nitrogen–cooled surface to give a purple solid; on warming to room temperature it changes in a few seconds to a mixture containing about 40% of crystalline sulfur and 60% of amorphous sulfur. The activation energy of the change is 3.1 kcal.

During this work a greenish modification occasionally appeared at the edges of the purple material, and further investigation (22) showed that this green modification could be readily prepared by distilling sulfur from the molten liquid. On the Mansell system purple sulfur is characterized as 10.0 Red Purple 3/6 or 10 Red Purple 3/8 and on the National Bureau of Standards system it is characterized as dark purplish red, 1SCC; in the same way green sulfur is characterized on the National Bureau of Standards system (15) as 7.5 Green Yellow varying from 8/4 light yellowish green through 6/6 moderate yellowish green to 2/2 blackish green.

Electron spin resonance absorption (19) has been found in both of these colored forms of sulfur and there seem to be at least two types of trapped sulfur radicals present.

Red Sulfur

When sulfur is subjected to gamma radiation at about −200° C. it turns a bright red but does not give any ESR absorption. When warmed to room temperature, it reverts almost explosively to ordinary yellow sulfur.

At the suggestion of Charles Herzfeld we made single crystals of sulfur, both rhombic and monoclinic, obtained from saturated solutions of sulfur in toluene crystallized at appropriate temperatures. The crystals were placed in borosilicate glass tubes which were evacuated and sealed at both ends. The tubes containing the monoclinic crystals were kept at liquid nitrogen temperatures to prevent transition to the rhombic form, which is stable at room temperature.

These tubes were then subjected to gamma radiation at 0.5 megaroentgen per hour for 87.2 hours. An attempted electron spin resonance determination of the radical content yielded no evidence of the presence of radicals.

Sulfur Formed in Electrical Discharge Decomposition of H_2S

In these experiments H_2S in a flowing system at a pressure of a few tenths of a millimeter was decomposed electrically and the products were brought in contact with a liquid nitrogen–cooled finger. We used two kinds of electrical discharge: a Raytheon microtherm unit generating radio-frequency energy at a wave length of 12.2 cm., and another obtained by connecting a voltage of 15,000 volts (maximum) to two aluminum electrodes in the gas stream. We obtained only ordinary yellow sulfur on the cold finger, except when the power in each case was at a minimum. In the micro discharge experiments, if we kept the discharge as close as possible to the cold finger and the power output at 50% (or lower) of the maximum, we obtained a green deposit which had a dark ring around it. On warming to room temperature, all these deposits reverted to ordinary yellow sulfur.

With the electrical discharge experiment both purple and green sulfur were repeatedly obtained according to conditions. When purple sulfur was obtained, on warming a transition to green sulfur occurred at about −150° C. and finally ordinary yellow sulfur was obtained on warming to room temperature. Mixing the H_2S with helium or argon made no appreciable difference in our results.

Divalent Radicals

There are three simple divalent radicals—CH_2, NH, and O—and since two of them are inorganic it seems appropriate to discuss them here. Even though most of the work has been done on methylene, it seems likely that the type of reaction characteristic for CH_2 will be the same for NH and O. Methylene was first characterized by Rice and Glasebrook (20, 26), who prepared it by the thermal decomposition of diazomethane; it is a particle of short half life of only a very few hundredths of a second. It combines with tellurium to form a red polymer, $(HCHTe)_n$, which permits its identification. It can be carried in a current of butane, but if the temperature is raised to about 650° C., methyl radicals are formed. This behavior led the original workers erroneously to suppose that methylene behaved like the univalent radicals and picked off hydrogen atoms. Later work showed that methylene actually "insinuates" itself in between CH bonds and its action is indiscriminate (6, 9, 12, 13). The NH radical behaves like CH_2 (21). It also "insinuates" itself between CH bonds, forming amines.

Oxygen atoms may be formed by the photochemical decomposition of either NO_2 or N_2O (4) and these also react with saturated hydrocarbons to form alcohols.

It seems therefore to be definitely established experimentally that the simple divalent radicals in their ground state do not behave like univalent radicals, whose main reaction with saturated molecules is to remove hydrogen atoms; instead, the divalent radicals incorporate themselves into molecules. We may understand this behavior by considering an old paper by Thomson (31) on the constitution of the atom. This paper, written only eight years after Becquerel's discovery of radio-activity, postulated that the chemical atom consists of a ball of positive electricity containing electrons embedded in it. Thomson addressed himself to the problem of how the electrons would arrange themselves to form a stable system. He suggested that the electrons would arrange themselves in rings very much resembling the periods in Mendeleyev's classification of the elements. This picture is, of course, entirely wrong and was disproved in 1912 when the famous Rutherford experiment was performed.

However, the Thomson atom provides a basis for the description of a chemical molecule, which actually consists of a smear of negative electricity having embedded in it the nuclei of atoms. The negative cloud is, however, not uniformly distributed but has a higher density between the nuclei. The outside of the negative cloud in organic molecules consists of electron pairs located between the nuclei of hydrogen atoms and carbon atoms.

If we consider the molecule of neopentane, our picture would be a particle consisting of 12 protons each carrying a single positive charge and five carbon kernels each carrying four positive charges. The whole is embedded in a sphere of negative electricity. We may now consider a bivalent radical and what happens when it collides with a molecule such as neopentane. It seems reasonable to assume that if the bivalent radical is in the ground state, there will be incipient bond formation by interaction with one of the electron pairs of the neopentane. This can be expected to be followed by rearrangement to form a stable molecule; in deciding what arrangement to postulate we would be guided by the principle of least motion (29). In the case of neopentane this would result in movement of one of the 12 protons and formation of an alcohol, amine, or higher hydrocarbon according to whether the divalent radical is O, NH, or CH_2. If instead of neopentane, containing only primary hydrogen atoms, the hydrocarbon contains also secondary or tertiary atoms, we would expect the same sort of result. However, bond strengths would not be expected to affect the picture and the relative proportions of isomers would be determined simply by the number of the different kinds of hydrogen atoms. Furthermore, we would expect the speed of reaction of bivalent radicals with hydrocarbon molecules to be represented by

$$C_1 \times C_2 \times n$$

where C_1 represents the concentration of the bivalent radicals, C_2 is the concentration of the hydrocarbon, and n is the number of electron pairs in the sphere of negative electricity that are associated with C-H bonds. I have preferred to take this number of electron pairs because those between the carbon kernels would not be expected to interact appreciably.

The foregoing discussion is limited to molecules having zero or near-zero dipole moment. Reaction of a divalent radical with a dipole will be expected not only to be strongly oriented but also to proceed with a rather low activation energy. There should be none of the indiscriminate attack by hydrocarbons that occurs with paraffin. We may understand this by noting that NH has a permanent dipole and the oxygen atom will have an induced dipole caused by the permanent dipole of the reacting molecule. The net effect of this will be to locate interaction between the molecule and divalent radical at the negative or positive end of the molecule.

We may illustrate this with reference to the blue material formed by freezing the decomposition products of hydrazoic acid (25). The primary reaction presumably may be written

$$HN_3 \rightarrow NH + H_2$$

so that it is tempting to ascribe the blue color to the NH radical. Foner and Hudson (8) attempted to identify NH by passing the decomposition products of NH_3 directly into a mass spectrometer. They were unable to find any trace of NH but did find diimide, N_2H_2.

Before attempting to understand the thermal decomposition of hydrazoic acid, it seems well to mention an x-ray diffraction study of the blue material made by Bolz, Mauer, and Peiser (2). It appeared to be a low temperature glass, mainly ammonium azide but also containing hydrazoic acid.

According to the foregoing hypothesis, after the preliminary decomposition

$$HN_3 \rightarrow NH + H_2 \tag{P_1}$$

various reactions can occur, depending on the conditions. Suppose first the decomposition occurs in a flowing system (hot tube, 800° to 950° C., at low pressures, 0.01 to 1.0 mm.) and the gases are quickly cooled to −200° C.; we may then consider the following reactions:

$$NH + NH \rightarrow N_2H_2 \tag{Q_1}$$

$$NH + HN_3 \rightarrow HN\text{—}N\text{—}N\text{—}NH \tag{Q_2}$$

$$NH + HN_3 \rightarrow H_2N\text{—}N\text{—}N\text{—}N \tag{Q_3}$$

$$HN\text{—}N\text{—}N\text{—}NH \rightarrow 2H\text{—}N\text{—}N \tag{R_1}$$

$$H_2N\text{—}N\text{—}N\text{—}N \rightarrow H_2 + 2N_2 \tag{R_2}$$

$$H\text{—}N\text{—}N + HN_3 \rightarrow H\text{—}N\text{—}N\text{—}H + N_3 \tag{S_1}$$

We may suppose that in the hot tube, reaction Q_1 is negligible; N_2H_2 could hardly form in this way because of the difficulty of getting rid of the energy of formation. Reactions Q_2 and Q_3 are probably highly exothermic and so we may suppose that they occur readily and are followed by Reactions R_1 and R_2. In the hot tube R_1 would be quickly followed by S_1, thus providing for the production of diimide. On the other hand, suppose that the first decomposition is photochemical, the hydrazoic acid being maintained at −200° C.: As before, we may then consider the reactions:

$$NH + NH \rightarrow N_2H_2 \tag{Q'_1}$$

$$NH + HN_3 \rightarrow HN\text{—}N\text{—}N\text{—}NH \tag{Q'_2}$$

$$\text{NH} + \text{HN}_3 \rightarrow \text{H}_2\text{N}\text{—N}\text{—N}\text{—N} \tag{Q$'_3$}$$

$$\text{HN}\text{—N}\text{—N}\text{—H} \rightarrow 2\text{H}\text{—N}\text{—N} \tag{R$'_1$}$$

$$\text{H}_2\text{N}\text{—N}\text{—N}\text{—N} \rightarrow \text{H}_2 + 2\text{N}_2 \tag{R$'_2$}$$

$$\text{H}\text{—N}\text{—N} + \text{HN}_3 \rightarrow \text{H}\text{—N}\text{—N}\text{—H} + \text{N}_3 \tag{S$'_1$}$$

While it is true that the photochemical decomposition will produce a very "hot" NH, the surroundings are at $-200°$ C. We may then expect stabilization of the NH and Reaction Q′ may be an important source of diimide; it might be expected, too, that at $-200°$ C. Reactions R'_1 and R'_2 would not be important until warming up occurred.

Support for these considerations is given by Papazian (*17*), who studied the ultraviolet and visible absorption spectra of HN_3, photochemically decomposed at $-200°$ C. He postulated the primary production of NH radicals, followed by reactions in the matrix to produce diaminohydrazine ($HN{=}N{-}N{=}NH$), triazene ($H_2N{-}N{=}N{-}H$), and the radical $H{-}H{-}N$; he ascribed the blue color and paramagnetism of the solid to this radical.

Acknowledgment

The experiments with red sulfur were conducted partly with V. de Carlo and partly with J. D. Kelley. Experiments on sulfur formed in the electrical discharge composition of H_2S were conducted with J. D. Kelley.

Literature Cited

(1) Bass, A. M., Broida, H. P., eds., "Formation and Trapping of Free Radicals," p. 400, Academic Press, New York, 1960.
(2) Bolz, L. J., Mauer, F. A., Peiser, H. S., *J. Chem. Phys.* **30**, 349 (1959).
(3) Chilton, H. T. J., Porter, G., *Spectrochim. Acta* **16**, 390 (1960).
(4) Cvetanovič, R. J., *Can. J. Chem.* **36**, 623 (1958) and other papers.
(5) Dewar, J., Jones, H., *Proc. Roy Soc. London* **A85**, 574 (1911) and earlier papers.
(6) Doering, W. von E., Buttery, R. G., Laughlin, R. G., Chaudhuri, N., *J. Am. Chem. Soc.* **78**, 3224 (1956).
(7) Dyne, P. J., Ramsay, D. A., *J. Chem. Phys.* **20**, 1055 (1952).
(8) Foner, S. N., Hudson, R. L., *Ibid.*, **28**, 719 (1958).
(9) Frey, H. M., *J. Am. Chem. Soc.* **80**, 5005 (1958).
(10) Hogg, M. A. P., Spice, J. E., *J. Chem. Soc.* **1958**, 4196.
(11) Ingalls, R. B., Wall, L., *J. Chem. Phys.* **35**, 370 (1961).
(12) Kistiakowsky, G. B., Sauer, K., *J. Am. Chem. Soc.* **78**, 5699 (1956).
(13) Knox, J. H., Trotman-Dickenson, A. F., *Chem. and Ind.* (*London*) **1957**, 268.
(14) Mandelcorn, L., *Chem. Revs.* **59**, 827 (1959).
(15) Natl. Bur. Standards, Circ. **553** (1955).
(16) Norman, I., Porter, G., *Nature* **174**, 508 (1954).
(17) Papazian, H. A., *J. Chem. Phys.* **32**, 456 (1960).
(18) Pauling, L., "Nature of the Chemical Bond," 3rd ed., p. 343, Cornell Univ. Press, Ithaca, N. Y., 1960.
(19) Radford, H. E., Rice, F. O., *J. Chem. Phys.* **33**, 774 (1960).
(20) Rice, F. O., *J. Am. Chem. Soc.* **61**, 213 (1939).
(21) Rice, F. O., Cosgrave, D., Miller, E., unpublished work.
(22) Rice, F. O., Ditter, J., *J. Am. Chem. Soc.* **75**, 6066 (1953).
(23) Rice, F. O., Ditter, J., unpublished work.
(24) Rice, F. O., Freamo, M. J., *J. Am. Chem. Soc.* **73**, 5529 (1951).
(25) *Ibid.*, **75**, 548 (1953).
(26) Rice, F. O., Glasebrook, A. L., *Ibid.*, **56**, 2381 (1934).
(27) Rice, F. O., Luckenbach, T., unpublished work.
(28) Rice, F. O., Sparrow, C.. *J. Chem. Soc.* **75**, 848 (1953).
(29) Rice, F. O., Teller, E., *J. Chem. Phys.* **6**, 489 (1938); **7**, 199 (1939).
(30) Staudinger, H., Kreis, W., *Helv. Chim. Acta* **8**, 71 (1925).
(31) Thomson, J. J., *Phil. Mag.* **7**, 237 (1904).
(32) Warren, B. E., Burwell, J. T., *J. Chem. Phys.* **3**, 6 (1935).
(33) Whittle, E., Dows, D. A., Pimentel, G. C., *Ibid.*, **22**, 1943 (1954).

RECEIVED June 3, 1962.

2

Production of Free Radicals and Their Physical Properties in the Liquid and Solid State

G. WILSE ROBINSON

Gates and Crellin Laboratories of Chemistry,
California Institute of Technology, Pasadena, Calif.

Methods of preparing free radicals are described and semiquantitative answers are given to the question: In what way are the physical properties of free radicals modified by a high density environment? Particular problems dealt with are negative experiments on trapped HO_2 radicals, rotations of molecules in solids and liquids, vibrational solvent shifts, an experimental example of a harmonic oscillator in a box, singlet-triplet shifts, and effects of environment on electron-electron repulsion terms and ionization potentials in molecules.

The chemical reactivity of "molecular fragments" depends upon the presence of unpaired electrons or the availability of low-lying unfilled orbitals. These electronic properties are also precisely the ones that cause molecular fragments to be of interest in spin resonance or in optical spectroscopic studies. Many of the physical properties of molecular fragments may be obtained very precisely from gas-phase optical spectroscopic measurements, since the line widths are very narrow. For the chemist, however, there is also interest in the question: "In what way are the physical properties of free radicals modified by a high density environment?"

The effect of high density environments on chemical and physical properties of molecules is an interesting problem, but environments, since they consist of a great number of electrons and some nuclei, are complex even in their simplest form. It would seem that good progress could be made in the real understanding of solvent effects if more time were spent on a few fundamental experiments dealing with the simplest solvents available. Thus the simplest hydrocarbon solvent would perhaps be liquid or solid methane. However, even this molecule is a more complex representative of a nonpolar solvent than is necessary, since molecular hydrogen and the rare gases—helium, neon, krypton, and xenon—are available. Under only slightly exotic experimental conditions (42), H_2 and the rare gases in solid, liquid, or supercritical form, provide a set of chemically inert, optically transparent, and physically simple solvents over the temperature range from $0°$ K. to $20°$ C. and above. The purpose of this paper is to discuss the effects of such solvents on the molecular properties of some small molecules and free radicals.

Preparation of Free Radicals

Solid Phase Experiments. The production of trapped free radicals in solid rare gases is a very simple matter, if the rare gas is present in at least 25 to 1 excess and the number of collisions between the free radicals and other molecules or the wall is held to a minimum (*46*). Use of the optical spectra of the free radical, if known, offers a usually reliable method by which it can be identified.

ELECTRICAL DISCHARGES. An electrical discharge containing the rare gas and the parent molecule from which the free radical is to be prepared was found to be a very successful device for the production of such trapped molecular fragments as CN, C_2, OH, NH, CH, NH_2, HNO, HCO, NCO, C_3, PH, and PH_2 (*30, 33, 41, 46*). The parent molecules which can be used are, for example, acetylene or methane for C_2, CH, and C_3; water or alcohol for OH; ammonia or hydrazine for NH and NH_2; ammonia plus oxygen for HNO (NO_2 also formed); air plus hydrocarbon for CN, NCO, HNO, HCO, OH, NH, and NH_2; and phosphine for PH and PH_2. Actually almost any discharged mixture of rare gas plus parent molecules containing the appropriate atoms can be used to produce the above trapped radicals. In addition, some other as yet unidentified radicals are produced. A mixture of excess H_2 and NH_3 containing no rare gas resulted in a good yield (*15*) of NH radicals trapped in solid H_2! Hydrogen atoms from electrical discharges trapped in argon, krypton, and xenon matrices have been studied by ESR techniques (*19*) and a great deal of work has been carried out on other atomic species using both optical and ESR detection (*4*).

PHOTODECOMPOSITION. A second useful method which is a little more selective employs photodecomposition of the parent molecule trapped in a solid rare gas. In this way the molecular fragments NH and NH_2 (by a secondary reaction) can be produced from photolyzed hydrazoic acid (*27*). Photolysis of trapped acetylene using light of wavelength shorter than λ 2000 A. yields C_2 (*20*). The photolysis at wavelengths shorter than 1500 A. of ammonia (*47*) trapped in argon yields NH and NH_2, while light having longer wavelengths than 1700 A. produces only NH_2. Recently (*1*) ESR was used for detection of HCO produced from the photolysis of formaldehyde in argon with Hg λ 2537 plus λ 1849 A. light or from the photolysis of methanol in argon using λ > 1450 A. radiation. In earlier experiments (*30*), no easily detectable HCO optical absorption was produced from H_2CO photolysis using λ > 2600 A. light. Brown and Pimentel (*7*) showed that the labile molecule HNO could be produced from the photodecomposition of CH_3NO_2 in an argon matrix.

The photolysis of trapped diazomethane (*21, 45*) yields a complicated mixture of mostly unidentified products, one of which has been definitely identified as CH and another tentatively identified as CH_2 in its ground triplet state. One strong, relatively sharp feature at 4240 A. occurs in the photolysis of diazomethane and deuterated diazomethane, and also in discharges of acetylene plus a rare gas possibly contaminated with a trace of air. This feature remains unidentified.

RADIATION DAMAGE. The use of x-rays, electron beams, or high energy particles would serve the same purpose as ultraviolet light, except that the production of radicals might be much more efficient and new radicals might be found. Unfortunately, such excitation sources have not been used very extensively (*10*) for the production and study of small inorganic free radicals in simple matrices, probably simply because such equipment does not happen to be in the hands of those people interested in this problem. This is radiation damage in its simplest form, and such experiments might be more enlightening than those involving large molecules.

CHEMICAL REACTIONS. Products from gas-phase chemical reactions can also be trapped in rare gas matrices, and those products which absorb light can be studied by optical spectroscopic techniques. For example (31), the products from a low pressure ($\sim$ 1 mm. of Hg) atomic flame of oxygen atoms plus acetylene were allowed to leak through a small orifice in a borosilicate glass reaction chamber, where they were mixed with an excess of gaseous krypton at 10^{-4} mm. of Hg pressure. The mixture was condensed on a quartz window cooled to liquid helium temperature. The only detectable small free radical found was HCO, but it was present in considerable quantities. Similar experiments by Harvey and Brown (23) showed that HNO could be easily produced and trapped from the gas-phase reaction of hydrogen atoms plus nitric oxide.

CHEMICAL REACTIONS NEAR 0° K. Still another technique, which makes use of the fact that chemical reactions can take place even at temperatures near the absolute zero, consists of first trapping one reactant in a rare gas matrix at 4.2° K. and then allowing the second reactant to impinge on the solid surface. This technique requires that the second reactant can readily diffuse through the solid, so the technique is pretty much limited to reactions of the type

$$H + M = HM$$

In addition, the reaction must proceed with near zero activation energy. Thus far the reaction of H plus trapped NO to give HNO is the only known example of the use of this technique (16). Chemical reactions in the solid at such low temperatures are, however, not too unusual. The previously mentioned (27) photolysis of trapped HN_3 at 4.2° K. to give NH and NH_2 must involve a reaction of this type. One presumes that a primary photochemical step producing NH, followed by a secondary reaction,

$$NH + HN_3 = NH_2 + N_3$$

can account for these observations. Diffusion of NH radicals through the solid was not required here, however, since at the concentrations of HN_3 employed, a certain fraction of the HN_3 molecules had HN_3 nearest neighbors. Recently, Ewing, Thompson, and Pimentel (18) have shown that the photolysis at 20° K. of HI trapped in CO yields HCO by the low temperature addition of H atoms to CO.

NEGATIVE RESULTS ON HO_2. Perhaps the most interesting, puzzling, and somewhat frustrating series of negative results carried out in our laboratory (15) concerns the search for the free radical HO_2. The techniques discussed above have been so very successful in the study of labile molecules that any one of them would be expected to yield trapped HO_2. There are theoretical reasons (43, 49) why HO_2 is expected to have an electronic spectrum in the visible or photographic infrared. Certainly such predictions that are found to be valid for all known first-row triatomic molecules are not expected to fail in the case of HO_2.

Nevertheless a number of experiments have been tried and have thus far not produced a spectrum anywhere between 3500 and 8500 A. which can be identified with this molecule. Discharges of H_2O, H_2O_2, and H_2 plus O_2 mixed with rare gases were tried; discharges of these molecules were leaked into a gaseous mixture at 10^{-4} mm. of Hg pressure of rare gas plus O_2 or H_2O_2 and the products solidified at 4.2° K; hydrogen atoms were mixed with O_2 plus a rare gas both in the gas phase as above or in the solid; photolysis of trapped H_2O_2 was tried; and the products from an atomic flame of $H + O_2$ were trapped. Identical techniques are known to produce large amounts of the similar molecule HNO. Perhaps HO_2 rapidly photodissociates. To prevent this, the spectra should be searched for, starting in the photographic infrared and moving toward the blue, always filtering out the higher energy radiation as one proceeds. This technique was tried in a few of the above experiments. Perhaps the HO_2 spectrum is too broad in the solid or perhaps not enough of the optimum conditions were massed in any one of the above experiments. Also it is not exactly known just how much the electronic spectrum would be affected by a change in molecular geometry from a supposed bent H—O—O configuration to, say, a triangular form, $\overset{.H.}{O-O}$. If the most stable form were not the supposed one, the positions of the actual excited electronic states would not correspond to those now predicted.

Liquid Phase Experiments. Simple polyatomic molecules, if not too polar, dissolve in liquid argon, krypton, and xenon. A lower limit to the solubility of a substance in a liquid rare gas can be estimated from the vapor pressure of the substance at the liquid rare gas temperature. Pressures up to only about 50 atm. need to be used to extend the liquid range of argon, krypton, and xenon, so that they form a useful set of solvents over the continuous temperature range −182° to +16° C., the critical temperature of xenon. Experiments can also be carried out in the supercritical rare gases. Rare gas liquid solvents have a tremendous advantage over other solvents in that solvent effects are simple, the solvents are definitely chemically inert, they can be highly purified when solvent purity is of importance, and they are optically transparent from well into the vacuum ultraviolet, through the visible and the infrared regions of the spectrum.

A low-temperature reaction chamber has been built which can employ lithium fluoride, barium fluoride, or sapphire windows mounted to a metal cell by means of metal flange fittings, indium metal gaskets, and Teflon pressure rings. This cell has been used for the study of low-temperature infrared spectra of HCl in liquid xenon and of CH_4 in liquid argon. It has been more fully described in a recent paper (29).

The cell is also admirably suited to free radical studies in the liquid phase at low temperatures. Flash photolysis or steady-state photolysis may be used, depending upon the chemical lifetime of the free radical. Pulsed or steady-state x-ray excitation may prove advantageous here, since penetration of the radiation into the solution is required. In these heavy-atom solvents much of the energy can be absorbed by the solvent and gently transferred to the solute. Experiments using liquid neon, hydrogen, or even liquid helium as solvents may be possible when pulsed electron beams are used. Solutes in these cases may be atomic hydrogen, excited states of helium atoms or molecules, and possibly ionic species.

Experiments using liquid rare gases may prove valuable in the study of simple solvent effects upon free radical reactions, in the study of energy relaxation phenomena where solvents of exceedingly high purity are required, or in the production of new reactive molecules of questionable chemical stability. The possible photodimerization of acetylene to cyclobutadiene is a good example of one kind of experiment which can be carried out at low temperatures in these inert solvents.

Detection. Molecular properties of radicals in liquid or solid solution may be studied by use of nuclear magnetic resonance, microwave spectroscopy, infrared rotation-vibration spectroscopy, electron spin resonance, and electronic spectroscopy. The first two methods are not very useful for low concentrations or for situations where the radicals are labile. Direct microwave or far-infrared observation of rotational motions of small molecules in solids does not seem out of the question, but no work of this kind has yet been reported.

Near-infrared detection suffers somewhat because relatively high concentrations ($> 0.1\%$) are required compared with those usually needed for the detection of electronic transitions. Another problem is that fast-scanning infrared instruments are not yet available for the study of rapidly reacting radicals which might be encountered in the liquid phase. Infrared detection further suffers because the vibrational spectrum of the desired free radical may not be easy to distinguish from that of the reactants or of other products. The difficulties are not insurmountable, however, as evidenced from the successful experiments cited above. The use of high resolution infrared provides a more powerful method for the study of free radical spectra in the solid state, but again identification is not necessarily easy, since even the rotation-vibration spectra of known molecules in a solid matrix are complex and difficult to interpret. Such spectra, for example, are known to be very sensitive to environmental perturbations caused by concentration changes (36).

Electron spin resonance is, of course, a well established method by which the molecular properties of free radicals in the solid phase may be investigated. When the technique is applied judiciously, a considerable amount of information about simple free radicals can be gained. Some of this work has been cited above.

Actually, almost all of the known molecular properties of small free radicals in the gas phase have been determined by flash photolysis combined with photographic spectroscopy in the vacuum ultraviolet, the ultraviolet, the visible, and the photographic infrared. Recent reviews have been given by Ramsay (40) and Robinson (43). Nearly all of this work has been carried out at the National Research Council of Canada by G. Herzberg, D. A. Ramsay, A. E. Douglas, and coworkers. This work therefore serves as a sound basis for the study of free radicals in the solid and liquid phase, since the problem of identification is largely removed.

Rotational Motions of Molecules in Dense Media

Liquid Phase. Quantized rotational motion in the liquid phase has rarely been reported. This is not necessarily because molecules do not undergo rotational motions in solution, but because there are various broadening mechanisms present which do not allow resolution of the individual rotational lines. One therefore expects that the optimum conditions for the spectral observation of rotational motions exist when the molecule possesses small moments of inertia. This criterion is fairly rigid and pretty much limits studies of quantized rotational motions in solution to hydrides and deuterides. Even in these cases, the presence of degenerate vibrations, such as exist in CH_3, CH_4, NH_3, and BH_3, might cause an additional line broadening because of random removal of vibrational degeneracies by the local solvent fields. Other contributions to rotational line broadening in solution spectra are a result of local density fluctuations in the liquid, of superposition of random quasi-lattice vibrations on the molecular spectrum, of interactions of the molecular rotation with these vibrations, or of uncertainty broadening caused by relaxation processes. It is not surprising then that the very best example of rotation in the liquid phase is illustrated by molecular hydrogen (2, 3, 22, 34). Of the chemically stable molecules, HF is the next most obvious, but low-temperature liquid solutions cannot be formed because of extensive polymerization of HF.

HCl in liquid xenon at $T \approx 185°$ K. has been studied (29). A spectrum consisting of three broad maxima is observed in the region where HCl vapor absorbs. The maxima have been interpreted as arising from a vibrational transition where the rotational angular momentum can increase by one quantum, decrease by one quantum, or remain the same. In the gas phase only the first two kinds of transitions are allowed. The third type of transition is expected when an unsymmetrical electrostatic field, such as that existing locally in the liquid, is present. In this case the major contribution to the field arises indirectly from the HCl dipole which induces a dipole in the neighboring polarizable xenon. This reaction field can act back on the HCl dipole. The field is unsymmetrical because of the defect structure of the liquid state. When there is high symmetry, as in the case of HCl in solid xenon (28), the perturbed spectrum does not occur!

Small diatomic hydrides such as BH, CH, NH, OH, NH_2, etc., would present further examples of molecules whose rotational structure in solution might be observed by use of flash photolysis techniques. Unfortunately, this kind of experiment is not likely to furnish much more information about rotational motions in solution than is already known about H_2 and HCl.

Solid Phase. While free radical studies in the liquid phase are not likely to contribute to our knowledge about molecular rotations in dense media, solid phase free radical experiments are better able to furnish such information than are experiments on stable molecules. The reasons are clear. Simple, low molecular weight, chemically stable molecules do not possess low-lying electronic states. Thus only infrared techniques are available for the study of rotational structure in the solid phase. Perhaps the best examples are NH_3 in solid argon (35, 36) and HCl in solid argon, krypton, and xenon (28). The results are tricky to interpret, however, since nearest neighbor as well as long-range rotational and vibrational resonance interactions apparently can become important as the concentration of absorbers increases. At low temperatures only a few vibrational levels are accessible in an infrared transition and for each of these only one or at most two rotational lines are expected. Increasing the temperature allows more initial rotational levels to be populated, but for small hydrides it is not possible to gain more than two or three lines in the temperature range available. At higher temperatures, the matrices allow diffusion, tend to sublime, and may undergo phase transitions. In addition, higher lattice vibrational levels become populated, and these may couple with the rotational motions, giving great breadth to the lines. One often hears that "hindered rotation in the lowest rotational level of a molecule in a solid may become free in the higher levels because the barriers have been surmounted." This philosophy is fine, except that it says nothing about the onset of rotational-lattice coupling which presents new complications at higher temperatures.

Study of rotational fine structure in the electronic spectrum has the advantage that the number of vibrational levels which occur is not bound by harmonic oscillator selection rules. Often long progressions of vibrations can be studied as in the case of trapped NH_2 molecules (46). Unfortunately, rotational selection rules are still present and these limit observation to a small number of rotational lines per vibrational transition. The solid can be warmed, but without very satisfactory results. A much better way by which higher rotational levels may be populated is by optical pumping Electronic transitions are relatively intense, and bright light sources are available for this region of the spectrum. Absorption of light populates vibrational levels of the excited electronic state. Portions of this energy are degraded into heat as vibrational and rotational relaxation processes take place in the upper electronic state. A change of electronic state will subsequently occur by a radiative or a nonradiative process. Excited vibrational levels in the ground electronic state are therefore populated; they then transfer their energy to lower vibrational levels and the excess is converted into lattice heat. In the process of vibrational relaxation, higher rotational levels may also become populated. Since lattice vibrational relaxation is faster than the intramolecular rotation and vibration relaxation processes, and since the entire solid is heated only slightly in any case, optical pumping offers a good method by which nonequilibrium populations of rotational and vibrational levels may be attained. When the surrounding lattice is very cold, say about 4.2° K. in a liquid helium experiment, rotational-lattice mixing is not so important, and the rotational lines should remain reasonably sharp. Since the relaxation processes occur during a time interval of milliseconds or microseconds, flash techniques will have to be used. As an important sideline here, the relaxation process itself can be studied. Preliminary observations indicate that rotational and vibrational relaxation processes in simple rare gas crystal fields are slow, and easily measurable on readily available time scales. Solid laser light sources would be a tremendous advantage here, providing the laser line superposed an absorption line in the low-temperature spectrum, or could be tuned to do so.

NH$_2$ in Solid Rare Gases. The case of NH$_2$ in solid rare gases probably presents the best known case, other than H$_2$, for quantized rotational motions in the solid phase. The rotational fine structure in the electronic spectrum of NH$_2$ trapped in solid argon was first reported in 1958 (44). At that time it was stated that "rotational structure in the electronic spectrum of trapped NH$_2$ indicates that this molecule is experiencing nearly free end-over-end rotation in the matrix phase." Later (46) a number of tentative rotational assignments were made, based upon line frequency, expected selection rules, and expected low-temperature Boltzmann populations. The intensity of lines originating from the rotationless ground state should not possess a temperature coefficient, while the intensity of lines arising from low-lying excited rotational levels should be strongly dependent upon temperature in the range 4.2° K. $\leq T \leq$ 20° K. If optical pumping is used to populate the excited levels, absorption intensities should be dependent upon light intensity. In other words, an exposure at intensity I_0 for time t should show half the absorption intensity as one at intensity $2I_0$ for time $t/2$, since the equilibrium populations of the excited rotational states depend linearly upon light intensity. Such experiments have now been carried out (11), and the new assignments which are consistent with these experiments are shown in Table I. Some of the older tentative assignments of Robinson and McCarthy (46) are now considered doubtful, since many of the lines were found to be insensitive to temperature and to intensity in optical pumping experiments and can therefore not have an excited rotational level as initial state. Two other lines at 16,775.1 and 20,323.8 cm.$^{-1}$ not included in Table I were found to be sensitive to the above tests but could not be easily assigned. Lines originating in $N''\tau = 0_0$, the rotational ground level of the ground vibronic state, are of course insensitive to temperature and to radiation intensity as expected. There still remain about 50 unassigned weak lines in the NH$_2$-argon spectrum. The moderately strong line at 14397.8 cm.$^{-1}$ is coincident with the ruby laser line. This rather fortunate circumstance might provide a

An examination of the new NH$_2$-argon assignments in Table I shows that the argon matrix provides a constant perturbation of ~ 25 cm.$^{-1}$ in the lower vibronic good pumping mechanism for further study of higher rotational lines in this system.

Table I. Rotational Assignments

Argon Matrix,[a] ν_{vac}	*Gas[b]* ν_{vac}	*M-G[c] Argon,* Cm.$^{-1}$	*Assignment[d]* ν_1' ν_2' ν_3'	$N_{T'} - N_{T''e}$	*M—G,* Cm.$^{-1}$ *Krypton[f]*	*Xenon[f]*
12661.0	12638.2	+22.8	(0 4 0)Π	$1_{+1} - 0_0$		
12669.1	12647.7	+21.4				
14388.4	14362.1	+26.3	(0 6 0)Π	$1_{+1} - 0_0$	−2.6	−32.6
14397.8	14374.7	+23.1			−10.7	−37.1
15040.3	15012.7	+27.6	(0 7 0)Δ	$2_{+1} - 1_0$		
15048.8	15023.0	+25.8				
15931.0	15903.6	+27.4	(0 8 0)Π	$1_{+1} - 0_0$	−3.8	−34.9
15934.1	15906.5	+27.6				
16636.7	16608.0	+28.7	(0 9 0)Δ	$2_{+1} - 1_0$	−3.6	
17588.0	17559.1	+28.9	(0 10 0)Π	$1_{+1} - 0_0$	−4.4	−36.5
17774.5	17755.1	+19.4	(1 6 0)Π	$1_{+1} - 0_0$	−18.7	−64.1
18282.8	18256.9	+25.9	(0 11 0)Δ	$2_{+1} - 1_0$		
19244.3	19226.9	+17.4	(1 8 0)Π	$1_{+1} - 0_0$	−23.6	−67
19412.2	19393.5	+18.7	(0 12 0)Π	$1_{+1} - 0_0$	−20.9	−66
20191.8	20179.7	+12.1	(0 13 0)Δ	$2_{+1} - 1_0$		
21220.7	21215.2	+5.5	(0 14 0)Π	$1_{+1} - 0_0$	−36.1	−81
23145.8	—	—	(0 16 0)Π	$1_{+1} - 0_0$		
25056.8	25059.3	−2.5	(0 18 0)Π	$1_{+1} - 0_0$	−54.6	−106
27022.3	—	—	(0 20 0)Π	$1_{+1} - 0_0$		

a (*46*).
b (*13*).
c Matrix–gas frequency shifts.
d ν_1 = symmetric stretch; ν_2 = bend; ν_3 = antisymmetric stretch. Prime refers to upper electronic state; Π and Δ refer to upper state vibronic symmetries.
e N refers to rotational quantum number and τ is the asymmetric rotor index.
f (*30*).

levels. Since there is little relative shift of $1_{+1} - 0_0$ and $2_{+1} - 1_0$ lines in the low vibronic bands, it is probable that neither the Renner splittings (*13*) nor the ground state $1_0 - 0_0$ energy separation are much affected by the environment. Thus the original conclusions concerning nearly free end-over-end rotation of NH_2 in the solid appear still to hold. Unfortunately, now the evidence for unperturbed 1_{-1}, 1_{+1}, and $N = 2$ levels is lacking and further search for these is necessary. The largest perturbation on the rotational structure here appears to be associated with the spin splittings in the first four doublets listed in Table I. These splittings are caused by spin-orbit interactions (*38*) and are observed to be generally smaller in the solid than in the gas. The vibrational perturbations in this spectrum are discussed below.

Vibrational Structure of Free Radicals in Dense Media

Bonding-Stretching Vibrations. BUCKINGHAM'S THEORY. Buckingham (*8*) has treated the problem of the effect of nonpolar solvent interactions on frequencies, intensities, and shapes of infrared absorption bands of dissolved molecules. The

Hamiltonian in terms of the dimensionless displacement coordinate $\xi = (r - r_e)/r_e$ for a gaseous diatomic molecule may be written as

$$H = H_0(\dot{\xi}^2, \xi^2) + H_a(\xi^3, \ldots)$$

where H_0 is the harmonic oscillator Hamiltonian and H_a contains the anharmonic terms. When the molecule is placed in a surrounding medium, there will in general be a solute-solvent interaction energy, U. U is dependent upon a variable, τ, which represents the form of the local solvent environment, and, in order to get infrared shifts, U must also be dependent upon ξ. A change in equilibrium internuclear separation r_e is expected because of the presence of the intermolecular potential. For the gaseous molecule, this minimum in the potential function $V(\xi)$ is determined by setting $dV/d\xi = 0$, while in the solvent one must set $d(V + U)/d\xi = 0$. Buckingham takes a Taylor's expansion of U,

$$U(\tau, \xi) = U_e(\tau) + U'(\tau)\xi + \frac{1}{2} U''(\tau)\xi^2 + \ldots$$

where $U_e(\tau)$ is the potential energy of interaction between the solvent and the solute in its equilibrium nuclear configuration. He then uses the potential

$$H' = H_a + U - U_e$$

as a peturbation on the harmonic oscillator Hamiltonian, H_0. Only the zeroth rotational angular momentum state is treated. Neglecting terms in U of higher power than ξ^2, the relative solvent shift is given by

$$\frac{\Delta\omega_{n \leftarrow m}}{\omega_e} = (n - m) \frac{B_e}{hc\omega_e^2} \{U'' - 3aU'\}$$

for a transition from the mth to the nth vibrational state. In the above equation $B_e = h/8\pi^2 mcr_e^2$; the constant a, which is always negative for diatomic molecules, is the dimensionless coefficient of the cubic term in $H_a(\xi)$; and ω_e is the unperturbed harmonic oscillator frequency. Higher terms in U could be included and easily handled by perturbation theory. In this way further adjustable parameters would be added to the above simple expression.

The simple expression or the more complicated ones can be used to describe solvent perturbations on infrared spectra. They do not explain solvent shifts, since their explanation requires *a priori* calculations of $U', U'', \ldots$. This kind of calculation demands a detailed quantum mechanical examination of the intricate many-body interactions between the electrons and nuclei of the solvent and those of the dissolved molecule. Such calculations may be just barely possible for, say, a system of hydrogen atoms dissolved in liquid helium. They are not tractable for most solvent-solute systems unless drastic approximations are made.

PHYSICAL SIGNIFICANCE OF U''. In spite of the complexity of the quantitative theory, one can make certain qualitative statements about the effect of these interactions upon molecular vibrations. The physical significance of U'' is that it is the difference between the force constant for the free molecule and that for the molecule in the solvent. We neglect the term in U', since it is always modified by the small anharmonicity constant, a. There are two limits of interest: that where U'' is negative and that where it is positive. The first case occurs when the dispersion interactions caused by the nonzero polarizability of the solvent dominate exchange repulsive interactions caused by "overlapping" electronic eigenfunctions of solvent and solute. U'' becomes positive when the exchange repulsive forces dominate. Electrons belonging to the solute polarize the nearby solvent molecules and are attracted to the positive end of these instantaneous induced dipoles. Conversely, the electrons of the solvent are attracted towards the solute. The force of attraction is called an induction force, and for an electron of charge e interacting with a sphere of constant polarizability α at a distance r, the potential energy is given by

$$\varphi = -\frac{1}{2} e^2 \alpha r^{-4}$$

For example, the potential energy of an electron in the field of a krypton atom at a distance of 3.6 A. is about 0.1 e.v. The net result of these kinds of interactions is that the electrons of the solute and of the solvent are delocalized into the intermolecular bond (32). This generally has the effect of decreasing the force constant of the solute, giving U'' a negative sign, and contributing a red shift of the infrared band.

A general theory would have to be more precise as to the nature of the electronic eigenfunctions of solvent and solute. For example, if the electrons of the solute are loosely bound, and there are low-lying unfilled orbitals of the solvent, one must take into account solute-solvent charge transfer states $U+V-$ which are expected to make important contributions to the interaction. Here the change in force constant would be of larger relative magnitude than the case where the electronic excited states of solvent and solute were high. When the most loosely bound electrons are antibonding, attractive interactions are expected to cause smaller red shifts than if these electrons are bonding. In some cases even blue shifts may be encountered. However, the so-called most loosely bound electrons need not be much more affected than the "inner" bonding electrons, since in the language of perturbation theory the relative sizes of the energy denominators may not be too much different. Thus, the infrared blue shift of stretching vibrations in an attractive environment is a rare phenomenon.

REPULSIVE INTERACTIONS (HARMONIC OSCILLATOR IN A BOX). In most stable solutions and in pure liquids where the components are at or near relatively deep intermolecular potential minima, attractive interactions dominate the intermolecular repulsive terms. Unstable solutions of large solute molecules dissolved in a solution of small solvent molecules can be prepared in the solid phase by trapping experiments. Certain trapped free radicals may therefore show the effects of solvent-solute repulsive interactions, which would be evidenced by blue shifts in the infrared spectrum of these "cramped" solutes. Diatomic carbon (C_2) trapped in solid xenon shows this effect strongly (30, 31, 32) in both the upper and lower electronic states of the $^3\Pi_g \longleftrightarrow {}^3\Pi_u$ (Swan) transition. Since the $1 \to 0$ vibrational relaxation time in the $^3\Pi_g$ upper state is slow compared with the electronic lifetime (2×10^{-7} second), five emission bands involving both the $n = 0$ and $n = 1$ levels in the upper state and $n = 0$, $n = 1$, and $n = 2$ in the lower state can be easily excited in fluorescence. The wave number difference $\omega_{1 \leftarrow 0}$ in the upper electronic state was found to be 1940 cm.$^{-1}$ as compared with only 1755 cm.$^{-1}$ for free C_2. This is a vibrational perturbation which amounts to over 10% of the unperturbed frequency! In the lower electronic state ($^3\Pi_u$) the perturbation is not much less spectacular, $\omega_{ \to}$ and $\omega_{1 \leftarrow 0}$ being 1740 and 1720 cm.$^{-1}$, respectively, in the solid and 1590 and 1618 cm.$^{-1}$, respectively, in the gas (24). The normal negative anharmonicity in the free molecule has been reversed by the presence of the solid environment. This system seems to present a good illustration of the effect of repulsive interactions. The fact that C_2 has low-lying unfilled bonding orbitals cannot, however, be neglected in any theory which attempts a quantitative explanation of these results.

Even in those cases where a small red shift or no shift is observed on the $\omega_{1 \leftarrow 0}$ frequency, repulsive blue shifts are expected to take over at large vibrational amplitudes. The recent work of Broida and Peyron (5, 6) shows that for O_2 and N_2 trapped in "similarly sized" solvents, there is little or no vibrational perturbation in the ground electronic states up to vibrational quantum numbers of the order of 13. For the excited electronic state of the Schuman-Runge bands of O_2, however, the molecule is about 0.4 A. larger than in the ground state (24). Repulsive interactions should be more prominent here. Dressler and Schnepp (14) have found large vibrational repulsive perturbations of increasing magnitude for vibrational quantum numbers from about 12 upward. It is fairly certain that infrared detection, which must be limited to the lower vibrational quantum numbers, will not be able to turn up these repulsive perturbations except possibly in tailor-made systems such as ICl in solid argon, CO in solid hydrogen, etc. It is not surprising therefore that infrared blue shifts of this kind have not been reported as yet in the literature.

A physical explanation of vibrational blue shifts would be that, as the solvent-solute distances become smaller, the electrons of the solute, simply because of the Pauli exclusion principle, meet a high energy barrier as they attempt to crowd into the already filled orbitals of the solvent. The presence of repulsive interactions often has the effect of increasing the molecular force constant, since electrons of the solute as well as the solvent are forced into the molecular bond. U'' is positive under these conditions. In addition, an inverse anharmonicity might occur. The situation at small intermolecular separations may be likened to the quantum mechanical problem of a harmonic oscillator in a box. To calculate the vibrational energy levels for such a system one must solve the harmonic oscillator problem numerically using finite boundary conditions (26). Characteristic values are nonintegral but approach integral quantum numbers as the cavity size approaches infinity. The energy levels for a harmonic oscillator in a box behave in a manner consistent with the above two sets of experimental results for C_2 and O_2. Since the actual repulsive potentials are not infinitely steep, however, one would not expect exact quantitative agreement between this theory and the experiments.

NONEXISTENCE OF SIMPLE THEORIES FOR COMPLEX PHENOMENA. From the above considerations, it is clear that a simple theory of infrared solvent shifts cannot exist. Buckingham's widely used theory, which expresses the intermolecular potential as a simple power series in the vibrational displacement coordinate, most probably would have to be extended to higher powers than ξ^2, in order to keep track of many of the interesting types of perturbations. This feature detracts from the usefulness of such a theory. For example, the repulsive contribution to $U(\tau, \xi)$ must be a sharply varying function of ξ, and it is not easy to see how a highly truncated expansion of $U(\tau, \xi)$ would have much validity over a very great range of ξ. The repulsive interactions are important even where they are not dominant. For this reason, theories like those of Pullin (39), where the solvent is considered to be only a dielectric medium, are incomplete. As Buckingham (9) has pointed out, the significance of a simple dielectric effect may have been overstressed in the past, since any attempt to attribute shifts solely to long-range dipolar attractions must necessarily fail because of the neglect of short-range (exchange) repulsive interactions. This was also pointed out by the present author (43). To this comment should also be included the effect of short-range (exchange) attractive interactions which occur when there are low-lying unfilled orbitals in the solvent or solute. This last consideration is especially important in the discussion of vibrational solvent shifts of trapped free radicals.

Bond-Bending Vibrations. The above discussion pertains particularly to bond-stretching vibrations. Many of the concepts can be carried over to bond-bending vibrations, except that now the direction and magnitude of the perturbation are somewhat more difficult to predict. Accompanying bond bending is a change in bond hybridization, and one must now ask, "What are the relative magnitudes of hybridization energies in solution and in the vapor phase?" The bending vibration may be accompanied by an oscillating local dipole moment in the molecule which the solvent electrons may be able to follow but which the solvent nuclei cannot. This kind of interaction can cause one hybrid form to be relatively more stable than the other when the molecule is placed in solution. The increased inversion barrier for NH_3 in argon (*35*) gives a possible illustration of this type of interaction.

The free radical NH_2 trapped in solid rare gases (*30, 46*) probably gives the best example of a simple molecule undergoing bond bending in the solid phase. Vibrational quanta from $n = 4$ to $n = 20$ in the excited electronic state have been observed. Transitions to odd quanta are much weaker than those to even ones at $4.2°$ K, since selection rules require an excited rotational level 31.9 cm.$^{-1}$ above the rotationless ground state to be populated in order for such transitions to take place. This can be accomplished by heating or preferably by optical pumping. These transitions have been observed weakly. The small perturbations observed allow one to say that the Renner splittings are not measurably changed in the solid phase—that is to say, the magnitude of the interaction between vibrational and electronic motions is not a strong function of the environment in this system.

Strong Fermi resonance occurs (*13*) in NH_2 between the vibrational levels (0 10 0) and (1 6 0) and between the levels (0 12 0) and (1 8 0). The first of the above two Fermi doublets appears more sensitive to environmental perturbations than the latter. For example, the energy splitting between the two members of the lower doublet decreases steadily from 196 cm.$^{-1}$ for vapor-phase NH_2 to 168 cm.$^{-1}$ for NH_2 in xenon. For the higher doublet, the splitting remains essentially constant at 167 cm.$^{-1}$ This peculiar effect is not understood. It does indicate that the anharmonicities which give rise to the Fermi interaction are affected to some extent by the environment.

The perturbations on the bond-bending vibrations of NH_2 in argon are not very appreciable in the II and Δ vibronic levels in the excited state up to (1 6 0). This is evidenced in Table I by the nearly constant matrix shift up to this point. In krypton and xenon, measurable vibrational perturbations also appear suddenly at this point, as indicated in the last two columns of Table I. Beyond (1 6 0) a gradually increasing vibrational red shift contribution occurs in all three matrices. These vibrational perturbations are small. The perturbation is largest in xenon, where, between (0 6 0) and (0 18 0), inclusive, it amounts to only about 70 cm.$^{-1}$ out of a total vibrational energy of about $10,000$ cm.$^{-1}$! It is not clear how a truncated Taylor's expansion in the vibrational coordinate could explain the observed sharp onset, and then the gradual increase, of the perturbation energy. The point here is that small perturbations do not necessarily justify the use of theories which use highly truncated expansions. For many "normal" solvent-solute systems at low vibrational amplitudes, Buckingham's expansion is expected to have wider applicability, but it is well to keep in mind the possible pitfalls in its use.

Solvent Effects on Electronic Transitions

The Physical Origin of Electronic Solvent Shifts. The motion of electrons in the solute sets up oscillatory fields in the solvent. The solvent thereby becomes polarized always in a sense opposite from the polarization of the solute by the solvent. These interactions may be described formally in a complete Hamiltonian (25) for the total solvent-solute system which includes coulombic interactions between the electrons and nuclei of the solute with those of the solvent. If the intermolecular distances are not too close, these fields can give rise to an attractive potential between solute and solvent which dominates the effect of exchange repulsive interactions. The electrons of both the solvent and the solute will therefore tend to delocalize into the intermolecular bond. The situation is of course identical to that discussed in the vibrational case. The vibrational perturbation resulted in a decrease in vibrational force constant. Here we are interested in the effect of delocalization on the various contributions to the electronic energy terms. Qualitatively one would expect the electrons of the solute to be now less firmly bound to the molecular frame than in the free molecule. Therefore electronic excitation energies should be smaller, giving electronic red shifts. This is generally the observed direction when both the solute and solvent are reasonably nonpolar.

Quantitative Calculations for Nonpolar Interactions. Unfortunately, just as for vibrational perturbations, any oversimplified quantum mechanical theory of electronic spectral shifts is bound to be invalid. Such theories suffer for two main reasons and a number of minor ones. When the many-body problem is reduced to a second-order perturbation approach, similar to that encountered in London dispersion theory, the same kind of errors are present which arise in any calculation of this type. It is known for instance, that except for H_2 or He interactions, calculated energies are small by a factor of 2. Part of this error is caused by the necessary reduction for complex systems of the perturbation sum to a single term involving an average oscillator strength and an average excitation energy (37). Even when the dispersion calculation is carried out correctly, the details of the electronic structure of the interacting molecules may cause higher than dipole terms to become important at the intermolecular distances of interest. For low-lying excited states, the effect of the environment on the e^2/r_{ij} terms for the outer electrons must be considered. Last, but not least, the repulsive exchange interactions are important and must be considered in any calculation which is to describe spectral shifts. It would be truly remarkable if this contribution to the intermolecular energy remained constant upon electronic excitation!

Using the London theory in its simplest form, and with the above reservations, one can show that the solvent shift of electronic excitation energy for attractive interactions only is (42)

$$\Delta E = - \frac{3}{8} z \alpha_v \alpha_u E_u r_{uv}^{-6}$$

where α_v is the molecular polarizability of the solvent, α_u is the molecular polarizability of the solute, E_u is the transition energy for the electronic transition in the solute, r_{uv} is the intermolecular distance, and z is the nearest neighbor density. The intermolecular distance and the effect of repulsive interactions are difficult to evaluate (42), but this equation does give shifts of the right order of magnitude.

Polar Interactions. For molecules which have permanent dipole moments in either or both of the combining electronic states, a red-shift or blue-shift contribution to the energy can result, depending upon whether the dipole moment increases or decreases in the excited state. Many n-π^* transitions are accompanied by a decrease of dipole moment in the excited state, since the transition takes a lone-pair nonbonding electron from the outside of the molecule towards the center of the molecule. The nonbonding electrons make a large contribution to the dipole moment and by essentially removing half of this contribution the dipole moment in the excited state is expected to decrease to perhaps half its ground state value. Because of this, n-π^* transitions of molecules in a nonpolar environment are usually blue-shifted (48) relative to the vapor phase. If the environment is also polar, so that dipole-dipole interactions are prominent, the effect may be very large, amounting to a few kilocalories per mole in some instances.

The spectrum of NH_2 in argon presents a 25-cm.$^{-1}$ blue shift which can be ascribed to this effect. The molecule is bent in the ground state, the angle being 103.3° which is about that of water. The dipole moment may be comparable to that in water. In the excited state the NH_2 molecule becomes linear and the dipole moment vanishes. Assuming a dipole moment of 1.0 debye in the ground state, a calculation of the dipole-induced-dipole interaction energy gives 40 cm.$^{-1}$ (112 cal. per mole). The usual van der Waals dispersion red shift must be added to this blue-shift contribution to obtain the over-all shift. A 15-cm.$^{-1}$ contribution from this source would therefore explain the observed value. In krypton the two contributions must approximately cancel, since the over-all electronic shift is very small. In xenon the dispersion red shift dominates the dipole contribution (see Table I).

Repulsive Interactions. In the case where the solute is cramped by a small solvent cavity, the electronic energies increase compared with the free molecule energies. The prototype problem here is that of a hydrogen atom or a helium atom in a box (12), and the quantum mechanical electronic problem may be handled by a method similar to that used for the harmonic-oscillator-in-a-box problem. Blue shifts will occur which increase with increasing orbital size. In a real solvent the repulsive potentials are not infinitely steep, so that this effect on the electronic energy levels will not be so pronounced as that predicted from the rigid-box model. Nevertheless an electron in a Rydberg orbital of a size comparable to or larger than the solvent cavity size is expected to meet considerable repulsive resistance with the environment, and large blue shifts are expected for these transitions.

Ionization Potentials in Dense Media. Now one has the right to ask "What about the ionization potential? Is it not expected to be smaller for a molecule immersed in a dielectric medium, and if so, how is this fact compatible with the increase of energy in the Rydberg transitions?" A detailed quantitative answer to this question cannot be made as yet, since no calculations have been carried out. A good model would be a hydrogen atom in a potential well of depth corresponding approximately to the energy of the lowest unfilled orbitals of the solvent. If the solvent states lie above the solid state ionization potential of the solute, the potential acts like a barrier through which the electron must tunnel in order to leave the solute. The electronic energy spacings of such a system would indeed increase in the lower states, then start to converge and broaden as the top of the barrier is approached. The broadening would be caused by an autoionization process as the partly bound electron tunnels through the barrier into the lattice. If the solvent states are comparable to or lower than the ionization potential of the solute, a discussion of the ionization of the solute molecule becomes indistinct, since the electronic states of solvent and solute are so thoroughly mixed. The ionization process in this case corresponds to a promotion of a solute electron into the exciton band of the solvent-solute system.

Effect of Environment on e^2/r_{ij} Terms. In the case of a trapped helium atom, as well as for molecular solutes, in attractive or repulsive environments, consideration of the effect of the environment upon the e^2/r_{ij} repulsive terms in the solute

Hamiltonian becomes important. If the environment is attractive, the solute eigenfunctions have a greater expanse than in the free molecule because of the attractive induction interactions of the solute electrons with the environment. The e^2/r_{ij} terms are accordingly expected to be smaller than in the free molecule. On the other hand, if the environment is repulsive, the eigenfunctions of the solute must go to zero at large distances much faster than they do in the free molecule. Since the eigenfunctions are normalized, their amplitude must increase near the center of the solute molecule. One then expects the e^2/r_{ij} terms to be larger than in the free molecule.

These electron repulsion terms are important in molding the details of the electronic eigenstates. In particular, they remove configurational degeneracies and are responsible for configuration interaction. These energy contributions are therefore expected to be changed when the molecule is placed in the solvent. This change in electron correlation energy is an important contribution to solvent shifts for electronic transitions. It has been essentially ignored in all previous calculations of electronic spectral shifts. For example, in a molecule like benzene the first excited configuration consists of six states, three singlets and three triplets, one pair of the singlets and one of the triplets being doubly degenerate. In the absence of e^2/r_{ij} terms all of these states would have the same energy, aside from some extremely small magnetic contributions. The presence of such terms causes the lowest of these states to lie 22,000 cm.$^{-1}$ below the highest one! Some of this energy difference is caused by diagonal coulomb and exchange contributions to the energy which result from the e^2/r_{ij} interactions. A smaller part is due to interaction with other configurations. Considering attractive solute-solvent interactions only, the diagonal energy contribution to the total electronic energy is decreased in the solid. A small percentage perturbation on the e^2/r_{ij} terms, particularly when they are large as in the case of benzene, can lead to a solvent shift contribution of comparable or larger magnitude than the usual dispersion red shift. For repulsive interactions, the e^2/r_{ij} terms increase, and again this contribution for some states may dominate the usual repulsive blue shifts. Effects of this kind are of especial interest in the low-lying electronic states of free radicals and molecules, since here e^2/r_{ij} effects are larger and other contributions to the shifts are smaller than for higher electronic states.

Environmental Effects on Singlet-Triplet Splittings. One important manifestation of the above effect concerns singlet-triplet splitting in molecules having no atoms other than hydrogen and first-row atoms. This splitting is caused directly by e^2/r_{ij} terms and should therefore be sensitive, in the way outlined above, to the presence of an environment. If polar contributions to the shifts are neglected and one assumes an attractive environment, a singlet state should be shifted to lower energy and its corresponding triplet state should be shifted to higher energy than predicted solely by a London dispersion-type argument. A number of singlet and triplet states of molecules in solid media have now been studied (42). In those cases where the interactions are attractive the triplet state is indeed found to be shifted very little to the red or shifted to the blue relative to the vapor phase spectrum. In one case (17) where solid hydrogen was used as matrix, and the interactions are expected to be repulsive, the reverse of the above was found. There is left little doubt that such solvent shift contributions are present and important. One should therefore not carry solvent shift arguments for singlet states over to triplet states without regard for these effects. For example, $\pi-\pi^*$ transitions, which are red-shifted for singlets, may show no shift or even a small blue shift in the lowest singlet-triplet transition.

Literature Cited

(1) Adrian, F. J., Cochran, E. L., Bowers, V. A., *J. Chem. Phys.* **36,** 1661 (1962).
(2) Allin, E. J., Feldman, T., Welsh, H. L., *Ibid.,* **24,** 1116 (1956).
(3) Allin, E. J., Hare, W. F. J., MacDonald, R. E., *Phys. Rev.* **98,** 554 (1955).
(4) Bass, A. M., Broida, H. P., eds., "Formation and Trapping of Free Radicals," Academic Press, New York, 1960.
(5) Broida, H. P., Peyron, M., *J. Chem. Phys.* **30,** 139 (1959).
(6) *Ibid.,* **32,** 1068 (1960).
(7) Brown, H. W., Pimentel, G. C., *Ibid.,* **29,** 883 (1958).
(8) Buckingham, A. D., *Proc. Roy. Soc. (London)* **A248,** 169 (1958).
(9) *Ibid.,* **A255,** 34 (1960).
(10) Cole, T., Pritchard, H. O., Davidson, N. R., McConnell, H. M., *Mol. Phys.* **1,** 406 (1958).
(11) Dalby, F. W., Duardo, J., unpublished manuscript.
(12) DeGroot, S. R., ten Seldam, C. A., *Physica* **12,** 669 (1946); **18,** 891 (1952).
(13) Dressler, K., Ramsay, D. A., *Phil. Trans. Roy. Soc. (London)* **A251,** 553 (1959).
(14) Dressler, K., Schnepp, O., private communication.
(15) Duardo, J., unpublished manuscript.
(16) Duardo, J., Robinson, G. W., unpublished manuscript.
(17) El Sayed, M. A., Robinson, G. W., *Mol. Phys.* **4,** 273 (1961), Table I.
(18) Ewing, G. E., Thompson, W. E., Pimentel, G. C., *J. Chem. Phys.* **32,** 927 (1960).
(19) Foner, S. N., Cochran, E. L., Bowers, V. A., Jen, C. K., *Ibid.,* **32,** 963 (1960).
(20) Frosch, R. P., Robinson, G. W., unpublished manuscript.
(21) Goldfarb, T. D., Pimentel, G. C., *J. Am. Chem. Soc.* **82,** 1865 (1960).
(22) Hare, W. F. J., Allin, E. J., Welsh, H. L., *Phys. Rev.* **99,** 1887 (1955).
(23) Harvey, K. B., Brown, H. W., *J. Chim. Phys.* **56,** 745 (1959).
(24) Herzberg, G., "Spectra of Diatomic Molecules," 2nd ed., Van Nostrand, New York, 1950.
(25) Hirschfelder, J. O., Curtiss, C. F., Bird, R. B., "Molecular Theory of Gases and Liquids," pp. 922 et seq., Wiley, New York, 1954.
(26) Keyser, L. F., unpublished results.
(27) Keyser, L. F., Robinson, G. W., *J. Am. Chem. Soc.* **82,** 5245 (1960).
(28) Kwok, J., Keyser, L. F., unpublished manuscript.
(29) Kwok, J., Robinson, G. W., *J. Chem. Phys.* (June 15, 1962).
(30) McCarty, M., Jr., Ph.D. thesis, Johns Hopkins University, Baltimore, Md., 1960.
(31) McCarty, M., Jr., Robinson, G. W., *J. Chim. Phys.* **56,** 723 (1959).
(32) McCarty, M., Jr., Robinson, G. W., *Mol. Phys.* **2,** 415 (1959).
(33) McCarty, M., Jr., Robinson, G. W., Preprints, "Informal Discussion on Free Radical Stabilization," Sheffield, September 1958; *J. Chem. Phys.* **28,** 349, 350 (1958); *Can. J. Phys.* **36,** 1590 (1958); *J. Am. Chem. Soc.* **81,** 4472 (1959); *J. Chim. Phys.* **56,** 723 (1959).
(34) McLennan, J. C., McLeod, J. H., *Nature* **123,** 160 (1929).
(35) Milligan, D. E., Hexter, R. M., Dressler, K., *J. Chem. Phys.* **34,** 1009 (1961).
(36) Pimentel, G. C., Bulanin, M. O., Van Thiel, M., *Ibid.,* **36,** 500 (1962) and papers cited.
(37) Pitzer, K. S., *Advan. Chem. Phys.* **2,** 59 (1959).
(38) Pople, J. A., *Mol. Phys.* **3,** 16 (1960).
(39) Pullin, A. D. E., *Proc. Roy. Soc. (London)* **A255,** 39 (1960).
(40) Ramsay, D. A., *Advan. Spectry.* **1,** 1 (1959).
(41) Ramsay, D. A., in "Formation and Trapping of Free Radicals," A. M. Bass and H. P. Broida, eds., pp. 169–211, Academic Press, New York, 1960.
(42) Robinson, G. W., *J. Mol. Spectry.* **6,** 58 (1961).
(43) Robinson, G. W., in "Methods of Experimental Physics," D. Williams, ed., Vol. 3, Academic Press, New York, 1962.
(44) Robinson, G. W., McCarty, M., Jr., *Can. J. Phys.* **36,** 1590 (1958).
(45) Robinson, G. W., McCarty, M., Jr., *J. Am. Chem. Soc.* **82,** 1859 (1960).
(46) Robinson, G. W., McCarty, M., Jr., *J. Chem. Phys.* **30,** 999 (1959).
(47) Schnepp, O., Dressler, K., *Ibid.,* **32,** 1682 (1960).
(48) Sidman, J. W., *Chem. Revs.* **58,** 689 (1958).
(49) Walsh, A. D., *J. Chem. Soc. (London)* **1953,** 2288–96.

RECEIVED May 16, 1962. Contribution 2841, California Institute of Technology. Work supported in part by U. S. Atomic Energy Commission and U. S. Army Research Office.

3

Spectroscopic Studies of Some Excited Inorganic Free Radicals

NORMAN BASCO

Department of Chemistry, The University, Sheffield 10, Yorks, England

Vibrationally excited nitric oxide, arising directly from the absorption of energy in excess of that required for dissociation, has been observed spectroscopically following the flash photolysis of nitrosyl halides. The generality of this type of process is discussed in relation to the photolysis of cyanogen halides and of ozone. A series of reactions in which an electronically excited oxygen atom reacts with ammonia, hydrogen, hydrogen chloride, methane, or water to produce vibrationally excited hydroxyl radicals is described and related to a class of exothermic abstraction reactions in which the newly formed bond is always excited. Vibrational excitation of the cyanogen radical and of nitric oxide has been achieved without chemical reaction by prior electronic excitation. In the former case a virtually infinite vibrational "temperature" was attained. Relaxation, resonance energy exchange, and the chemical properties of vibrationally excited species are also described.

M any inorganic free radicals can be produced by flash photolysis in sufficient concentrations to be detected spectroscopically in absorption. Usually the radical is observed to be in equilibrium at the temperature of the system and this is always so within 1 msec. after the photoflash. In some cases, however, there may be extreme departures from equilibrium conditions and in these the vibrational "temperature" of the radicals may be some thousands of degrees above that of the other degrees of freedom.

Three types of processes responsible which may lead to this situation and in which inorganic free radicals are involved are described.

Experimental

The apparatus has been described in detail (7). Flash energies of 1600 to 2500 joules were obtained by discharging a 50-μf. condenser at 8 to 10 kv. through a quartz tube 50 cm. long containing Kr at ~ 8-cm. Hg pressure. The reaction vessel, also 50 cm. long and of quartz, was double-walled, the annular space between the vessel and the outer jacket being 0.6 cm. and containing gaseous or liquid filters when required. It lay alongside the flash lamp and the arrangement was enclosed within a cylindrical reflector of aluminum coated with magnesium oxide.

The spectroscopic flash lamp dissipated 100 joules (2 μf. at 10 kv.) and was triggered from the photoflash by means of a photocell, delay unit, and spark gap, so that photographs of the spectra could be taken at any time from slightly before the peak of the photoflash up to 30 msec. All delay times quoted are relative to the shortest taken as zero. The output of the spectroscopic lamp after passing lengthways through the reaction vessel was focused on the slit of a Hilger Littrow spectrograph.

In all experiments, the reactant was mixed with a large excess of an inert gas (usually N_2) to prevent the temperature of the system rising more than a few degrees.

The Hydroxyl Radical

Mixtures of ozone (4 to 6 mm. of Hg pressure) and ammonia, hydrogen, hydrogen chloride, methane, or water (up to 150 mm. of Hg pressure) were flashed (7). In each system the spectrum of the OH radical was observed in the 0,0; 1,0; 1,1; 2,1; 2,2; and 3,2 bands of the $A^2\Sigma^+ - X^2\pi$ system. Transitions from vibrationally excited levels were visible for 15 μsec. and those from the zeroth level for up to 75 μsec. In addition, the spectra of NH, O_2, and ClO were recorded, the latter persisting for 1 msec. The only spectrum visible after this time was that of formaldehyde.

The primary step must be

$$O_3 + h\nu \rightarrow O^1D + O_2 \tag{1}$$

the ^1D atom being 45 kcal. per mole above the ground (^3P) state. This is proved merely from the fact that OH is observed at all at room temperature, since the reactions

$$O^3P + HR \rightarrow OH + R \tag{2}$$

where R = H, OH, Cl, NH_2, or CH_3, all have an appreciable activation energy.

The reaction with H_2O is actually endothermic by some 16 kcal. per mole and the others are approximately thermoneutral and, to produce OH radicals with two vibrational quanta, an additional 20 kcal. is required.

The reactions responsible are therefore

$$O^1D + H_2 \rightarrow OH^* + H \tag{3}$$

$$O^1D + HCl \rightarrow OH^* + Cl \tag{4}$$

$$O^1D + H_2O \rightarrow OH^* + OH \tag{5}$$

$$O^1D + CH_4 \rightarrow OH^* + CH_3 \tag{6}$$

$$O^1D + NH_3 \rightarrow OH^* + NH_2 \tag{7}$$

where OH* represents a vibrationally excited OH radical in its ground electronic state. These reactions are exothermic by 45 kcal. (29 kcal. for H_2O) and some, at least, of this energy appears in the form of vibration of the OH bond.

These are examples of a class of exothermic reactions of the type

$$A + BCD \rightarrow AB + CD \tag{8}$$

in which the newly formed bond, AB, can possess up to the full exothermicity of the reaction in the form of vibrational energy. The molecule CD, however, has not been observed to be vibrationally excited. Some further examples of this type are relevant to the flash photolysis of ozone.

When ozone is flashed with only inert gases present, vibrationally excited oxygen, O_2^*, is produced (13) in the reaction

$$O^1D + O_3 \rightarrow O_2^* + O_2 \tag{9}$$

Molecules with up to 20 quanta of vibrational energy have been observed (4), corresponding to 75 kcal. In the presence of excess water, ammonia, etc., this reaction is suppressed, though usually the spectra of O_2^* and OH^* occur together, showing that Reactions 3 to 7 and 9 are of comparable speed.

The rapidity with which the OH disappears is explained by the reaction

$$OH + O_3 \rightarrow HO_2 + O_2 \tag{10}$$

though the HO_2 radical has not been observed spectroscopically—in this system probably because of the reaction

$$HO_2 + O_3 \rightarrow OH + 2O_2 \tag{11}$$

Reactions 10 and 11 explain why the quantum yield for the decomposition of wet ozone by ultraviolet radiation greatly exceeds 2 (14). In the absence of water, the yield is much less, but also > 2 because of the reaction

$$O_2^*(v \geqslant 17) + O_3 \rightarrow O^1D + 2O_2 \tag{12}$$

The 17th level has the minimum energy required for this reaction and the fact that levels higher than the 20th have not been observed may be explained by the increasing rapidity of this reaction.

Following Reactions 3 to 7 the other fragments can also react further—e.g.,

$$H + O_3 \rightarrow OH + O_2 \tag{13}$$

$$Cl + O_3 \rightarrow ClO + O_2 \tag{14}$$

The ClO spectrum is observed for 1 msec. and also that of NH (from NH_2) and HCHO (from CH_3). Reaction 13 has been studied by introducing H atoms into O_3 (16) by flashing Cl_2 in the presence of O_3 (15) (using a glass filter to prevent appreciable decomposition of the O_3). In both cases the radicals produced are vibrationally excited and a similar reaction with Br_2 produces excited BrO (15); these and other examples of Reaction 8 have been discussed (4, 5, 18, 20).

The production of OH^* described here has two features of special interest, being the only case where the vibrational energy is supplied by the electronic energy of an atom and where the proportion of energy appearing as vibration has been estimated. It appears that at least 30% of the OH radicals produced are vibrationally excited and this approximate figure is obtained on the basis that the relative proportions observed do not represent an appreciable relaxation from a state of higher excitation. This appears to be a reasonable assumption in this case, since Reaction 10 may well be faster than relaxation.

Nitric Oxide

Vibrationally excited NO has been produced in two ways and, at least in the first method described, its free radical properties are not important.

Electronic Excitation of NO. Nitric oxide absorbs discretely in the regions 2270, 2150, and 2050 corresponding to the 0,0; 1,0; and 2,0 bands of the γ system $(A^2\Sigma^+ - X^2\pi)$ and, subsequently, either by fluorescence or collisional quenching, the ground state is regained. With pressures of 1 to 5 mm. of Hg and a 1600-joule flash the following sequence of reactions produces sufficient concentrations of vibrationally excited NO to be observed spectroscopically in absorption (*1*)

$$NO.X^2\pi(v = 0) + h\nu \rightarrow NO.A^2\Sigma^+(v = 0,1,2) \tag{15}$$

$$NO.A^2\Sigma^+(v = 0,1,2) \rightarrow NO.X^2\pi(v = 0,1,2,3..) + h\nu \tag{16}$$

$$NO.A^2\Sigma^+(v = 0,1,2) + M \rightarrow NO.X^2\pi(v = 0,1,2,3..) + M \tag{17}$$

The maximum concentration of $NO(v = 1)$ observed is 0.1 mm. of Hg and this represents a 500-fold overpopulation of this level at room temperature. The second excited level can also just be detected, but its concentration and that of higher levels are rapidly reduced by resonance exchange reactions of the type

$$NO(v = 2) + NO(v = 0) = 2NO(v = 1) \tag{18}$$

Equilibrium is regained by the reactions

$$NO(v = 1) + M \rightarrow NO(v = 0) + M + K.E. \tag{19}$$

but this is a relatively slow process whose rate with various molecules, M, can be measured by plate photometry for up to 250 μsec. The probability of Reaction 19 per collision is 7×10^{-3} for H_2O, 3.6×10^{-4} for NO, 2.5×10^{-5} for CO, and 4×10^{-7} for N_2. The figures for CO and N_2, although very low, are still higher than expected and it seems probable that in these cases the reaction involves near-resonance exchange

$$NO(v = 1) + CO(v = 0) + K.E. \rightarrow NO(v = 0) + CO(v = 1) \tag{20}$$

the calculated rate of which is in satisfactory agreement with the experimental results. This reaction is supported by the observation (*2*) of $CO(v = 1)$ in the vacuum ultraviolet.

Flash Photolysis of Nitrosyl Halides. Both NOCl and NOBr absorb throughout the visible and ultraviolet regions of the spectrum, the absorption increasing greatly in the ultraviolet below 2500 A. The N-Cl and N-Br bonds are weak (38 and 28 kcal. per mole), so that when photolyzed with the full output of a flash lamp, most of the decomposition follows absorption of energy very considerably in excess (70 to 120 kcal. per mole) of that required to break the bond.

It now appears that at least half of this excess energy can be carried by the NO fragment in the form of vibration.

When the nitrosyl halides are flashed, NO is observed in absorption in the γ, β, δ, and ϵ systems at short delays with up to 11 quanta (55 kcal.) of vibrational energy (*6, 8*). The highest level observed is overpopulated by a factor of $\sim 10^{35}$ and, since the decay of NO* is extremely rapid, this probably represents an appreciable relaxation from a situation of an even higher degree of excitation. It is thus evident that the reaction

$$NOCl + h\nu \rightarrow NO.X^2\pi(v \gg 0) + Cl \tag{21}$$

could account for much, if not all, of the excess energy of the quantum absorbed.

Sometimes in a case of this sort the excess energy produces electronically excited fragments and this possibility was investigated. The only electronic excitation possible energetically here is the production of the $^4\pi$ state of NO, though this contravenes the spin conservation rule. The following sequence would then explain the results observed.

$$NOCl + h\nu \rightarrow NOCl^* \tag{22}$$

$$NOCl^* \rightarrow NOCl' \tag{23}$$

$$NOCl' \rightarrow NO.^4\pi(v = 0) + Cl \tag{24}$$

$$NO^4\pi + M \rightarrow NO.X^2\pi(v \gg 0) + M \tag{25}$$

Since NOCl is a singlet and the absorption strong, NOCl* is also a singlet. This state would cross a repulsive triplet state, NOCL', which dissociates. Unfortunately, very little information is available about the $^4\pi$ state of NO, but what theoretical and experimental evidence there is indicates that it lies 103 kcal. above the ground state. Therefore the radiation absorbed by the nitrosyl halides was restricted by means of a glacial acetic acid filter to 2500 A., so that the excess energy available was reduced to 75 or 85 kcal. Vibrationally excited NO was still observed, so that on present evidence the direct mechanism reaction (Equation 21) appears much more probable.

Three other interesting sets of results were obtained from this system. When Cl_2 + NOCl mixtures are flashed with a borosilicate glass filter, so that only the Cl_2 is appreciably photolyzed, the NOCl is decomposed in the reaction

$$Cl_2 + h\nu \rightarrow 2Cl \tag{26}$$

$$Cl + ClNO \rightarrow Cl_2 + NO \tag{27}$$

This is a reaction of the type

$$A + BCD \rightarrow AB + CD \tag{8}$$

and, as expected, no NO* was observed—i.e., it represented $<5\%$ of the NO produced.

The great efficiency of certain molecules in removing vibrational energy from another is often ascribed to resonance energy exchange. The NOCl system has provided the first clear demonstration that this process actually occurs. Mixtures of NOCl with various pressures of NO were flashed with a NO filter to prevent direct excitation of the NO. As the NO:NOCl ratio is increased, the spectra of all the excited levels are seen to decrease progressively in intensity—with the notable exception of the first excited level which increases. With additives other than NO, all levels decrease. Thus the reaction is

$$NO(v = n) + NO(v = 0) \rightarrow NO(v = n - 1) + NO(v = 1) \tag{28}$$

and this process continues until most of the excited NO is in the first excited level, since it is even faster than the reaction

$$NO(v = 1) + NO(v = 0) \rightarrow 2NO(v = 0) + K.E. \tag{29}$$

In connection with the decomposition of ozone with ultraviolet radiation, the energy chain (Reactions 9 and 12) explains the high quantum yield. A similar chain might be expected in the case of NOCl; thus

$$NOCl + h\nu \rightarrow NO(v \gg 8) + Cl \tag{30}$$

$$NO(v \gg 8) + NOCl \rightarrow 2NO + Cl \tag{31}$$

$$Cl + NOCl \rightarrow Cl_2 + NO \tag{32}$$

The quantum yield of 2 should be increased by Reaction 31 to 4; but at least with 2537-A. radiation, the quantum yield does not exceed 2 (9). It is clear that the efficiency of vibrationally excited species in chemical reactions may be limited. Thus although vibrationally excited N_2 produced in the reaction

$$N + NO \rightarrow N_2 + O \tag{33}$$

seems to have enough energy to decompose ozone (*17*), the fact that the quantum yield for ozone decomposition with visible light is ~ 2 implies that either or both of the reactions

$$O^3P + O_3 \rightarrow O_2^* + O_2 \tag{34}$$

$$O_2^* + O_2 \rightarrow O^3P + 2O_2 \tag{35}$$

are relatively inefficient.

The Cyanogen Radical

Cyanogen and the cyanogen halides absorb fairly weakly in the quartz ultraviolet region, but when these compounds are flash-photolyzed, the CN radical produced can be observed spectroscopically in the $v = 0, \pm 1,2$ sequences of the violet ($B^2\Sigma - X^2\Sigma$) system and in the red ($A^2\pi - X^2\Sigma$) system.

All vibrational levels of the ground electronic state are populated up to at least $v'' = 6$ (*3*). The relative population of the first five levels has been measured as a function of time and of pressure in the range $C_2N_2 = 0.14$ to 56 mm., $CNBr = 3.6 \times 10^{-3}$ to 36 mm., and $CNI = 2.5 \times 10^{-2}$ to 0.27 mm. At short delay times and moderately low pressures, these populations are approximately equal—i.e., there is an infinite vibrational temperature. In about 100 μsec. all excited levels decay, but the zeroth level can be followed for ~ 600 μsec. At very low pressures, the population of the fourth excited level can exceed that of the zeroth level by a factor of 4 and the decay is much slower.

These observations could be explained in two ways. First, since the energy of the radiation absorbed exceeds that required to break the C—C, C—Br, or C—I bond by 35 to 85 kcal. per mole, it seems possible that some of this could appear as vibrational energy of the CN radical, just as it does in the case of NO produced from NOCl or NOBr. Thus, for example,

$$CNBr + h\nu \rightarrow CNX^2\Sigma(v > 0) + Br \tag{36}$$

Secondly, following the photolysis,

$$RCN + h\nu \rightarrow R + CN.X^2\Sigma(v = 0) \tag{37}$$

where R = CN, Br, or I, the CN radical could absorb radiation in the regions 3590, 3883, 4216, and 4606 A. and thus undergo excitation in a similar way to that observed when NO is flashed:

$$CN.X^2\Sigma(v = 0) + h\nu \rightarrow CN.B^2\Sigma(v = 0,1,2) \tag{38}$$

$$CN.B^2\Sigma(v = 0,1,2) \rightarrow CN.X^2\Sigma(v = 0,1,2,3\ldots) + h\nu \tag{39}$$

$$CN.B^2\Sigma(v = 0,1,2) + M \rightarrow CN.X^2\Sigma(v = 0,1,2,3\ldots) + M \tag{40}$$

To distinguish between these mechanisms, CNBr was flashed using a solution of $NiSO_4$ as filter to remove radiation between about 3500 and 4300 A. This solution also absorbs strongly in the ultraviolet below about 2200 A., so that the results were compared with those obtained using various mixtures of methyl and ethyl alcohols and of acetic acid and water as filters, these substances absorbing only in the shorter wavelength region. With the $NiSO_4$ filter, no vibrationally excited CN was observed, but with all other filters it could clearly be seen, even when the total amount of CN produced was less. It follows that it is the radiation in the region 3500 to 4300 A. which is responsible for the production of vibrationally excited CN—an upper limit of 6% could be due to the direct mechanism (Reaction 36).

In some ways this is an unexpected conclusion, since the idea that some of the excess energy should appear as vibration is, intuitively, very plausible. There is, however, apart from the case of the nitrosyl halides, very little experimental evidence that this in fact occurs. The reaction

$$CH_2CO + h\nu \rightarrow CH_2 + CO \tag{41}$$

produces $CO(v \lessgtr 2)$ which is observed in the vacuum ultraviolet (12) and there is indirect evidence that the CH_2 radical produced from diazomethane (11) and various radicals of the type CHXY produced from polyhalomethanes (19) are also vibrationally excited. There are, on the other hand, reasons for believing that the reaction

$$O_3 + h\nu \rightarrow O_2.{}^3\Sigma_g^-(v \gg 0) + O^3P \tag{42}$$

does not contribute significantly (if at all) to the production of the O_2^* observed in the flash photolysis of ozone (5), although there is up to 125 kcal. of excess energy.

In the production of CN*, Reactions 38 to 40 cannot by themselves account for the observed distribution. Knowing the relevant transition probabilities, it can be calculated that, after this sequence, only 15% of the radicals will be vibrationally excited. Since the CN radical absorbs very much more strongly than NO, the process of excitation can occur many times and can involve excited levels as well as the zeroth level. If all the CN radicals are initially in the zeroth level, then after six excitation processes it can be shown that 50% of them will be excited—of which half will have two or more vibrational quanta. After 14 processes 70% will be excited and, of these, half will have three or more quanta. After about 25 to 30 processes, the difference in the population of the first five levels would be <10%, a close approximation to the observed distribution. Since each process takes about 10^{-8} second, there is time, unless the relaxation is extremely rapid (high pressures of CNR) or the intensity of the photoflash is low, for the observed distribution to be attained. Ultimately, in the absence of relaxation, an infinite vibrational temperature results, though, of course, the radical dissociates before this by absorption from higher levels. The relaxation rate is in fact very high—only 100 collisions between $CN(v = 4)$ and CNBr being required to remove a vibrational quantum. At the lowest pressures used, a CN radical will suffer only one collision in ~ 30 μsec. with a CNBr molecule, and, even at the more usual pressures, an excited CN radical lasts ~ 2 μsec., which is still a long time compared to the time required for excitation.

The decay of the zeroth level is found to be second-order with respect to the concentration of CN. The value of the rate constant obtained, which can be expressed as 6×10^{11} cc. mole^{-1} sec.$^{-1}$ or as 1.6×10^{16} cc.^{2} mole^{-2} sec.$^{-1}$ with N_2 as the third body, depended on the absolute estimation of CN concentration, but is probably accurate to within an order of magnitude. The latter figure is close to that obtained for halogen atoms.

Vibrationally excited CS radicals have been observed in the photolysis of carbon disulfide (10) and it seems likely that the mechanism here is similar to that involved in the excitation of the CN radical, though the alternative mechanism has not been investigated.

This type of excitation is evidently of general applicability and should be taken into account whenever a strongly absorbing radical or molecule is produced in a system subjected to high intensity radiation. Likewise, the production of excited radicals and molecules in atom abstraction reactions, being a general phenomenon, could raise problems in a wide field of kinetic studies. The outstanding questions here and in the case of reactions of the type illustrated by the nitrosyl halides—of the proportion of molecules produced in excited vibrational levels, the distribution of molecules among the various levels, and any special chemical reactivity the possession of vibrational energy may confer on them—largely remain to be studied.

Acknowledgment

The author gratefully acknowledges the award of an I.C.I. fellowship, during the tenure of which the experimental work described was done.

Literature Cited

(1) Basco, N., Callear, A. B. C., Norrish, R. G. W., *Proc. Roy. Soc.* A260, 459 (1961).
(2) Basco, N., Callear, A. B. C., Norrish, R. G. W., to be published.
(3) Basco, N., Nicholas, J. E., Norrish, R. G. W., Vickers, W. H. J., to be published.
(4) Basco, N., Norrish, R. G. W., *Can. J. Chem.* 38, 1769 (1960).
(5) Basco, N., Norrish, R. G. W., *Discussions Faraday Soc.* (April 1962).
(6) Basco, N., Norrish, R. G. W., *Nature* 189, 455 (1961).
(7) Basco, N., Norrish, R. G. W., *Proc. Roy. Soc.* A260, 293 (1961).
(8) *Ibid.*, in press.
(9) Basco, N., Norrish, R. G. W., Wayne, R. P., to be published.
(10) Callear, A. B., Norrish, R. G. W., *Nature* 188, 53 (1960).
(11) Frey, H. M., *Proc. Roy. Soc.* A250, 409 (1959).
(12) Herzberg, G., *Proc. Chem. Soc.* 1959, 116.
(13) McGrath, W. D., Norrish, R. G. W., *Proc. Roy. Soc.* A242, 265 (1957).
(14) *Ibid.*, A254, 317 (1960).
(15) McGrath, W. D., Norrish, R. G. W., *Z. physik. Chem.* 15, 245 (1958).
(16) McKinley, J. D., Garvin, D., Boudart, M. J., *J. Chem. Phys.* 23, 784 (1955).
(17) Morgan, J. E., Phillips, L. F., Schiff, H. I., *Discussions Faraday Soc.* (April 1962).
(18) Polanyi, J. C., *J. Chem. Phys.* 31, 1338 (1959).
(19) Simons, J. P., Yarwood, A. J., *Trans. Faraday Soc.* 57, 2167 (1961).
(20) Smith, F. T., *J. Chem. Phys.* 31, 1352 (1959).

RECEIVED May 8, 1962.

4

Mass Spectrometry of Inorganic Free Radicals

S. N. FONER and R. L. HUDSON

Applied Physics Laboratory, The Johns Hopkins University, Silver Spring, Md.

Use of a mass spectrometer with a collision-free molecular beam sampling system has facilitated observations of certain free radicals, such as O atoms, and excited species which are readily destroyed by wall collisions. Data were obtained on the production of HO_2 by several reactions and on the rate constant for the homogeneous reaction of two HO_2 radicals. Electrical discharges in nitrogen compounds were used to produce N, NH_2, N_2H_3, and $HN_2(CH_3)_2$ radicals, and the unstable compounds N_2N_2, N_3H_3, N_4H_4, and HN_2CH_3. Metastable He and N atoms and N_2 molecules were obtained from electrical discharges. Substantial concentrations of $N(^2P)$ and $N(^2D)$ atoms were observed, in addition to ground state $N(^4S)$ atoms, from an electrical discharge in a mixture of N_2 with a large excess of helium. Nitrogen molecules in this system have excitation energies up to several electron volts.

Mass spectrometric studies have furnished considerable information on free radicals in gaseous systems. The scope of these studies includes: detection and identification of free radical species, measurement of radical concentrations, determination of radical ionization potentials, determination of bond-dissociation energies, and elucidation of the role of free radicals in chemical reactions. In addition, mass spectrometry has recently been extended to the investigation of electronically excited atoms and molecules. One aspect of information on a free radical which is not accessible to mass spectrometry is knowledge of its geometry (bond lengths and angles). Fortunately, for simple free radicals this information is often obtainable by optical spectroscopy.

A major problem in mass spectrometry of free radicals is the extraction of the gas sample from the reacting system and its transport into the ionization chamber without materially changing the composition of the sample and, in particular, avoiding loss of the free radicals in the process. In some cases, spurious free radical signals may be produced in the mass spectrometer by ion-molecule reactions and by reactions of incoming molecules with the heated filament. The mass spectrometer used in the studies reported here employs a collision-free molecular beam sampling system to avoid loss of reactive chemical species, and is designed to discriminate strongly against background signals and extraneous effects generally present in conventional instruments.

Although this paper is primarily concerned with inorganic free radicals and reactions of inorganic free radicals, it also discusses some unstable nitrogen compounds, and metastable atoms and molecules. The production, detection, and identification of free radicals, and the determination of bond-dissociation energies for the radicals, are considered in some detail. Radicals produced by heterogeneous reactions, such as the catalytic reactions on heated filaments in the mass spectrometer ion source, are not considered.

Experimental

The mass spectrometer and its collimated molecular beam sampling system (6, 12) have been especially designed for the study of reactive free radicals.

The gas being sampled enters the molecular beam system shown in Figure 1 through a small circular aperture in a glass or quartz cone and is collimated by two additional slits. The three sections of the molecular beam sampling system are separately evacuated by high speed diffusion pumps, the pressures typically being 10^{-3} mm. of Hg in the first section, 10^{-5} in the second section, and 10^{-7} in the ion source section. The molecular beam traverses a distance of 10 cm. from the entrance aperture to the center of the ion source. This corresponds to a transit time of about 230 μsec. for an oxygen molecule at room temperature. The molecular beam is mechanically interrupted at 170 cps. by a vibrating reed beam chopper in the first section in order to provide discrimination against background signals.

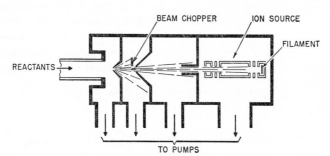

Figure 1.   Molecular beam sampling system of mass spectrometer

A block diagram of the mass spectrometer and the ion detection system is shown in Figure 2.

Molecules that are ionized by electron impact in the ion source are accelerated, sent through a conventional 90° magnetic sector analyzer, postaccelerated by a few thousand volts, and arrive at the electron multiplier detector. The output of the electron multiplier detector consists of pulses of about 10^{-13} coulomb per ion. The pulses are amplified and sent through a gated amplifier and an electronic switch which is synchronized with the beam chopper so that one of the ion counters records ions only when the beam chopper is open, the other only when the beam chopper is closed. The difference between the two ion counts represents the ion intensity contributed by the molecular beam, while the square root of the sum of the two ion counts is approximately equal to the standard deviation of the measurement and serves as a useful indicator of the quality of the data being obtained.

With this arrangement it has been possible to measure ion currents as low as 0.01 ion per second under favorable conditions, and measurements are often made down to the 0.1-ion per second level.

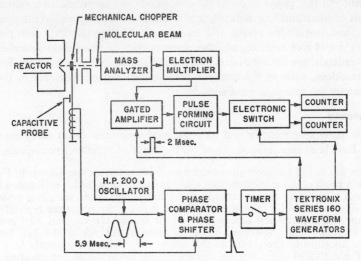

Figure 2. Block diagram of mass spectrometer and ion detector system

The lifetime of free radicals in very low pressure systems, such as mass spectrometer ion sources, is determined principally by the probability of destruction of the radical by surface reactions. The relative ease with which CH_3 radicals have been detected in conventional mass spectrometers and the corresponding difficulty in detecting O atoms are related to the speed of surface reactions, as shown by the following experiments.

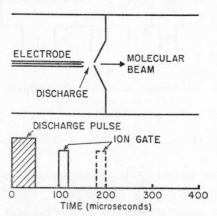

Figure 3. Pulsed discharge source of free radicals

Ion counter activated for 20-μsec. interval by adjustable ion gate

An electrical discharge source of free radicals was set up as indicated in Figure 3. The selected gas was introduced at high flow rate through the small center tube and was repetitively subjected to short discharge pulses (50 μsec.) just in front of the pinhole, producing each time a burst of radicals. For this experiment the beam chopper was inactivated and the ion counter was controlled by an adjustable electronic gate of 20-μsec. width.

The CH_3 intensity as a function of time from a pulsed discharge in CH_4 is shown in Figure 4. The transit time of the radicals into the instrument is responsible for the time lag of about 0.2 msec. between initiation of the discharge and the attainment of peak intensity. The decay of the CH_3 intensity with time is

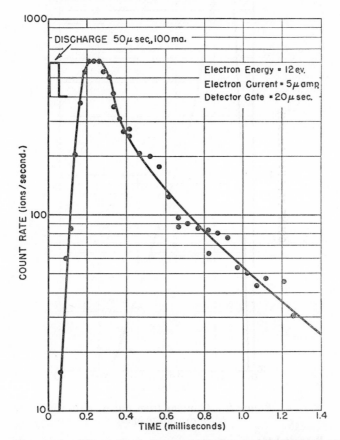

Figure 4. CH_3 radicals from pulsed electrical discharge in
CH_4

much slower than predicted on the assumption that the molecules in the trailing part of the pulse are the slow molecules in a Maxwell-Boltzmann velocity distribution. In contrast, O atoms from an electrical discharge in O_2 follow the curve shown in Figure 5. Here the O atom intensity decays by a factor of 100 in 0.7 msec. as compared to the decay by only a factor of 6 in this time for CH_3 radicals. The O atom curve is reasonably close to what is theoretically predicted for a step function of radicals having a Maxwell-Boltzmann distribution. This indicates that incoming O atoms are destroyed by single, or at most a few, collisions with the walls of the ion source. On the other hand, CH_3 radicals obviously survive many collisions with the walls. These experiments indicate why CH_3 radicals can be readily observed in instruments that may often not detect comparable inputs of O atoms and other highly reactive species. Experiments have shown that propyl radicals can undergo many thousands of collisions with cold surfaces without reaction (5). The fact that many hydrocarbon free radicals are observed in mass spectrometers is probably due to their ability to survive many wall collisions.

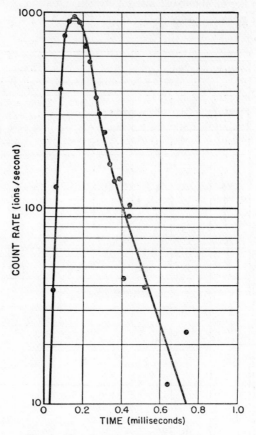

Figure 5.   O atoms from pulsed elec-trical discharge in O_2

Appearance Potential Measurements

The detection and identification of free radicals are intimately connected with measurements of appearance potentials. The appearance potential, $A(R_1^+)$, of the R_1^+ ion from the molecule R_1R_2 in the ionization process

$$R_1R_2 + e \rightarrow R_1^+ + R_2 + 2e \tag{1}$$

is given by

$$A(R_1^+) \geq I(R_1) + D(R_1 - R_2) \tag{2}$$

where $I(R_1)$ is the ionization potential of the radical R_1, $D(R_1 - R_2)$ is the dissociation energy of the $R_1 - R_2$ bond, and the inequality indicates that in some cases the fragments may possess excess energy. Since bond-dissociation energies are usually of the order of a few electron volts, it is possible in principle to detect the presence of the free radical R_1 by using electron energies well below the appearance potential of the R_1^+ ion from all stable molecules in the system that are potential sources of this ion. In many instances, the ionization potential of the radical can be measured rather accurately. This is useful not only in clearly establishing the identity of the radical, but by application of Equation 2 may lead to the determination of bond-dissociation energies. When the radicals are present in large concentrations, they can be analyzed as ordinary components in a gas mixture using electrons with 50- to 75-e.v. energy (*19*). However, for radicals at low concentration, operation of the mass spectrometer at reduced electron energy results in a much higher effective sensitivity for radical detection.

An example of an ionization potential measurement of a free radical is illustrated in Figure 6, where the radical being studied is OH produced by an electrical discharge in H_2O (*9*). In this method, which is one of several currently in use for appearance potential measurement, the ionization curve of the unknown is compared with the ionization curve of a reference gas, argon in this case, whose ionization potential is known spectroscopically. From the voltage scale shift required to match the curves in Figure 6, 2.59 e.v., and the ionization potential of argon, $I(Ar) = 15.76$ e.v., the ionization potential of OH was determined in this experiment as 13.17 e.v. Thus far, although the OH radical has been extensively studied by optical spectroscopy, a spectroscopic check on the value of $I(OH)$ quoted here has not been available. The appearance potential of the OH^+ ion

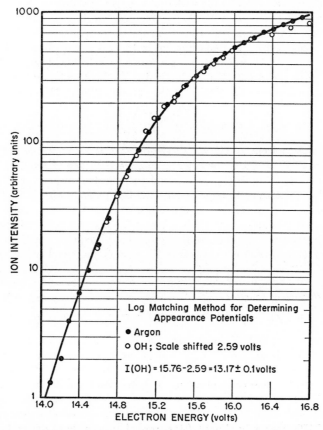

Figure 6. Determination of ionization potential of OH free radical

from H_2O was measured to be 18.19 e.v. This leads to a value of $D(H-OH) = 5.02 \pm 0.15$ e.v., and in combination with thermochemical data to $D(O-H) = 102.9 \pm 3$ kcal. per mole, which is in good agreement with the spectroscopic determination of $D(O-H) = 101.3 \pm 0.3$ kcal. per mole (2).

Studies of HO_2 Free Radical

Because the HO_2 free radical plays an important role in oxidation, combustion, and explosion phenomena, substantial efforts have been made by optical spectroscopy and mass spectrometry to establish the participation of HO_2 in various reactions, to determine its structure, and to measure the thermochemical energies associated with it. As one phase of the mass spectrometric investigation of HO_2, a series of experiments was carried out to find reactions producing significant concentrations of HO_2 radicals in relatively simple chemical systems. Reactions found to produce HO_2 were: H atoms with O_2, H atoms with H_2O_2, O atoms with H_2O_2, OH with H_2O_2, photolysis of H_2O_2, and electrical discharge in H_2O_2.

The reaction of H atoms with O_2 molecules, the classical method for HO_2 production and the reaction used in the mass spectrometric detection of the HO_2 radical (7), does not yield high concentrations of HO_2 radicals. This is partly due to the requirement of a third-body M to remove excess energy, which makes the reaction inefficient at low pressures. However, the introduction of stabilizing gas molecules into the reaction has the undesirable effect of reducing the sensitivity of the mass spectrometer, because the ion source pressure is approximately the same for the various experiments and, therefore, the detectability of a free radical is essentially determined by its mole fraction in the gas rather than by its absolute concentration. Furthermore, H atoms can react with HO_2 radicals, and attempts to increase the HO_2 concentration by increasing the H atom input were unsuccessful, probably for this reason. Typically, the concentration of HO_2 obtained by the reaction

$$H + O_2 + M \rightarrow HO_2 + M \tag{3}$$

at pressures of 1 to 4 cm. of Hg was of the order of 0.001% and corresponded to the conversion of about 1% of the H atoms in a reaction time of about 0.01 second.

Reactions involving H_2O_2 were found to be rather useful sources of HO_2 radicals. The reactions of H and O atoms and OH radicals with H_2O_2 to produce HO_2 are not limited by third-body requirements and, therefore, are operable at low pressure. It is not always possible to decide on the particular primary reaction involved, because radicals may be generated in subsequent reactions. For example, in the reaction of H with H_2O_2 the HO_2 can be produced either by

$$H + H_2O_2 \rightarrow H_2 + HO_2 \tag{4}$$

or by the sequence of reactions

$$H + H_2O_2 \rightarrow H_2O + OH \text{ and } OH + H_2O_2 \rightarrow H_2O + HO_2 \tag{5}$$

The concentration of HO_2 obtained from the $H + H_2O_2$ reaction at a pressure of about 0.5 mm. of Hg and reaction time of about 0.01 second was of the order of 0.1%. The reaction of O atoms with H_2O_2 was found to generate HO_2 radicals, but at substantially lower concentration. The reaction involved is

$$O + H_2O_2 \rightarrow OH + HO_2 \tag{6}$$

The yield of HO_2 was only about 0.01%, probably because of destruction of HO_2 radicals by O atoms which were necessarily present in large concentration. The reaction of H_2O_2 with OH radicals from an electrical discharge in H_2O or H_2O_2 proceeds very rapidly by the reaction

$$OH + H_2O_2 \rightarrow HO_2 + H_2O \tag{7}$$

and has yielded HO_2 in concentrations of about 0.3%. It was also determined that small quantities of HO_2 could be generated by photolysis of H_2O_2. This was not particularly surprising, since the primary photolytic decomposition step is the production of OH radicals which had been shown in our previous experiments to produce HO_2 radicals.

A generally applicable technique for the generation of free radicals and other unstable species is the use of a confined low power electrical discharge in a high speed gas stream of a suitable compound. By the partial decomposition of the compound in the discharge an assortment of free radicals, ions, and excited molecules are generated which can react immediately with the undecomposed parent compound. The reaction products are quickly removed from the discharge zone by the streaming gas. The apparatus used is rather simple, consisting of two wire loop electrodes wrapped around the quartz or glass reactor tube, spaced about 1 cm. apart, and connected to a radio-frequency generator. While it is desirable to operate discharges at high power levels when generating simple radicals such as atoms, it is essential in attempting to manufacture complex radicals to be able to operate at low power levels in order to avoid complete decomposition of the parent compound.

The yield of HO_2 radicals from an electrical discharge in H_2O_2 as a function of decomposition is shown in Figure 7. The 0.003- and 0.006-second curves were taken by positioning the electrodes at appropriate distances from the molecular beam entrance aperture. Two features are worth noting. First, the production of HO_2, which attains a peak value of 0.4%, is relatively insensitive to H_2O_2 decomposition over the range from about 5 to 30%. Secondly, OH radicals are not observable at 0.003 second for decomposition less than 60%, indicating that the removal of OH by reaction with H_2O_2 is very rapid. A lower limit of 4×10^{-13} cc. per molecule per second has been deduced for the rate constant of the OH +

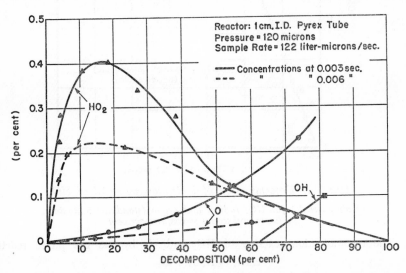

Figure 7. HO_2 radical production by electrical discharge in H_2O_2

H_2O_2 reaction. O atoms which are formed in the discharge are considerably less reactive than OH radicals, since they persist long after OH has disappeared. If the discharge power is low, the system after a few milliseconds becomes extremely simple chemically, the major radical component being HO_2 flowing in a stream of H_2O_2 with small amounts of H_2, O_2, and H_2O, all of which are nonreactive toward HO_2.

The ionization potential of HO_2 has been measured using the low-power electrical discharge in H_2O_2 as the radical source. Ionization curves for HO_2 and argon are shown in Figure 8, from which it is found that $I(HO_2) = 11.53$ e.v. with a precision of measurement of ± 0.02 e.v. The bond-dissociation energy, $D(H-O_2)$, can be calculated from $I(HO_2)$ and the appearance potential of HO_2^+ from HO_2, $A(HO_2^+) = 15.36 \pm 0.05$ e.v., together with some well established thermochemical energies. The bond-dissociation energy, $D(H-O)_2$, thus calculated is 45.9 ± 2 kcal. per mole at $0°K.$, and 47.1 ± 2 kcal. per mole at $25°C.$

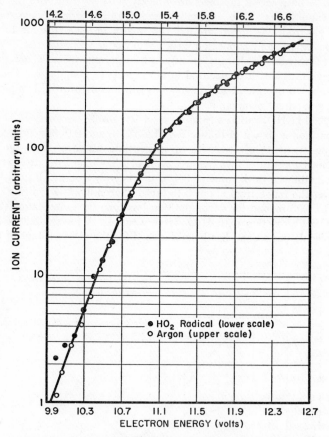

Figure 8.   Determination of ionization potential of HO_2

*Voltage scales for HO_2 radical and argon (standard) indicated
on lower and upper scales, respectively*

The recombination reaction of HO_2 radicals by the gas phase reaction

$$2HO_2 \rightarrow H_2O_2 + O_2 \tag{8}$$

is, in principle at least, one of the simplest HO_2 reactions to study. Estimates for the collisional efficiency of this reaction vary from about 10^{-6} (*18*) to unity (*4*). A comprehensive series of experiments was carried out to measure the recombination of HO_2 radicals (*13*). The concentration of HO_2 radicals was followed as a function of time in a flow system. A typical concentration *vs.* time curve is given in Figure 9, which presents data for a borosilicate glass tubing reactor 1.9 cm. in diameter. The decrease in HO_2 radical concentration follows approximately a second-order rate law, as expected, for Reaction 8. However, measurements taken

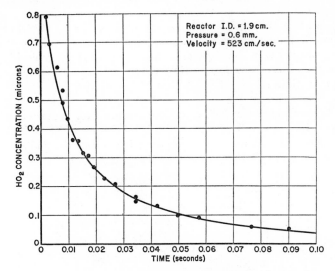

Figure 9. HO$_2$ concentration as a function of time in a 1.9-cm. diameter borosilicate glass

at different pressures and in reactors of different surface-volume ratios showed conclusively that HO_2 radicals were being consumed not only by the homogeneous reaction but also by a heterogeneous reaction, which also followed a second-order rate law. The surface reaction is very complicated, and is experimentally found to be a function of the partial pressures of the condensable components in the system, indicating that HO_2 radicals and condensable molecules are competing for surface sites. The data have been analyzed to give a value of about 3×10^{-12} cc. per molecule per second for the rate constant of the homogeneous Reaction 8. This corresponds to a collisional efficiency of about 1% for the gas phase reaction of two HO_2 radicals.

Radicals and Unstable Molecules from Nitrogen Compounds

In some instances the distinction between inorganic and organic free radicals will be interpreted loosely—for example, when we consider the reaction of H atoms with a methyl-substituted hydrazine. The radicals discussed were produced either by mixing the products of an electrical discharge with a suitable reactant or by applying an electrical discharge directly to the reactant.

The NH_2 radical was observed in several reactions, including OH with NH_3, H atoms with N_2H_4, N atoms with N_2H_4, H atoms with $H_2N_2(CH_3)_2$, and electrical discharge in N_2H_4. As expected from bond-energy considerations, the NH_2 radical was not produced by reaction of NH_3 with H, O, or N atoms. The ionization potential of the NH_2 radical has been measured to be 11.4 ± 0.1 e.v.

(11), which when combined with the appearance potential of NH_2^+ from NH_3, 16.0 ± 0.1 e.v., leads to the dissociation energy $D(NH_2\text{-}H) = 106 \pm 3$ kcal. per mole, in good agreement with the value 104 ± 2 kcal. per mole reported by Altshuller (1).

The N_2H_3 radical was observed as a product of an electrodeless electrical discharge in N_2H_4, and also when N_2H_4 reacted with the products of a high power microwave discharge in H_2 or N_2. The N_2H_3 radical has a low ionization potential, $I(N_2H_3) = 7.88 \pm 0.2$ e.v., and as a result it has been detected in concentrations of about 1 part in 10^7.

A related free radical, $HN_2(CH_3)_2$, was obtained by an electrical discharge in unsymmetrical dimethylhydrazine. An appearance potential curve for this radical is shown in Figure 10. The ionization potential of the radical is 6.6 ± 0.3 e.v. If the radical is assumed to be $HN_2(CH_3)_2$, then one finds from appearance potentials that $A[HN_2(CH_3)_2^+] - I[HN_2(CH_3)_2] = D[H - HN_2(CH_3)_2] = 3.4 \pm 0.3$ e.v. $= 78 \pm 8$ kcal. per mole. The N-H bond-dissociation energy thus calculated is in good agreement with a similar calculation for hydrazine, which gives $A(N_2H_3^+) - I(N_2H_3) = D(H\text{-}N_2H_3) = 3.3 \pm 0.2$ e.v. $= 76 \pm 5$ kcal. per mole. The close agreement of the N-H bond-dissociation energies indicates that the radical observed is $HN_2(CH_3)_2$ rather than $H_2N_2CH_3CH_2$.

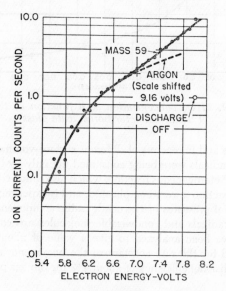

Figure 10. Appearance potential curve for $HN_2(CH_3)_2$ radical from discharge in $H_2N_2(CH_3)_2$

The NH radical has not yet been observed mass spectrometrically, despite its demonstrated presence by optical spectroscopy in systems that have also been examined by mass spectrometry. The difficulty is apparently due to the low concentrations of NH radicals in these systems, coupled with the interference generally present at mass 15 from CH_3 and isotopic ^{15}N.

A number of unstable nitrogen compounds have been produced by electrical discharges. These include diimide (N_2H_2), triazene (N_3H_3), tetrazene (N_4H_4), and methylimide (HN_2CH_3), none of which had been previously identified. Diimide was discovered (*10*) during an unsuccessful search for the NH radical in the decomposition of hydrazoic acid. The other compounds were discovered in the products of electrical decomposition of hydrazine and dimethylhydrazine. The discharge arrangement was similar to the one used for HO_2 production from H_2O_2. The yield of N_2H_2 and N_3H_3 from an electrical discharge in N_2H_4 is given in Figure 11. The similarity of these curves with the HO_2 production curves in Figure 7 is apparent. The maximum concentration of N_2H_2 was obtained with radio-frequency power of about 5 watts. The conversion efficiency of N_2H_4 into N_2H_2 is high at low values of decomposition—for example, at 5% decomposition, 30% of the reacted N_2H_4 shows up as N_2H_2, while at the peak of the curve about 15% of the N_2H_4 is converted to N_2H_2.

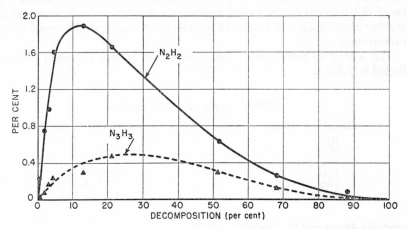

Figure 11. Diimide and triazene production by electrical discharge in hydrazine

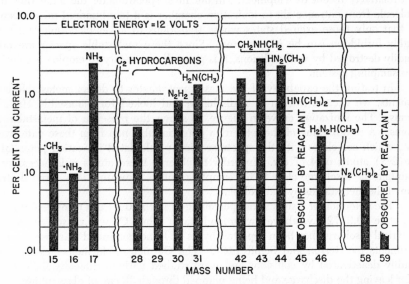

Figure 12. Products of reaction of H atoms with 1, 1-dimethylhydrazine

Low electron energy (12 e.v.) used to reduce dissociative-ionization interferences

The reaction of H atoms from an intense microwave discharge in hydrogen with unsymmetrical dimethylhydrazine produced an interesting array of products. In Figure 12 the ion intensities are referred to the parent hydrazine peak, whose intensity is arbitrarily taken as 100. The reaction reduces the parent peak by about 2%. Except for the dissociative-ionization peaks at mass 45 and mass 59, the ion intensities at the various mass numbers represent ion currents obtained from discharge products. Since the ionization potentials of the components are different, the relative intensities should not be directly used to infer relative concentrations. The presence of the NH_2 and CH_3 radicals is easily recognized. Among the stable components, the identification of NH_3, N_2H_2, H_2NCH_3, and $N_2(CH_3)_2$ is straightforward. The peak at mass 44 has been assigned to methylimide (HN_2CH_3) rather than to a free radical. This assignment is substantiated by the fact that some of this material survives condensation and re-evaporation from a cold trap. The other identifications in Figure 12 represent the most probable assignments of the components.

The ionization potentials of the nitrogen compounds discussed above are collected in Table I.

Table I.   Ionization Potentials

Radical or Compound	Ionization Potential, E.V.
NH_2	11.4 ± 0.1
N_2H_3	7.88 ± 0.1
$HN_2(CH_3)_2$	6.6 ± 0.3
N_2H_2	9.85 ± 0.1
NH_2CH_3	9.27 ± 0.1
N_3H_3	9.6 ± 0.1

Metastable Atoms and Molecules

The study of electronically excited atoms and molecules by mass spectrometry is a relatively recent development. In our mass spectrometer the flight time of a molecule from entrance slit to ionization chamber is a few hundred microseconds, so that only those excited states whose transitions to lower electronic states are highly forbidden can be investigated. Since these metastable species are often readily destroyed by wall collisions, it is generally necessary to employ a collision-free sampling system.

In testing the capability of the mass spectrometer to detect metastable components, we excited helium in a discharge and looked for metastable $He(2^3S)$ atoms. The ionization curve in Figure 13 shows the presence of metastable He atoms. A rough value of the ionization potential obtained from these data was 5 e.v., which correlates with the spectroscopically calculated ionization potential of $He(2^3S)$ atoms of 4.77 e.v. In order to observe these atoms it is necessary to maintain the discharge close to the sampling orifice, indicating very rapid destruction of the metastables by wall collision.

The detection of a substantial percentage (10 to 20%) of O_2 molecules in the $^1\Delta_g$ state (0.9772 e.v. above the ground state) when O_2 was passed through an electrical discharge has been reported by us (8) and confirmed in subsequent experiments by Herron and Schiff (16). The O_2 metastable molecules were not readily deactivated by collisions and were studied without difficulty 0.05 second after leaving the discharge and being pumped through 30 cm. of glass tubing.

Active nitrogen has been the subject of a large number of investigations. The principal energetic species in the afterglow are ground state N atoms and

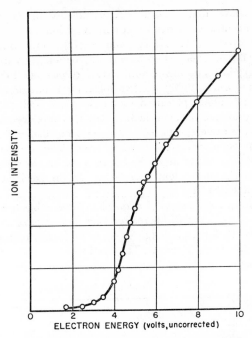

Figure 13.   Ionization curve of metastable
He atoms from electrical discharge in He

vibrationally excited N_2 molecules.   Previous mass spectrometric studies of nitrogen subjected to electrical discharge have indicated only the presence of unexcited $N(^4S)$ atoms and unexcited N_2 molecules (*3, 15, 17*).   Optical absorption

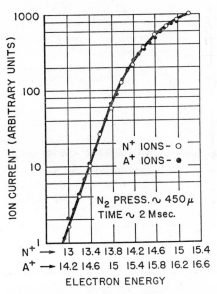

Figure 14.   N atom ionization curve

Voltage scales for N atom and argon
(standard) indicated

studies (20) have shown that metastable $N(^2P)$ and $N(^2D)$ atoms are present in the afterglow at concentrations much lower than $N(^4S)$ atoms.

We have observed $N(^4S)$, $N(^2P)$, and $N(^2D)$ atoms and have found N_2 molecules with excitation energies up to several electron volts when nitrogen was subjected under certain conditions to an electrical discharge (14). Under normal discharge conditions these highly excited species are not observed. A typical ionization curve for N atoms produced by an electrical discharge in N_2 is shown in Figure 14. The atomic nitrogen in this case was produced by a high power (80-watt) microwave discharge in N_2 at a pressure of 0.45 mm. of Hg and was observed about 2 msec. after leaving the discharge. The N-atom ionization curve is very closely matched by an argon ionization curve scale shifted by 1.20 e.v., giving an N-atom ionization potential of 14.56 e.v., in excellent agreement with the spectroscopic value, 14.54 e.v.

If nitrogen with a large excess of added helium is subjected to electrical discharge and observed very shortly thereafter, one finds excited N atoms. This is illustrated in Figure 15 for a discharge in N_2 at 0.16 mm. of Hg plus He at 2.2 mm. of Hg observed within 1 msec. The synthetic N^+ curve was fitted to the experimental curve, using the spectroscopically known energies of the $N(^4S)$,

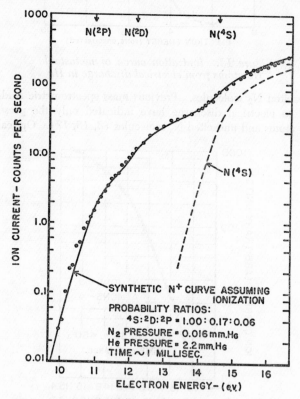

Figure 15.   Metastable N atoms from electrical discharge in mixture of N_2 and He

————   Calculated from known ionization potentials, indicated in figure, of ⁴S, ²P, and ²D states
- - - -   Estimated ion current due to unexcited $N(^4S)$ atoms

$N(^2D)$, and $N(^2P)$ states and assuming that the ionization cross-section curves for atoms in these states were identical in shape. For convenience in calculation, the atomic ionization probability functions were assumed to be linear. The dashed curve represents the contribution of $N(^4S)$ ionization to the total ion current. The relative concentrations of N atoms in the ^4S, ^2D, and ^2P states are estimated from this analysis to be in the ratio 1.00 to 0.17 to 0.06. The excited atoms were not observed except within a millisecond or so after leaving the discharge, presumably because they diffuse to the walls of the reactor and are destroyed there. Metastable N atoms have also been obtained from a high power discharge in pure N_2, although in this case the concentrations of $N(^2D)$ and $N(^2P)$ relative to $N(^4S)$ were lower than those obtained in the N_2-He mixture by a factor of about 25.

The N_2 molecules from the discharge in the N_2-He mixture have also been studied and found to have excitation energies up to several electron volts. The ionization curve for N_2 is complex and can be explained by the presence of N_2 molecules in known metastable electronic states and in various vibrational levels.

Conclusion

The application of mass spectrometry to the study of inorganic free radicals has been illustrated by several examples from current research. Considerable information has been obtained on the presence, identity, and concentration of free radicals in gaseous systems, and on the mechanism of reactions involving free radicals. From appearance potential measurements a number of bond-dissociation energies have been calculated. The extension of the study of free radicals to include electronically excited species, as illustrated by the study of metastable N atoms and N_2 molecules from electrical discharges, is an area of investigation which may prove to be very interesting. The production of unstable chemical compounds by electrical discharges in high speed gas streams is an area of research which merits further exploration.

Literature Cited

(1) Altshuller, A. P., *J. Chem. Phys.* **22**, 1947 (1954).
(2) Barrow, R. F., *Arkiv Fysik* **11**, 281 (1956).
(3) Berkowitz, J., Cupka, W., Kistiakowsky, G. B., *J. Chem. Phys.* **25**, 457 (1956).
(4) Burgess, R., Robb, J. C., "Reactions of Free Radicals in the Gas Phase," Chem. Soc., London, Spec. Pub. **9**, 167 (1957).
(5) Fabian, D. J., Robertson, A. J. B., *Trans. Faraday Soc.* **53**, 363 (1957).
(6) Foner, S. N., Hudson, R. L., *J. Chem. Phys.* **21**, 1374 (1953).
(7) *Ibid.*, **21**, 1608 (1953); **23**, 1364 (1955).
(8) *Ibid.*, **25**, 601 (1956).
(9) *Ibid.*, p. 602.
(10) *Ibid.*, **28**, 719 (1958).
(11) *Ibid.*, **29**, 442 (1958).
(12) *Ibid.*, in press.
(13) Foner, S. N., Hudson, R. L., to be published.
(14) Foner, S. N., Hudson, R. L., submitted for publication, *J. Chem. Phys.*
(15) Herron, J. T., *J. Research Natl. Bur. Standards* **65A**, 411 (1961).
(16) Herron, J. T., Schiff, H. I., *Can. J. Chem.* **36**, 1159 (1958).
(17) Jackson, D. S., Schiff, H. I., *J. Chem. Phys.* **21**, 2233 (1953); **23**, 2333 (1955).
(18) Lewis, B., von Elbe, G., "Combustion, Flames and Explosions of Gases," 2nd ed., p. 55, Academic Press, New York, 1961.
(19) Lossing, F. P., Tickner, A. W., *J. Chem. Phys.* **20**, 907 (1952).
(20) Tanaka, Y., Jursa, A. S., LeBlanc, F. J., Inn, E. C. Y., *J. Planetary Space Sci.* **1**, 7 (1959).

RECEIVED May 3, 1962. Work supported by the Bureau of Naval Weapons, Department of the Navy, under NOrd 7386.

5

ESR Studies of Inorganic Free Radicals in Photolytic Systems

FRANK J. ADRIAN, EDWARD L. COCHRAN, and VERNON A. BOWERS

*Applied Physics Laboratory, The Johns Hopkins University,
Silver Spring, Md.*

The spectra of simple photolytically produced free radicals trapped in solid argon at 4.2°K. are described. The spectra of S-state atoms resemble those expected for the free atoms, the major difference being small matrix perturbations in the g factors and in the hyperfine coupling constants. The spectra of polyatomic radicals depend on magnetic field orientation and for radicals rigidly and randomly oriented this results in a spectrum of broad complex lines. Rotation will partly or completely average out this orientation dependence. In general, rotations involving only the motion of protons seem to be virtually unrestricted. Heavier radicals are more restricted. Some can rotate about one axis only; others are rigid at 4.2°K. but have considerable rotational freedom at higher temperatures; still others are rigidly held at all temperatures. In a number of cases analysis of the polycrystalline ESR shapes gave a fairly complete description of the magnetic interactions of the radical.

The study of the structure and chemistry of free radicals by means of their electron spin resonance, while a fruitful field for research, is beset by a number of complicating factors. Chief among these for the simpler, highly reactive radicals is the problem of obtaining the radical in sufficiently high concentration in a resonant cavity. One solution to this problem is to immobilize the radical in an inert medium. This process of immobilization itself, however, leads to other complications which must be understood if the technique is to be applied effectively. Foremost among these is the problem of magnetic anisotropies, which for randomly oriented trapped radicals often leads to severe line broadening and line distortion. In addition, the surrounding molecules in the inert matrix affect slightly the interaction of the electron spin with the various nuclear spins in the radical and the applied magnetic field. This results in "matrix shifts" in the positions of the lines in ESR spectra, which are usually small and which vary from matrix to matrix and from trapping site to trapping site within a given matrix. Other complications may result if low temperatures are required to immobilize the radicals. For instance, the rate with which energy can be transferred from the electron spin system to the matrix is often markedly reduced, making these low temperature systems susceptible to power saturation. Also, unusual intensity distributions are sometimes observed as a result of symmetry restrictions on the nuclear spin states due to population of only one or two of the lowest rotational energy levels of the radical.

Despite the above limitations, ESR studies of condensed media can yield considerable information about certain simple radicals and their interaction with their environment. This paper reviews the results for various free radicals trapped in solid argon. In general, the radicals described are inorganic, though for radicals containing only a few atoms this distinction is not particularly meaningful. In a few cases these radicals are "stable"—i.e., coexist in significant concentrations with the parent molecule at room temperature—though in general they were prepared by photolysis in the solid matrix of a parent molecule, or by the reaction of photolytically produced H atoms with a matrix molecule containing multiple bonds.

Experimental

The cryostat used in this work (Figure 1) has been described in detail (14).

Samples were deposited on the liquid helium–cooled sapphire rod through two slits symmetrically placed in planes 45° removed from the plane of the drawing. In general, the gas deposited consisted of argon containing 1% of the material to be photolyzed. In some experiments up to 10% of a second reactant was added. Deposition and initial ESR observations were conducted with the sample at 4.2° K. The effect of temperature on the ESR of the sample was observed by removing the liquid helium and allowing the cryostat to warm up

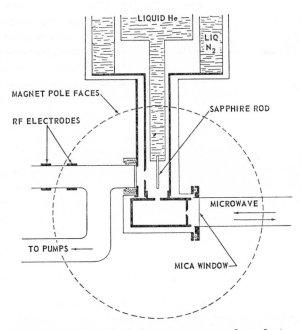

Figure 1. Liquid helium cryostat adapted for photolysis experiments

at a rate controlled by an adjustable heat leak. The usual light source for this work was an 8-Mc. discharge in H_2 gas at a pressure of approximately 0.1 mm. of Hg. in the discharge tube shown in Figure 1. Using this source, the actinic light was filtered by appropriate window materials. Windows used were: lithium fluoride (lower transmission limit = 1000 A.), sapphire (transmission limit = 1450 A.), and fused quartz (transmission limit = 1800 A.). In some experiments the discharge tube was replaced by a Hanovia SC 2537 low pressure mercury lamp operated in conjunction with windows of fused quartz or Vycor 7910 (transmission limit = 2400 A.). The bridge-type microwave spectrometer was of conventional design and employed 400-cycle field modulation (*14*).

Atomic Spectra

The simplest of all free radicals, the hydrogen atom, has been observed by ESR techniques in the gas phase, in liquids, and in various solid materials. The ESR transition frequencies for this $^2S_{1/2}$ atom are approximately given by

$$h\nu(M_I) = g\beta H_o + AM_I \tag{1}$$

where H_o is the applied magnetic field, β is the Bohr magneton, and M_I is the nuclear magnetic quantum number, which takes the values $I, I-1, \ldots -I$, where I is nuclear spin quantum number. g and A are parameters which describe the magnetic interaction of the electron with the magnetic field and the nucleus, respectively. A is a function of $|\psi_o|^2$, the density of the unpaired electron at the nucleus. Since for the proton $I = {}^1/_2$, the ESR multiplet for the free hydrogen atom consists of two lines, the positions of which can be both measured and calculated with high accuracy. H atoms are produced in good yield by the photolysis of many simple inorganic molecules such as HI, NH_3, PH_3, SiH_4, CH_4, HCN, etc., in inert matrices. When trapped in this manner, the atoms exhibit a spectrum consisting of two or more doublets whose g and A values differ slightly from those of the free atom (*10*).

In Figure 2 is shown the spectrum obtained by photolysis of water in solid argon at wavelengths longer than 1450 A. This spectrum consists of two doublets, one having a value of A 1.15% greater than, and the other a value of A 0.46% smaller than, the free atom values. The corresponding deviations in g are

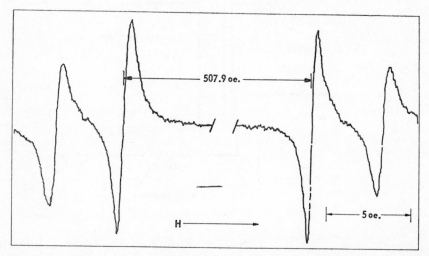

Figure 2. ESR spectrum of hydrogen atoms produced by photolysis of water in solid argon at 4.2° K.

−0.032 and −0.003%, respectively. In other matrices the results are similar, though the number, relative intensities, and deviations from the free state of the doublets vary. Adrian (1) has given a theoretical treatment of the matrix shifts observed for H atoms in rare gas matrices which correlates the various observed doublets with particular sites in the face-centered cubic rare gas crystal. A similar multiplicity of sites is observed when alkali metal atoms are deposited in rare gas matrices (13). The treatment of Adrian can be extended to describe the Li resonances fairly well, but the more complex spectra observed for Na, K, and Rb cannot be accounted for by this simple picture.

The ESR spectrum of the nitrogen atom whose ground electronic state is $^4S^3/_2$ can also be described approximately by Equation 1. Since $I = 1$ for the nitrogen nucleus, one expects a triplet spectrum, and this is observed as shown in Figure 3.

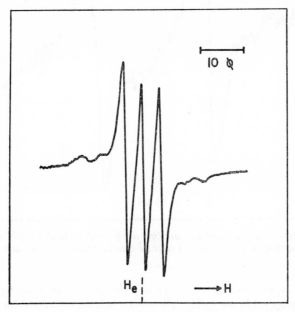

Figure 3. ESR spectrum of nitrogen atoms pro-
duced by photolysis of NO in solid argon at 4.2° K.

Here the nitrogen atoms were prepared by photolysis of NO. Since there are three unpaired electrons, each line of the triplet in Figure 3 is triply degenerate, and it has been postulated that in certain types of crystal fields this degeneracy can be lifted (7), causing the additional weak lines shown on either side of the main triplet in Figure 3. Since the unpaired electrons in the N atom occupy $2p$ orbits which have $|\psi_0|^2 = 0$ the splitting (4.3 oe.) shown in Figure 3 must be the result of configuration interaction with the nitrogen $3s$ orbital. For this reason one might expect the line-to-line separation for N to be somewhat more sensitive to matrix perturbations than is that for H. This has been observed, with deviations of A from the free value ranging from 10 to 30% in such weakly bonding matrices as H_2, N_2, and CH_4 (12).

The spectrum shown in Figure 4 is believed to be due to the phosphorus atom. This spectrum was observed when PH_3 was photolyzed at 2537 A. An identical spectrum resulted from the photolysis of PD_3. The lack of proton hyperfine structure and the similarity of the line-to-line separation (23.8 oe.) to the free atom value (20.0 oe.) (8) support this assignment. On warm-up, the lines in Figure 4 sharpen markedly and the separation between lines increases to 28.8 oe. These changes are irreversible.

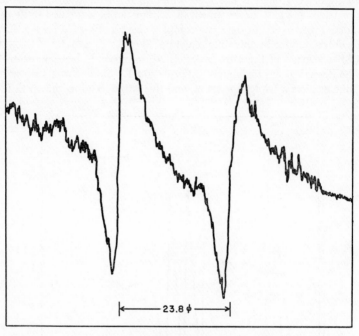

Figure 4.   ESR spectrum produced by photolysis of PH_3 in solid argon at 4.2° K. and believed due to phosphorus atoms

Atoms in an electronic S state such as those described give simple sharp line spectra when trapped in the solid. The situation is very different for atoms which have orbitally degenerate ground states. Here the electron spin is strongly coupled to the orbital angular momentum, which in turn is coupled to local crystal fields. As a result the positions of the resonance lines are strongly dependent on the direction of the local crystal fields. Since these are random, the lines are severely broadened. Attempts to observe halogen atoms and oxygen atoms in rare gas matrices have given negative results, probably for this reason (14). A similar argument may explain why OH and NO, orbitally degenerate diatomic radicals, have not been observed in solid argon (14), though there is evidence that this degeneracy may be lifted in very polar matrices, resulting in a line sufficiently narrow to be observed (18).

Spectra of Polyatomic Radicals

The ESR spectra of polyatomic radicals are inherently more complicated than the atomic spectra. In these nonspherically symmetric radicals the inter-action of the electron with the magnetic field and with the nuclei will depend on the orientation of the radical with respect to the magnetic field. Thus g and A in Equation 1 will no longer be constants, but will be functions of the magnetic field orientation. Take the simple yet common case in which all the magnetic interactions are axially symmetric and g and A vary only slightly with magnetic field orientation. Then if we consider hyperfine interactions with only a single nucleus, the ESR transition frequencies for these hyperfine components are given by the expression $(2, 3)$:

$$h\nu(M_I) = \left(\frac{1}{3}g_\| + \frac{2}{3}g_\perp\right)\beta H_0 + AM_I + \left[\frac{1}{3}(g_\| - g_\perp)\beta H_0 + BM_I\right](3\cos^2\theta_H - 1) \quad (2)$$

Here $g_\|$ and $g_\perp$ are the electronic g factors for the magnetic field, respectively parallel and perpendicular to the symmetry axis, A is now the isotropic hyperfine interaction constant, and B is the anisotropic hyperfine interaction constant. The dependence on magnetic field orientation is given by the function $(3\cos^2\theta_H - 1)$, where θ_H is the angle between the magnetic field and the symmetry axis.

The exact nature of a spectrum whose transition frequencies are given by Equation 1 depends on whether or not the radical is free to rotate. If the radical

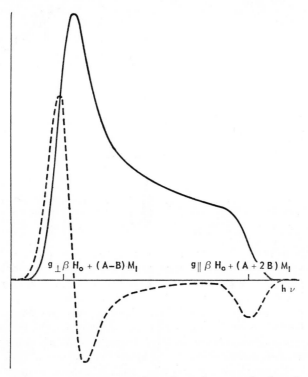

Figure 5. Typical ESR line shape for a randomly oriented, nonrotating free radical having an anisotropic g factor and an anisotropic hyperfine interaction as described by Equation 2

———— *Absorption curve*
– – – *Derivative of absorption*
        (*One unit on the ordinate scale of the dashed curve equals 7.56 units on the ordinate scale of the solid curve.*) *The strong positive peak in the derivative curve corresponds to the magnetic field oriented perpendicular to the symmetry axis, while the weak negative peak corresponds to the magnetic field oriented parallel to the symmetry axis.*

can rotate or reorient at a rate w_R such that $hw_R \gg \frac{1}{3}(g_\parallel - g_\perp)\beta H_o + BM_I$, then the observed spectrum will be an average over all field orientations. Since the average of the quantity $(3\cos^2\theta_H - 1)$ over all orientations is zero, this spectrum will be a simple sharp line spectrum described by the orientation-independent Equation 1. If, on the other hand, the radicals are rigidly and randomly oriented in a poly-crystalline matrix, the observed spectrum will be a superposition of spectra arising from all possible field orientations. The spectrum resulting in this case is illustrated in Figure 5 (3, 4). The two sharp peaks or "lines" in the derivative of the broad-ened absorption line (cf. Figure 5) correspond to definite orientations of the radical—namely, $\theta_H = 0$ and $\pi/2$. Therefore in simple cases where the various hyper-fine lines do not overlap appreciably, the broadened line shapes may be analyzed to obtain the constants in Equation 2. An alternative to analyzing the complex polycrystalline line shapes is to use single crystal samples, but the trapping of small highly reactive radicals in single crystal matrices is often not feasible.

The ESR spectrum of 0.014% of NO_2 in argon at 4.2° K. (2), which is shown in Figure 6, contains lines having the shape shown in Figure 5. The variation in width among the three lines of the nitrogen hyperfine structure multiplet shows that there is an anisotropy in both the electronic g factor and the nitrogen hyper-fine splitting. These two anisotropies combine in the broad low field line and

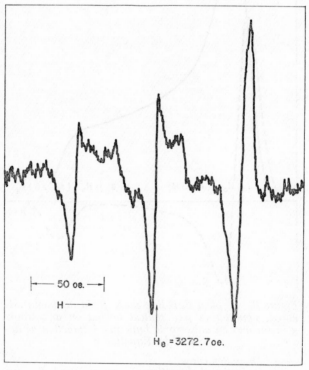

50 oe.

H

$H_e = 3272.7\,oe.$

Figure 6. ESR spectrum of NO_2 in solid argon at 4.2° K.

cancel in the narrow high field line. Analysis of the NO_2 lines gave the following values for the constants in Equation 2: $g_\parallel = 1.9920$, $g_\perp = 2.0033$, $A/h = 146$ Mc. per second, and $B/h = 21$ Mc. per second. The axial symmetry of the system NO_2 in argon is not an inherent property of the NO_2 molecule, but indicates that NO_2 is free to rotate about one axis. Using the results of a study of NO_2 in a single crystal of $NaNO_2$ where NO_2 has no rotational freedom and is not axially symmetric (19), it was shown that the rotation axis lies in the molecular plane and is perpendicular to the molecular symmetry axis.

Simple sharp line spectra are observed for a variety of free radicals trapped in solid argon at 4.2° K. The ESR spectrum of CH_3 is shown in Figure 7. In this experiment CH_3 was prepared by photolysis of CH_3I at 2537 A., but may also be

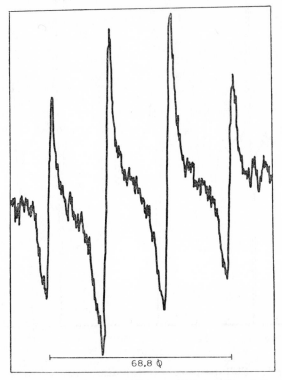

68.8 Φ

Figure 7. ESR spectrum of CH_3 produced by photolysis of CH_3I in solid argon at 4.2° K.

prepared by photolysis of a number of other appropriate molecules—e.g., CH_4 using a hydrogen discharge with a LiF window. This spectrum consists of four equally spaced lines, indicating that the three protons are equivalent, so that the spectrum may be described by Equation 1 with $M_I = {}^3/_2, {}^1/_2, -{}^1/_2$ and $-{}^3/_2$. The line-to-line separation is 22.9 oe., so that A/h in Equation 1 is 64 Mc. for this radical. The lines are sharp, indicating that the line broadening anisotropies in the magnetic hyperfine interaction of this radical are averaged to zero by the rotation of the radical in the argon matrix.

The ESR spectrum for NH_2, shown in Figure 8 (11), may be obtained by photolysis of NH_3 or N_2H_4. This spectrum consists of a triplet of triplets with a triplet-to-triplet separation of 23.9 oe., and a line-to-line separation within a triplet of 10.3 oe. By substituting deuterium for hydrogen in this radical, it was shown that the larger splitting was due to H and the smaller splitting to the N nucleus.

The triplet side lines are slightly broadened by residual hyperfine anisotropy due to the N nucleus. The integrated intensities of all lines in the spectrum are about equal, which would be expected on the basis of symmetry considerations if the radical occupies only the ground rotational level (15).

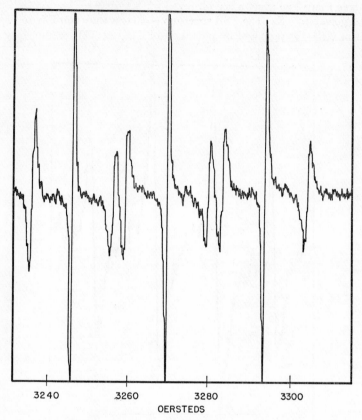

OERSTEDS

Figure 8.   ESR spectrum of NH₂ radical produced by photolysis of hydrazine in solid argon at 4.2° K.

The ESR spectrum of SiH_3 obtained by photolysis of SiH_4 is shown in Figure 9. The line-to-line separation in this spectrum is smaller by a factor of 3 than that for CH_3, which seems reasonable. The intensity ratio is not the expected 1:3:3:1, because of a line broadening which increases progressively from low field to high. The origin of this broadening is not known.

Cyanogen radical (CN) was prepared by the photolysis of HCN in argon using light of wavelengths greater than 1000 A. (5). This somewhat heavier radical is of interest in that it is not free to rotate at 4.2° K. but does rotate more or less freely at higher temperatures. The effect on the ESR spectrum of the transition from rigid to rotating molecule is shown in Figure 10. The center line is narrow and sharp at all temperatures, which indicates that the line broadening is due to an anisotropic hyperfine interaction with the nitrogen nucleus.

Another interesting feature of the photolysis of HCN in argon is that some of the H atoms formed add to the double bond in HCN molecules to produce the radical H_2CN. The existence of this reaction was suspected from the presence of additional weak lines in the ESR spectrum of the photolysis products of HCN which were not due to the primary products H and CN. This radical reaction was definitely identified by photolyzing a mixture of 1% HI and 9% HCN in argon using light of wavelength greater than 2400 A., which is absorbed by HI but not HCN. The resulting spectrum, which is shown in Figure 11, is a triplet of triplets —that is, there is a main triplet with an interline separation of 87.4 oe., and each line of the main triplet is split into a secondary triplet. The outer lines of each secondary triplet are weak and unsymmetrical, which indicates that the hyperfine interaction responsible for this splitting is anisotropic. For a number of reasons, strongest of which is the fact that the main triplet splitting is so large that it is almost certainly due to hyperfine interactions with two equivalent protons, we believe that this ESR spectrum is due to the radical $H_2C=N$ rather than the radical $HC=NH$. This interpretation also explains the observed anisotropy of the second-ary hyperfine splitting, because in the $H_2C=N$ radical the unpaired electron is in a nitrogen p orbital.

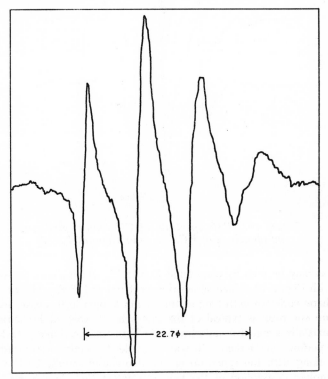

Figure 9.   ESR spectrum of SiH_3 radical produced by photolysis of SiH_4 in solid argon at 4.2° K.

Hydrogen atoms have been observed to add at 4.2° K. to a number of other molecules containing multiple bonds. Thus, Ewing, Thompson, and Pimentel (9) have studied the infrared spectrum of formyl radical produced by the photolysis of HI in solid CO. We have used this reaction to prepare the formyl radical in order to study its ERS spectrum. This spectrum is temperature-

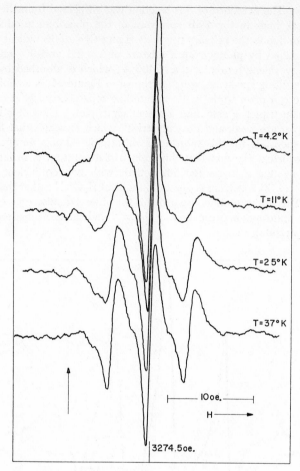

*Figure 10.   ESR spectrum of CN radical produced
by photolysis of HCN in solid argon at 4.2° K.*

sensitive, as may be seen by comparing Figure 12, which shows the spectrum at
4.2° K., with Figure 13, which shows the spectrum at 11° K.   The exact cause of
the line shape variation with temperature is not known in this case, but the high
temperature spectrum is typical of the line shapes expected for a rigid radical
having nonaxially symmetric anisotropies in both the electronic *g* factor and the
proton hyperfine interaction.   It was possible to analyze this rather simple
spectrum along with the spectrum of the deuterated radical DCO to obtain a
rather complete description of the magnetic interactions in this radical.   Since
the results of this analysis and their implications about the structure of the formyl
radical are somewhat involved, the reader is referred to the original article for a
complete account (*3*).

We consider here only the most striking feature of the formyl radical spectrum—namely, the very large isotropic proton hyperfine splitting of 137 oe.
Since this quantity is proportional to the charge density of the unpaired electron
at the proton, it suggests that the radical may be regarded as a resonance hybrid
of two states—namely,

1   2

A 25% admixture of the second state can account for the observed proton hyperfine splitting. The large admixture of the second state indicates that much of the energy lost in breaking the CH bond is regained, because it is no longer necessary to have the carbon atom promoted to the tetrahedral valence state to form the two remaining bonds, and also because the resonance energy of the CO molecule is regained in the second state. Experimental support for this hypothesis comes from the fact that the CH bond is very weak in this radical, having an upper limit of 1.71 e.v. (*17*). This explanation of the proton hyperfine splitting in the formyl radical requires that the unpaired electron occupy an orbital lying in the plane of the molecule, and not a π orbital perpendicular to the molecular plane as is typical of most radicals. If this condition is not met, states 1 and 2 have different symmetries and cannot be admixed. The assignment of the unpaired electron to a coplanar orbital makes the ground state of the radical symmetric with respect to reflection in the molecular plane, a conclusion which is in agreement with the results of optical studies of the formyl radical (*17*).

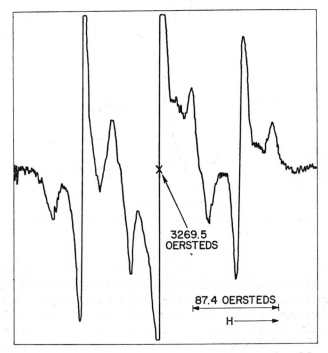

Figure 11.   ESR spectrum of H_2CN radical produced by addition of hydrogen atoms to HCN at 4.2° K.

The formyl radical can be produced in several other ways, one of which is the photolytic decomposition of formaldehyde. The formaldehyde system is interesting because the intensity of the HCO spectrum does not increase monotonically with ultraviolet irradiation time but reaches a maximum and then falls off. This indicates that the formyl radical is decomposed by the ultraviolet

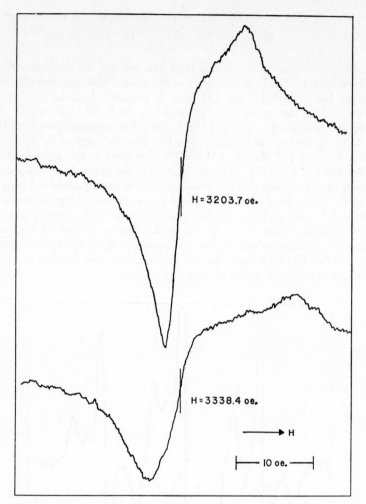

Figure 12.   ESR spectrum of HCO radical produced by addition of H atoms to CO at 4.2° K.

Spectrum taken at 4.2° K.

radiation.   Moreover, since the HCO concentration is always much less than the formaldehyde concentration, the formyl radical must absorb at 2537 A. much more strongly than formaldehyde.   The radical is also produced by the photolysis of methanol with light of wavelength greater than 1450 A.   This clearly requires a succession of photolytic decompositions.   Further proof for a multiple photolysis sequence comes from the fact that the photolysis of CH_3OD yields an ESR spectrum of both hydrogen and deuterium atoms.

The photolysis of a mixture of 1% HI, 10% HC≡CH, and 89% argon with ultraviolet radiation of wavelength greater than 2537 A. gave the ESR spectrum shown in Figure 14.   This spectrum is believed to be due to the vinyl radical, $H_2C=CH$, resulting from the addition of a hydrogen atom to the acetylene molecule, and contains a fairly large number of rather broad lines which overlap to a considerable extent.   For this reason a complete analysis of the spectrum was not feasible, but it is believed that the spectrum contains eight lines whose approximate locations are indicated in Figure 14. This is the number of lines expected for hyperfine interactions with three nonequivalent protons. The most significant feature of the spectrum is that one of the proton hyperfine splittings is again large (56 oe.). Presumably this hyperfine splitting is associated with the proton bonded to the carbon atom bearing the unpaired electron (α proton). Since the vinyl radical is similar in structure to the formyl radical, this suggests that the mechanism which produced the large hyperfine splitting in the formyl radical is also operative in the vinyl radical. The other two hyperfine splittings are of the expected order of magnitude for β protons located in the cis (36-oe.) and trans (16-oe.) positions relative to the sp^2 orbital occupied by the unpaired electron.

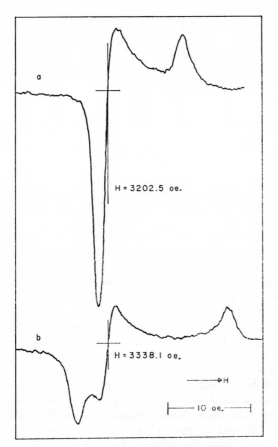

Figure 13.   ESR spectrum of HCO
Same sample as Figure 12.   Spectrum taken at
11° K.

Recently the preparation of tetrafluorohydrazine (N_2F_4) was reported (6), and it was found that this molecule spontaneously dissociates at low pressures into two NF_2 radicals. ESR techniques were used to measure the equilibrium constant for dissociation (16), and it was found that the ESR spectrum in the gas phase consists of a single very broad line, similar to that observed for NO_2. As

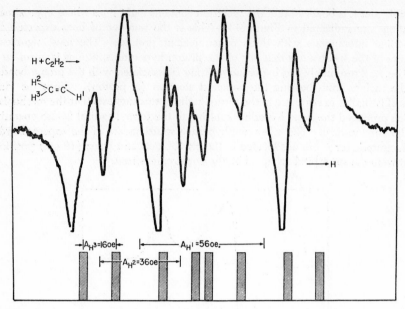

Figure 14.   ESR spectrum of vinyl radical produced by addition of H atoms to acetylene at 4.2° K.

described earlier, the NO_2 spectrum in solid argon, however, consists of an easily resolved triplet. The spectrum for NF_2 in solid argon is shown in Figure 15. Here the radical was prepared simply by expanding a 1% N_2F_4-argon mixture through the usual slit system. This spectrum consists of a relatively sharp, strong line in the center, which at 4.2° K. contains a fairly sharp subpeak on each side of the strong derivative-shaped center portion. Two weak asymmetrical lines are located, respectively, 16 oe. above and 16 oe. below this center line. Further removed are two other weak, asymmetrical, and exceedingly broad lines. The separation of these lines from the center line is $\pm \sim 47$ oe. The weak lines are indicated by the arrows in Figure 15, and using an expanded field scale and higher gain, the outside pair of lines was found to have the characteristic asymmetry expected for severe hyperfine anisotropy. When this sample was warmed up, the center line became more symmetrical and the two subpeaks disappeared. The two nearest weak lines became relatively much more intense, so that the center portion of the spectrum shown in Figure 16 was a more or less symmetrical triplet. The two side lines further removed from the center were barely detectable at 4.2° K. and disappeared on warm-up. We believe that the center triplet observed on warming the sample is due to the NF_2 spin state in which the two fluorine nuclei are antiparallel. The triplet structure is due to the hyperfine interaction with the nitrogen nucleus. This interaction is anisotropic, causing the lines to be broadened and weakened at low temperatures. The residual anisotropy due to the two antiparallel fluorine nuclei probably accounts for the subpeaks on the center line at 4.2° K. On warming, both these sources of magnetic anisotropy are partially averaged out by thermal motions of the radical. The very much larger anisotropic interaction with the two fluorine nuclei when they are parallel to each other makes the outside lines of this spectrum very weak and so broad that the additional hyperfine structure due to the nitrogen is washed out for these lines. Apparently these lines are not greatly narrowed on warming.

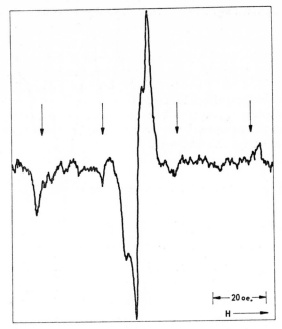

Figure 15.   ESR spectrum of NF$_2$ radical produced by depositing argon containing 1% N$_2$F$_4$ at 4.2° K.

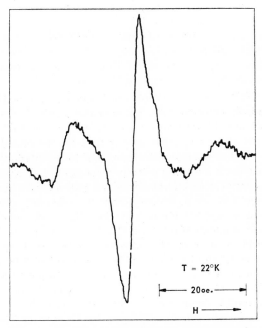

Figure 16.   Center portion of NF$_2$ spectrum shown in Figure 15 after warming sample to 22° K.

The spectrum shown in Figure 17 we believe due to another fluorine-containing radical—namely, CF_3—obtained by photolysis of CF_3I in argon at 4.2° K. Although this spectrum is obviously very complicated, it appears that it can be divided into four more-or-less equally spaced groups of lines, if several lines at the free electron g value are neglected. The hyperfine structure of CF_3 is expected to be a quartet, since I (F^{19}) $= \frac{1}{2}$, and the spacing between groups of roughly 95 oe. is in reasonable agreement with what might be expected for this radical. The large number of lines within a group, the lines at the free electron g value, the odd shapes and intensity ratios, and especially the very complex behavior observed on warming for this radical are not at all understood.

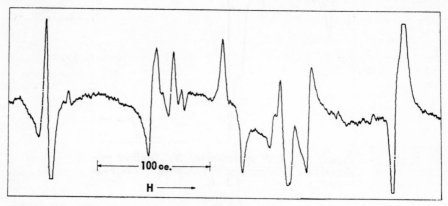

Figure 17. ESR spectrum produced by photolysis of CF_3I in solid argon at 4.2° K.

Believed to be due to CF_3 radical

Conclusion

Results of ESR observations of small radicals trapped at 4.2° K. in solid argon have been reported. A number of these radicals were freely rotating under these conditions, allowing an accurate determination of all isotropic nuclear coupling which results in a splitting greater than the associated line widths. A limited number of other radicals were found not to be rotating, or rotating in a very restricted manner, but were sufficiently simple so that a careful analysis of the line shape gave considerable information about the radical. In the general case magnetic anisotropy broadening severely limits the information one can obtain for randomly oriented trapped radicals and thus limits the use of ESR as an analytical tool in experiments of this type. Two experimental techniques by means of which the problem of magnetic anisotropy in free radicals can be handled are: (1) single crystal studies, which give very complete information about the radical, but often lead to an exceedingly complicated data reduction problem; (2) fluid media studies, which generally give simpler spectra, but give information only about the isotropic magnetic interactions of the radical.

Literature Cited

(1) Adrian, F. J., *J. Chem. Phys.* **32**, 972 (1960).
(2) *Ibid.*, **36**, 1692 (1962).

(3) Adrian, F. J., Cochran, E. L., Bowers, V. A., *Ibid.*, **36**, 1661 (1962).
(4) Cochran, E. L., Adrian, F. J., Bowers, V. A., *Ibid.*, **34**, 1161 (1961).
(5) *Ibid.*, **36**, 1938 (1962).
(6) Colburn, C. B., Kennedy, A., *J. Am. Chem. Soc.* **80**, 5004 (1958).
(7) Cole, T., McConnell, H. M., *J. Chem. Phys.* **29**, 451 (1958).
(8) Dehmelt, H. G., *Phys. Rev.* **99**, 527 (1955).
(9) Ewing, G. E., Thompson, W. E., Pimentel, G. C., *J. Chem. Phys.* **32**, 929 (1960).
(10) Foner, S. N., Cochran, E. L., Bowers, V. A., Jen, C. K., *Ibid.*, **32**, 963 (1960).
(11) Foner, S. N., Cochran, E. L., Bowers, V. A., Jen, C. K., *Phys. Rev. Letters* **1**, 91 (1958).
(12) Foner, S. N., Jen, C. K., Cochran, E. L., Bowers, V. A., *J. Chem. Phys.* **28**, 351 (1958).
(13) Jen, C. K., Bowers, V. A., Cochran, E. L., Foner, S. N., *Phys. Rev.*, in press.
(14) Jen, C. K., Foner, S. N., Cochran, E. L., Bowers, V. A. *Ibid.*, **112**, 1169 (1958).
(15) McConnell, H. M., *J. Chem. Phys.* **29**, 1422 (1958).
(16) Piette, L. H., Johnson, F. A., Booman, K. A., Colburn, C. B., *Ibid.*, **35**, 1481 (1961).
(17) Ramsay, D. A., *Advan. Spectr.* **1**, 1 (1959).
(18) Siegel, S., Baum, L. H., Skolnik, S., Flournoy, J. M., *J. Chem. Phys.* **32**, 1249 (1960).
(19) Zeldes, H., Livingston, R., *Ibid.*, **35**, 563 (1961).

RECEIVED April 30, 1962. Work supported by Bureau of Naval Weapons, Department of the Navy, under NORD 7386.

6

Experimental Determination of the Electron Affinities of Inorganic Radicals

F. M. PAGE

Department of Chemistry,
College of Advanced Technology,
Birmingham 4, England

The magnetron technique is a powerful tool, not only to establish experimental values of electron affinities but also to provide data about bond energies. It is applicable to a wide variety of radicals, the only limitation on its use being the difficulty of finding suitably volatile substrates whose mode of fission is known. The suggested application of mass spectroscopy to the problem will further extend the availability and power of the technique.

One of the fundamental properties of an atom or radical is the decrease in its energy when an electron is attached. This decrease in energy is known as the electron affinity and is of course identical with the ionization potential of the negative ion produced.

Many methods have been devised by which the electron affinity could be estimated with a greater or less accuracy and these have been reviewed by Pritchard (20). Four are of prime importance: the Born-Haber cycle, electron impact studies, electron transfer spectra, and the magnetron method. A fifth method, the elegant photodetachment technique of Branscombe and Smith (3), has not so far been exploited as thoroughly as it deserves. The Born-Haber cycle is based upon an electrostatic calculation of the lattice energies of a series of salts of the anion concerned. Such calculations have been discussed by Waddington (24) and it is fair to say that the uncertainties for all but spherically symmetrical ions forming cubic salts may easily amount to 1 e.v., or 20 kcal. The electron impact studies have led to a great deal of information about negative ions, collected by Field and Franklin (6), but the results obtained rarely agree among themselves, or with other estimates, possibly because of kinetic energy contributions. The so-called "electron transfer spectra," the intense spectra around 2000 A. shown by aqueous solutions and characteristic of the anion concerned, are more useful guides. They have been discussed by Orgel (12) and Stein and Treinin (21), to name but two of many recent studies, and can be used to make fairly accurate estimates of electron affinities when the anion is stable towards water.

Magnetron Technique

The most accurate and versatile method is undoubtedly the magnetron technique devised by Mayer and his coworkers (*4, 10, 22*) and used to study the halide ions. In this method the negative ions and electrons emitted from a hot filament in the presence of a low pressure of gas are separated by a coaxial magnetic field. In the absence of a magnetic field and at a pressure of about 10^{-3} mm. of Hg, so that the mean free path is comparable with the dimension of the apparatus, the thermionic current from the filament is carried by both ions and electrons, and in an apparatus such as that shown in Figure 1, the charged particles leave the filament radially, and pass through a coaxial grid with no more than a geometric hindrance.

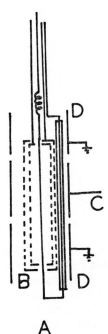

Figure 1. Coaxial
magnetron assembly

A. Filament
B. Suppressor grid
C. Anode
D. Guard ring

In the presence of a magnetic field of suitable intensity the electrons are constrained into spiral paths and, approaching the grid tangentially, are captured by it, while the heavy ions, the radii of curvature of whose paths are many times greater, are virtually unaffected, so that the limiting current is carried solely by the ions. At a constant pressure, the temperature dependence of the ion and electron currents can be related to the electron affinity of the radical under investigation. The sensitivity can be improved by including a second, or suppressor, grid whose function is to repel secondary ions and electrons formed by inelastic collisions either in the gas or at the grid surface, and it is this design which is illustrated.

Recently, a different form of apparatus has been devised (Figure 2), in which the layout has been altered from coaxial to linear, with the object of stabilizing the filament and grid assembly, which in the original form was very sensitive to mechanical vibration.

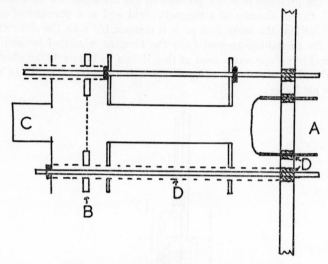

Figure 2.   Linear magnetron assembly

A. *Filament*
B. *Suppressor grid*
C. *Faraday cup*
D. *Glass insulation*

The experimental data obtained with either type of apparatus—the total thermionic current, the ion current, and the working pressure—may be regarded as arising from two rate processes, the emission of electrons from the surface, and the arrival of radicals at the surface followed by some fraction being emitted as negative ions.   The ratio of the electron current to the ion current per unit pressure of substrate will then have a temperature coefficient which corresponds to the difference in the activation energies of the two rate processes.   The activation energy for the emission of electrons will be χ, the work function of the filament surface, while that for negative ion emission will be $\chi - E$, where E is the electron affinity of the radical.   The temperature coefficient thus corresponds directly to the electron affinity of the radical.   Such a model is far too naive in view of the importance of the surface to the results obtained with certain substrates, and a more sophisticated formulation has been given by the author (16) based on the kinetics of adsorption and desorption at the surface.   The basic idea of computing the temperature coefficient of the ratio of two rate processes is unchanged, but the apparent electron affinity, E', is substituted for E.   This quantity is defined by the equation $E' = E + Q_r - D$, where E is the true electron affinity, D the energy necessary to produce radicals from the substrate, and Q_r the heat of adsorption, if any, of the unchanged residue of the substrate on the filament.

Very recently, Gaines, working in the author's laboratory, has shown that the total thermionic current may be used to measure the temperature of the filament, and that a logarithmic plot of the total and negative ion currents has a slope of $\chi - E'/\chi(8)$.   The work function has been taken to be that of the filament material, tungsten, even though Gaines has found that, as is well known with organic substrates, the filament becomes converted to tungsten carbide, a reaction which occurs rapidly under our experimental conditions; the work function of this is indistinguishable from that of clean tungsten, and tests with fresh and carbided filaments have shown no significant differences in results. This latter method is perhaps the most convenient to use, since measurement of the filament temperature is difficult, and the double logarithmic plot not only renders it unnecessary but also provides a continuous and instantaneous substitute for it. Furthermore, this method emphasizes the kinetic nature of the experiments leading to the ratio of the activation energies, an aspect of the experiment which is important because it makes clear that there is no necessity for even a significant portion of the total decomposition of the substrate at the surface to proceed through an ionic mechanism, any process not leading to ions being irrelevant as unobservable.

The apparent electron affinity, E′, which is the primary deduction from the observations, is a complex quantity, which may be broken down into the true electron affinity, E, the heat of breakdown of the substrate to the relevant entities which remain, D, and the heat of adsorption, Q_r, of all those nonionic products of the breakdown, the residue, on the surface. These are related by the equation:

$$E' = E + Q_r - D$$

Classes of Substrate

The heat of breakdown of the substrate, usually the energy required to break a single bond, is unimportant if it is less than approximately 75 kcal., the substrate then behaving as if it were broken into fragments before reaching the filament. It is possible to distinguish four classes of substrate which differ in their apparent electron affinities.

1. The electron acceptors which form negative ions directly, and where the apparent electron affinity is also the true electron affinity.
2. The compounds with low bond energies; such compounds break up to give electron acceptors before reaching the filament, and again E′ and E are identical.
3. The substrates with a high bond energy, which has to be taken into account, so that E′ is (E−D).
4. Perhaps the most interesting class, where the production of the electron acceptor is accompanied by the adsorption of a residue on the surface. This residue is usually hydrogen, and a study of the apparent electron affinities of suitable hydrides can yield information about the strength of hydride bonds, and thus provide a very valuable addition to the methods available to thermochemistry.

A number of ions have been studied by the magnetron technique, and, wherever possible, the parent electron acceptors have been derived from several different substrates. To emphasize the potentialities of the method, the results will be considered according to the class of substrate, rather than the electron acceptor, and any discussion of the individual acceptors be kept to the end. No members of the first class of substrate have yet been observed, although it would appear probable that sulfur hexafluoride, sulfur trioxide, nitrogen dioxide, and certain organic compounds such as tetracyanoethylene should be able to capture electrons directly.

The second class of substrates, which form electron acceptors by breaking a low energy bond, are very numerous, and are the most profitable for study. There are two subgroups, those such as the halogens, hydrazine (*18*), hydrogen persulfide (*1*), and thiocyanogen (*11*) which split symmetrically to give two electron acceptors, and those such as nitrous oxide (17) and the mercury alkyls (15) which split unsymmetrically to yield acceptors and inert products. It is often possible to deduce from the magnitude of the apparent electron affinity whether a substrate belongs to this class, and this may be of value in determining its structure. This occurred with thiocyanogen, expected to have an electron affinity less than that of cyanogen. The value observed, 46 kcal., could only be the true value, so that structures which would involve the fission of a link to carbon, which would have a high energy, were ruled out. Care must be exercised in cases of unsymmetrical fission to check that the other products are inert—for example, the mercury alkyls have been checked by a study of some lead tetra-alkyls. One interesting member of this class is benzil, which is believed to split symmetrically, to give benzoyl, which immediately splits unsymmetrically to give phenyl and carbon monoxide.

Substrates of the third group, involving fission of a high energy bond, are rarer, but two important examples are oxygen and cyanogen, while in the organic field such fission has been found in diphenyl and related compounds. It might be expected that carbon-carbon links would be broken in many alkyl compounds, but there is as yet no evidence that this occurs, presumably because the only ionic process involves the direct formation of the ion, and any more complex reaction involves only neutral species. Some evidence has been found that ethyl radicals can either form ethyl ions or disproportionate to give ethylene and methyl ions.

The fourth group involves the fission of a high energy bond, with the subsequent adsorption of the residual products on the filament surface. The apparent electron affinity is then given by the full expression $(E - D + Q_r)$. Such behavior has been found so far only with hydrides, where hydrogen is the residue adsorbed on the surface. Two reasons may be advanced for this. In the first place, the negative ion observed will be formed from the electronegative part of the substrate, so that the residue must be electropositive, and secondly, some slow rate process must intervene between the process liberating the negative ion and that desorbing the residue, so that the two processes are energetically isolated. These requirements are satisfied for hydrogen, which is desorbed as molecules but adsorbed as atoms, so that diffusion across the surface must occur before desorption can take place. It has been suggested (7) that the hydrogen may actually penetrate the tungsten lattice, which would make the over-all desorption an even slower process.

The heat of chemisorption of a hydrogen atom on tungsten was calculated by Eley (5) to be 73.5 kcal., and this was checked experimentally (14) by determining the apparent electron affinity of hydrogen chloride and found to be 72 kcal. in the temperature range of interest in these experiments. This value has been further checked with several other compounds and is now taken as established. Some indications have been found that, as might be expected, the heat of adsorption is different with different surfaces, and a platinum surface gives a lower value. The carbided tungsten surface referred to above has been examined carefully, but has been found to differ very little from a clean tungsten surface. Here, presumably, the tungsten dominates the carbon in the provision of the active centers on which adsorption can occur, as a naive view would suggest, so that little change is evident.

Interesting though such variations in the heat of chemisorption are, the most important aspect of these apparent electron affinities of the hydrides is thermochemical. If it is possible by any other experiment to obtain a value for the electron affinity of a radical, then the apparent electron affinity of the radical hydride will immediately yield a value for the radical-hydrogen bond energy. Many hydrides of the less electropositive elements have been prepared in recent years which are suitable for such studies, and in many cases the corresponding "twin radical" hydrides are also known.   One example which has been studied is ammonia, which gives the amino radical and the "twin radical" hydride—hydrazine (18).   The apparent electron affinity of the amino radical formed by the case II fission (weak bond, symmetrical split) of hydrazine was 33 kcal., while the case IV fission of ammonia led to an apparent electron affinity of only 3 kcal. The combination of these two figures leads to the value of 102 kcal. for the H—NH$_2$ bond energy, in good agreement with the pyrolysis studies of Szwarc (23).   In a similar manner, a combination of the apparent electron affinities of thiocyanogen, another case II fission, and thiocyanic acid has led to a value of 110 kcal. for the H—NCS bond energy.   Other monobasic acids, including selenocyanic, nitric, and possibly perchloric acids, can be studied by this method, while the hydrides of phosphorus, arsenic, antimony, and germanium can be treated in the same manner as ammonia.   In general, if a suitable source for the radical can be found, either the "twin radical" or as in the case of the nitrate radical a volatile compound (anhydrous copper nitrate), where the radical is produced by a case II split, the precise value of the bond that is broken is irrelevant, the apparent electron affinity is also the true electron affinity, and a comparison with the result for the hydride will give the hydrogen-radical bond energy and open

Table I.   Data Obtained by Magnetron Technique

Radical	Electron Affinity, Kcal./Mole	Substrate	Type of Split	Auxiliary Data Required
Cl	87	HCl	IV	$Q_r = 72$
Br	80	HBr	IV	$Q_r = 72$
I	74.5	I$_2$	II	. . .
O	33	N$_2$O	II	. . .
	34	O$_2$	III	$D(O—O) = 118.0$
	34	H$_2$O	IV	$D(H—O—H) = 219$, $Q_r = 2 \times 72$
S	48	H$_2$S	IV	$D(H—S—H) = 165$, $Q_r = 2 \times 72$
HS	53	H$_2$S$_2$	II	. . .
NH$_2$	28	N$_2$H$_4$	II	. . .
	28	NH$_3$	IV	$D(H—NH_2) = 102$, $Q_r = 72$
CN	64	C$_2$N$_2$	III	$D(NC—CN) = 112$
	64.5	HCN	IV	$D(H—CN) = 114$, $Q_r = 72$
SCN	46	(SCN)$_2$	II	. . .
	46	HNCS	IV	$D(H—NCS) = Q_r = 72$
CH$_3$	26	Hg(CH$_3$)$_2$	II	. . .
	26	Pb(CH$_3$)$_4$	II	. . .
	26	Pb(C$_2$H$_5$)$_4$	II + III	$\Delta H_f(C_2H_4, CH_3, C_2H_5)$
C$_2$H$_5$	22	Pb(C$_2$H$_5$)$_4$	II	. . .
	23	Hg(C$_2$H$_5$)$_2$	II	. . .
C$_3$H$_7$	16	Hg(n-C$_3$H$_7$)$_2$	II	. . .
C$_4$H$_9$	15	Hg(n-C$_4$H$_9$)	II	. . .
C$_6$H$_5$	53	C$_6$H$_6$	IV	$D(H—C_6H_5) = 102$, $Q_r = 72$
	50	(C$_6$H$_5$)CO$_2$	II	. . .
	50	C$_6$H$_5$.C$_6$H$_5$	III	$D(C_6H_5—C_6H_5) = 103$
C$_6$H$_5$.CH$_2$	23.5	C$_6$H$_5$.CH$_3$	IV	$D(H—CH_2.C_6H_5) = 77.5$, $Q_r = 72$
	25	(C$_6$H$_5$.CH$_2$)$_2$	II	. . .

the way for a full thermochemical investigation of the compound. If the bond energy is high, above about 75 kcal., the radical will be produced by a case III fission, and further information is required before such analysis can be made.

Many substances have now been examined by the magnetron technique, and the results obtained so far are listed in Table I. Only measurements made by the Birmingham group are included in the table, which covers both inorganic and organic radicals. Certain other results whose precise interpretation is not yet clear have been omitted.

So far the only means of identification of the ions produced has been the internal consistency and sense of the results obtained, but the increasing complexity of the radicals which are being examined, and the absence of any alternative estimates for comparison have made a more precise method of identification desirable. The construction of a radio-frequency mass spectrometer has therefore been put in hand for use in conjunction with the apparatus. Such mass spectrometers have a limited resolving power but will work at pressures of the order of 10^{-3} mm. of Hg, which is the usual operating pressure of the magnetron, so that the two pieces of apparatus will match each other very conveniently. The development of a suitable instrument will be doubly advantageous, for not only will it give precise identification, but it will also enable two radicals to be studied simultaneously, and their electron affinities compared. This will increase the available range of substrates, and will avoid many of the thermochemical drawbacks of having to split high energy bonds, since such bonds will be common to both fragments and therefore will cancel out in the comparison.

Electron Affinity of Hydroxyl Radical

One problem which is of great interest and which has not been tackled directly because of the great instability of the obvious substrate is the electron affinity of the hydroxyl radical. Lattice energy calculations, and thermodynamic cycles, can be made consistent with any value between 40 and 70 kcal., as can the electron transfer spectra. Some years ago the author interpreted a number of microwave studies of flames as indicating an electron affinity of hydroxyl of 62

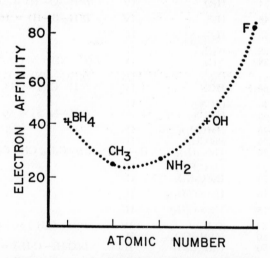

Figure 3. Isoelectronic interpolation of electron affinities

kcal. (*13*), but direct mass spectrometry of flames has failed to reveal the expected quantities of ions (*9*) and it is now believed that the effect may be due to the use of an incorrect electron collision frequency (*19*). The photodetachment studies of Branscombe and Smith gave a preliminary value of 40 kcal., but the resolution of the instrument used was not entirely satisfactory and a value 5 kcal. higher was possible (*2*). The data given in Table I may be used to make an isoelectronic interpolation in the series $F-OH-NH_2-CH_3$. Many quantities may be used as the independent variable; in Figure 3 the electron affinity is plotted against the atomic number, but whatever quantity is used, all lead to a value for hydroxyl in the range 45 to 50 kcal. While this is only one more piece of circumstantial evidence, it strengthens the support for a value in this range. The curve would suggest that the borohydride radical, BH_4, should have as high an electron affinity as hydroxyl.

Acknowledgment

The author's thanks are due to many people for their help and encouragement and in particular to the Royal Society for a grant for apparatus, and to the U. S. Army for financial support under contract DA-91-591-EUC-2142.

Literature Cited

(1) Ansdell, D. A., Page, F. M., *Trans. Faraday Soc.* **58**, 1084 (1962).
(2) Branscombe, L. N., private communication, 1956.
(3) Branscombe, L. N., Smith, S. J., *Phys. Revs.* **99**, 1957 (1955).
(4) Doty, P. M., Mayer, J. E., *J. Chem. Phys.* **12**, 323 (1944).
(5) Eley, D. D., *Discussions Faraday Soc.* **8**, 34 (1950).
(6) Field, F. H., Franklin, J. L., "Electron Impact Phenomena, "Academic Press, New York, 1957.
(7) Fox, R. E., private communication, 1961.
(8) Gaines, A. F., private communication, 1962.
(9) Knewstubb, P. F., Sugden, T. M., private communication.
(10) McCallum, K. J., Mayer, J. E., *J. Chem. Phys.* **11**, 56 (1943).
(11) Napper, R., Page, F. M., unpublished manuscript.
(12) Orgel, L. E., *Quart. Revs.* **8**, 422 (1954).
(13) Page, F. M., *Discussions Faraday Soc.* **19**, 87 (1955).
(14) Page, F. M., *Nature* **188**, 1021 (1960).
(15) Page, F. M., Proc. 8th Intern. Symposium on Flame and Combustion, Pasadena, Calif., 1960.
(16) Page, F. M., *Trans. Faraday Soc.* **56**, 1742 (1960).
(17) *Ibid.,* **57**, 359 (1961).
(18) *Ibid.,* p. 1254.
(19) Page, F. M., Williams, H., unpublished work, 1961.
(20) Pritchard, H. O., *Chem. Revs.* **52**, 529 (1953).
(21) Stein, G., Treinin, A., *Trans. Faraday Soc.* **55**, 1086 (1959).
(22) Sutton, P. P., Mayer, J. E., *J. Chem. Phys.* **2**, 145 (1934).
(23) Szwarc, M., *Proc. Roy. Soc.* **A198**, 267 (1949).
(24) Waddington, T. C., *Advan. Inorg. Chem. Radiochem.* **1**, 57 (1959).

RECEIVED May 3, 1962.

7

Electron-Spin Resonance of Some Simple Oxy Radicals

MARTYN C. R. SYMONS

Department of Chemistry, The University, Leicester, England

Recent results for certain known radicals of general type XO, XO_2, and XO_3 are presented and compared with those for unknown radicals formed and trapped in crystalline salts of nonmetal oxy acids, such as sulfates and phosphates, as a result of exposure to high energy radiation. Certain generalizations are made, regarding the values for isotropic and anisotropic hyperfine splittings to be expected from the nucleus of atom X for different isoelectronic series and these are linked to expected deviations of the g value from that of the free spin. Hence an attempt is made to rationalize the results of several recent studies of irradiated crystalline oxy salts.

The aim of this paper is to consider the interpretation of electron-spin resonance (ESR) data pertaining to simple inorganic radicals and to illustrate briefly the sort of structural information which can be derived therefrom. Oxy radicals of the nonmetals of groups 4 to 7, inclusive, are chosen as a basis, and results for related radicals are compared with these. Only radicals in doublet states are considered, thus excluding triplet species such as O_2 and SO.

Several of the radicals under consideration, such as the oxides of nitrogen, are relatively stable and have been studied extensively for many years. The resulting data have proved to be invaluable in the task of unraveling the information obtained from the application of ESR methods. Furthermore, the level schemes founded on this knowledge by Mulliken (34), Walsh (44), and others have formed an extremely useful platform for interpreting ESR data.

Electron Resonance Studies

Studies have been made on neutral radicals in the gas phase, and on these and radical ions in solution and in the solid state. Gas phase studies are complicated by the fact that many rotational states are populated, and, for linear molecules, orbital contribution to the magnetic states can be large, whereas in solution or the solid state rotations are nonquantized, and the orbital contribution is largely quenched by the medium. The present discussion is confined to results for radicals in condensed phases.

When a radical is in fluid solution or rotating freely in a rigid matrix, dipolar anisotropic interactions are averaged to zero, the residual isotropic hyperfine coupling, if any, being a measure of the s character of the odd-electron's wave function at the nuclei concerned. The g value, or electronic spectroscopic splitting factor, is then the weighted average of the three principal values of the g tensor of the radical concerned.

If a dilute solution can be frozen without separation of the solute, the ESR spectrum changes in a characteristic manner. Under favorable conditions each line will change as illustrated in Figure 1, and the magnitudes of the principal values of both the hyperfine coupling and g tensors can in principle be derived therefrom. Alternatively, resolution may be so poor that the over-all effect is simply a single line. This was the case, for example, in early studies of sodium ozonide, O_3^-, and SO_2^-. The situation is often so complex that unambiguous interpretation is impossible without prior knowledge of the relevant tensors. It is considerably simplified if the tensors have axial symmetry, so that two of the principal values coincide. This is often the case for simple radicals, and a typical result is illustrated in Figure 1, for trapped PO_3^{-2} radicals in powdered, γ-irradiated disodium hydrogen phosphite.

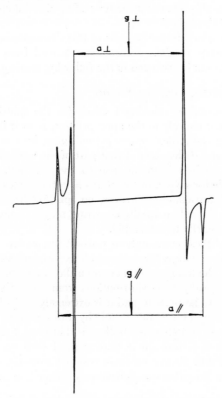

Figure 1. ESR spectrum of PO_3^{-2} radicals in powdered, γ-irradiated Na_2HPO_4 at room temperature

Data of Table I for this radical derived as indicated

Radicals with anisotropic magnetic properties are best studied when trapped in specific orientations in single crystals. They must be well separated from each other to avoid magnetic interactions between radicals. This is not always easy, but if it can be accomplished, it is relatively easy to derive the hyperfine coupling and g tensors (40), together with the directions of their principal axes relative to those of the crystal. This latter result, which cannot, of course, be derived from powder spectra, will be structurally informative if the orientation of the radicals in the crystal is known or can be reasonably predicted.

Somewhat surprisingly, many radicals, normally so reactive that they never exist in detectable amounts, can be formed and trapped in an oriented fashion in single crystals by exposure to high energy radiation. This fact, which was exploited recently in connection with the study of organic radicals, has been used for many years to create so called "color centers" in rare-gas ionic crystals such as the alkali halides. Only recently has it been realized that a "molecular" description of some of these centers is often appropriate, radicals such as Cl_2^- having been unambiguously recognized by their ESR spectra (10).

Unfortunately, although other aspects are ideal, the nature of the trapped radical is unknown, since in general it is not possible to predict the mode of breakdown of a given molecule or molecular ion. Therefore one depends upon the ESR results and other supporting evidence from ultraviolet spectra, reactivity in the solid state, or possibly chemical analysis after dissolution of the crystal, to establish the nature of the radical.

The oxy radicals which form the basis of this discussion are listed in Table I together with appropriate results. Information derived from the hyperfine coupling tensors and g tensors is discussed in the following sections.

Information from Hyperfine Coupling Tensors

If either experimental or calculated values for the splitting to be expected from an electron located entirely in the appropriate s, p, or d level are known, the experimental result for the radical concerned will give, by comparison, the total s and the sum of the p and d character of that part of the molecular orbital centered on the atom whose nucleus is giving rise to the splitting. Fortunately, such information is available for several of the atoms X in the oxides XO, XO_2, and XO_3 listed in Table I. Unfortunately, however, no splitting has ever been observed from oxygen, because the only naturally occurring magnetic nucleus, ^{17}O, is in too low an abundance to contribute detectably.

Several aspects of these computations warrant discussion. First, with respect to the isotropic coupling, unless the s character corresponding to this contributes about 10% or more of the total wave function on the atom concerned, little weight can be placed on the result, since contributions from excited states, both positive and negative, will always be present, and it is extremely difficult to make complete allowance for this, although for certain simple hydrides, such as the methyl radical, this has been attempted. An obvious corollary is that even if the molecular orbital of the unpaired electron is formally a pure p level with no contributions from atomic s levels, there will always be some residual isotropic splitting unless the positive and negative contributions fortuitously cancel, as is the case for the nitrogen atom.

Unfortunately, it is generally not possible to distinguish between p and d character from the anisotropic part of the hyperfine coupling tensor, since both give rise to a tensor of the same type. For simplicity, it is assumed, for radicals of the class under consideration, that the anisotropy arises largely from the (n) p level, and only slightly from the (n) d level. This neglect is not necessarily justified, however, except, of course, for oxy radicals of the first row nonmetals.

On the basis of this approximation it is possible, from the tables given by Coulson (*17*), to calculate the bond angle of 17-electron dioxides such as CO_2^- (Table I), and it is encouraging that for this radical (*36*) and for NO_2 (*3*) the bond angle estimated from the $s:p$ ratio is about $134°$, which is in good agreement with the value of $134°$ for NO_2 estimated by more direct methods.

Another class of radicals having a large s contribution from X is the 25-electron trioxides, typified by NO_3^{-2}. Just as on adding an extra electron to linear CO_2 the molecule bends, so also on adding an extra electron to planar NO_3^- one expects the resulting NO_3^{-2} to be pyramidal, since in each case the extra electron is thereby stabilized. If the results given in the table truly relate to NO_3^{-2}, this is a relatively slight effect. However, if one assumes no contribution to the anisotropic coupling from atomic d levels on X, then the groups PO_3^{-2}, SO_3^-, and ClO_3 deviate far more, the $p:s$ ratio being about 4 compared with 9.5 for NO_3^{-2}. Comparison with molecules whose shape is known leads to conflicting conclusions—thus on going from NH_3 to PH_3 the bond angle decreases by about $13°$, but angles for NF_3 and PF_3 are almost identical. Since the latter pair resemble more closely the oxides NO_3^{-2} and PO_3^{-2}, it seems that the situation is a subtle one. This question of the difference between NO_3^{-2} and PO_3^{-2} will be raised again later when substituted radicals are considered.

Another aspect of these calculations is that, knowing the net contribution from atomic orbitals on X, one can, by difference, estimate the contributions from levels on oxygen. In general, the trend for isoelectronic radicals is that the unpaired electron is more localized on X as the electron affinity of X falls. For example, it is more localized on carbon in CO_2^- than on nitrogen in NO_2.

This result, which appears contradictory at first sight, is a consequence of the total electron distribution in all the orbitals concerned. These are, in general, a set of bonding, nonbonding, and antibonding levels, the nonbonding being confined to oxygen. Thus if, as with NO_2, three electrons have to be distributed between X and O, the two in the low-lying bonding level will tend to concentrate more on X as its electron affinity increases, thus forcing the single electron in the antibonding level more onto oxygen. It is perhaps simpler to view the problem as the distribution of a positive "hole," which will clearly move onto oxygen the more as the electron affinity of X increases.

In contrast, the unpaired electron in linear radicals such as NO and O_2^-, and 19-electron dioxides such as NO_2^{-2}, O_3^-, and ClO_2, should be in a pure π level and hence the atomic s character with respect to X should be very small. This is in accord with the results tabulated.

Trioxides such as NO_3, however, have a "hole" in the nonbonding a_2 level on oxygen and hence both the isotropic and anisotropic coupling to nitrogen should be extremely small. This, together with g value considerations, has led us to postulate that radical 17 in the table is this trioxide.

Generally, the anisotropic coupling tensor has the form $(+2\alpha, -\alpha, -\alpha)$, the positive value arising when the external field is parallel to the p orbital on the atom concerned. (Contributions from dipolar interaction between the nucleus of X and the electron localized on adjacent oxygens are small, and can generally be neglected.) However, for linear radicals, such as NO or ClO, the unpaired electron is in a degenerate level and its dipolar interaction must be summed for both levels. This effectively alters the symmetry axis from that of the p orbital to that of the molecule, and the hyperfine tensor reduces to $(-\alpha, +\alpha/2, +\alpha/2)$. A similar reversal of sign and reduction by a factor of 2 from the "normal" value results when a molecule is free to rotate in one specific plane. Thus, for example, if NO_2 were to rotate about the y axis (the O—O direction) or the x axis (in the molecular plane), the anisotropic coupling should be thus modified. This has been verified for NO_2 radicals trapped in rare-gas matrixes (*31*), where they are thought to rotate about y (*3*) and for the dioxide formed in y-irradiated Pb $(NO_3)_2$, where they apparently rotate about x—that is, in the plane of the nitrate ion from which they were formed.

Information from g-Tensor. Although the hyperfine coupling tensor is the most helpful piece of information derived from the ESR spectra, the g tensor is also informative, especially if the components are clearly distinguishable and deviate considerably from the free-spin value of 2.0023.

For linear oxides and symmetrical trioxides the tensor should have symmetry about the molecular axis, but for bent dioxides three principal values are generally found.

For radicals in condensed media, g values rarely differ much from 2.0023. It is often stated that g values greater or less than 2.0023 are indications of "electron-deficit" centers or "electron-excess" centers, respectively. While this may well be the case, it is not a necessary condition. In general, there are competing excited states that can combine with the ground state for a given direction of the magnetic field, those which involve excitation of the magnetic electron into an outer vacant level giving a negative contribution, and those which involve excitation of an inner electron into the half-filled level giving a positive contribution to the g value. If there is a low-lying excited state that can combine, this will dominate. Thus for linear diatomic oxides with the unpaired electron in a π level, unless there is a very strong asymmetric intermolecular interaction, radicals such as NO with only one electron in the doubly degenerate level will have g less than 2.0023 while those with three electrons in this level, such as O_2^- or ClO, will have g greater than 2.0023. Experimental results for such radicals (*2, 6, 7*) are in agreement with this conclusion. The suggestion (*30*) that radical 9 in the table is NO trapped in KCl is therefore thought to be improbable.

Identification of Radicals

Bearing these generalizations in mind, we have endeavored to identify a variety of radicals which are formed on exposure of certain crystals to high energy radiation.

To start with, it seemed wise not only to compare experiment with theory, but to utilize results for radicals whose identity was known. This has been done for radicals O_2^- (*7*), ClO (*2*), NO_2 (*3*), and ClO_2 (*15*). The trio of radicals PO_3^{-2} (*27*), SO_3^- (*11*), and ClO_3 (*2, 14*) have been identified for a variety of reasons, in addition to the fact that their hyperfine coupling and g tensors are in accord with expectation. The steadily increasing delocalization onto oxygen in this series is in agreement with this formulation. The fact that the radical thought to be PO_3^{-2} can be made from the ion $H-PO_3^{-2}$ by γ-radiolysis is strong evidence in favor of this formulation, since it is common experience that hydrogen atoms are preferentially lost under these circumstances. The radical thought to be SO_3^- can be formed by irradiation of crystals containing the ion $O_3S-SO_3^{-2}$ and several other crystals likely to form SO_3^- give the same radical on irradiation. Finally, since so-called ClO_3 can be formed from a variety of perchlorates, and the parameters are totally different from those established for ClO and ClO_2, there can be little doubt that Cole's identification is correct also.

These data, combined with theoretical expectations, have enabled us to attempt an identification of a variety of radicals in this general class, some of which are given in Table I.   In several instances these suggestions differ from those of others: Reference should be made to the relevant publications for arguments in favor of these alternatives.

Apart from preparing more radicals within these groups, we hope to obtain some tetroxide radicals, XO_4. The most likely radical to be formed is the 31-electron tetroxide, such as PO_4^{-2}, which has an unpaired electron in a nonbonding t_1 level on oxygen.   Since this level is threefold degenerate, we anticipate that, in the absence of major distortions, there will be strong spin-lattice interactions, giving such efficient relaxation that a low temperature will be needed for their detection.   Also, the g values should be considerably greater than that of the free spin, and hyperfine coupling with the nucleus of X will be very small, probably comparable with that for nitrogen in NO_3 (Table I).   Unfortunately, such results will not be structurally very informative.   The 33-electron radicals would give more information, but, in contrast with comparable oxy ions in the transition metal series, such as MnO_4^{-2} (9), these ions will probably be extremely difficult if not impossible to prepare.

Recently a radical has been detected in γ-irradiated $Li_2SO_4.2H_2O$ crystals which has been ascribed to a "hole" on one of the oxygens of a sulfate ion (46). The properties of this radical are not in good accord with our expectations for SO_4^- as outlined above.   One important feature of the radical in lithium sulfate is that there is a remarkably large splitting from a single proton (Table I).   This coupling, as has recently been stressed by Ovenall (35), is what would be expected for an electron in a p orbital on an atom directly attached to the proton concerned.   An ambiguity arises as to whether the electron is on an oxygen atom of a sulfate group or of a water molecule from which a hydrogen atom has been lost. The latter possibility is favored by Ovenall, but, as he points out, there are certain interpretative difficulties which then arise, the major one being that axial symmetry would be expected.   Furthermore, hydroxyl radicals have been studied in ice (33, 38), and the hyperfine and g tensors recorded (Table I).

These results are in accord with expectation for a radical with axial symmetry, but whose orbital component has been quenched almost completely by the environment.   In particular, there is a remarkably large positive isotropic coupling to the proton.   This is about threefold larger than that for the radical in lithium sulfate, although the anisotropic couplings are fairly similar in magnitude. Unless the effect which is supposed to confine the electron to one of the p orbitals of ·OH also greatly decreases the isotropic coupling (and probably also changes the sign from positive to negative), this identification is not satisfactory.   The g values are also rather different, but this is thought to be a less useful guide to identity.

As Ovenall stressed, the results are comparable with those for a radical found in hydrogen peroxide irradiated with ultraviolet light (42).   This is almost certainly $HO_2\cdot$ rather than ·OH.   However, the proton hyperfine coupling tensor cannot be estimated from the spectrum, so it seems premature to identify the radical in $Li_2SO_4.2H_2O$ as HO_2.

If hyperfine coupling from ^{17}O in isotropically enriched oxy ions could be detected, a great deal more structural information would result, in addition to the extra information about the number of oxygens involved.   A less subtle approach is to replace one or more oxygens by fluorine, which has a nuclear spin of one half and should be fairly similar to oxygen in its bonding properties. Both these possibilities are being explored at present.

TABLE I.   **ESR Data for Oxides XO,**

No.	Outer Electrons	Class	Radical	Medium	x
		XO			
1	11		NO	Gas	
2[a,b]			N_2^-	KN_3	2.0027
3[d]			OH	H_2O	2.0077
4	13		O_2^-	NaO_2	2.00
5			ClO	H_2SO_4, 77°K.	1.9909
6	15		Cl_2^-	KCl	2.043
		XO₂		(z bisects OXO,	
7	17		CO_2^-	$NaHCO_2$	2.0032
8			NO_2	$NaNO_2$	2.0057
[a]				$Pb(NO_3)_2$	2.004
				Argon, 4°K	2.0037
9[a]	19		NO_2^{-2}	KCl	2.0038
10			NF_2	Gas	—
11			$N(SO_3)_2^{-2}$		2.0042
12			NH_2	Argon, 42°K.	
13			O_3^-	NH_3 KClO₃, 77°K.	2.0025
14[d,e]			HO_2	H_2O_2/H_2O, 77°K.	2.006
15			SO_2^-	$H_2O(S_2O_4^{-2})$ $Na_2S_2O_5$	2.0024
16			ClO_2	H_2SO_4, R,T. KClO₄	2.0036
		XO₃			
17[a]	23		NO_3	KNO_3	2.025
18[a]	25		NO_3^{-2}	KCl	2.0068
19[c]			R_2NO	CS_2	
20[c]			R_2CO^-	T.H.F.	
21			NH_3^+	NH_4ClO_4	—
22			$^-O_3SNH_2^+$	$^-O_3SNH_3^+$	
23			CH_3	CH_3I	
24			$ON(SO_3)_2^{-2}$		
25			PO_3^{-2}	Na_2HPO_3	2.001
26			HPO_2^-	NaH_2PO_3	2.0146
27			SO_3^-		2.004
28			ClO_3	NH_4ClO_4 $Mg(ClO_4)_2$	2.008 2.0103
29[d]			?	$Li_2SO_4 2H_2O$	2.002

[a] Identification either differs from that in specified reference, or no identification was offered.
[b] Identification tentative.
[c] R = *tert*-butyl and *n*-hexyl, respectively.
[d] Hyperfine tensor refers to proton.

Some Related Radicals

Radicals which can be regarded as being derived from the various classes of oxy radicals listed in Table I are considered here with respect to their ESR spectra. Replacements of oxygen by fluorine, protons, nitrogen, SO_3, and organic groups are discussed in turn.

Replacement by Fluorine. Although such replacement would be informative, because of the large doublet hyperfine splitting to be expected from fluorine, few radicals of this type have been studied. It has been claimed (20) that irradiation of CF_4 and SiF_4 gives CF_3 and SiF_3, respectively, which remain trapped in the matrix at 77° or 4°K. The resulting spectra are very complex,

XO₂, and XO₃, and Related Radicals

g Tensor			Hyperfine Coupling, Gauss				Ref.
y	z	Av.	Ax	Ay	Az	Aiso	
(z is X-O axis)							
(ca. 1.0)							
						10.6	(7)
2.0008	1.9832	1.9956	10.7	−5.3	−5.3	1.3	(28)
2.0077	2.0127	2.0094	−6	−6	12	41.3	(33)
2.00	2.175	2.058					(6)
1.9909	2.0098	1.9972	5.7	5.7	−11.4	−5.7	(2)
2.045	2.001	2.03	−30	−30	60	39	(10)
y joins oxygens)							
1.9975	2.0014	2.0006	−16.43	−11.43	27.86	167.2	(36)
1.991	2.0015	1.9994	−5.27	−7.95	13.22	54.71	(3)
1.995	1.995	1.998	−4.6	2.3	2.3	54.6	(23)
1.990	2.0037	1.9991	3.6	−7.2	3.6	54.2	(29)
2.0099	2.0070	2.0070	16.6	−9.3	−7.3	14.3	(30)
—	—	2.010					(37)
2.0082	2.0025	2.005	25	−12.5	−12.5	13.2	(26)
		2.0048				10.3	(21)
		2.012					(32)
2.0174	2.0013	2.0104					(2)
2.006	2.039	2.015		(A⊥ ca. 11)			(42)
		2.0057				14.2	(25)
2.0102	2.0057	2.0061					(2)
		2.0093				16.5	(2)
2.0183	2.0088	2.0102	57.6	−30.8	−26.8	15.4	(15)
(z ⊥ to O₃ plane)							
2.025	2.005	2.018	—	—	—	4.5	(18)
2.0068	2.0020	2.0052	−10.3	−10.3	21.7	40.8	(30)
						11	(5)
						7.6	(1)
—	—	2.0034	—	—	—	18.1	(14)
			−12.1	−6.4	18.6	18.2	(39)
						41	(16)
			−7	−7	14	13	(45)
2.001	1.999	2.0003	−53	−53	106	593	(27)
2.0146	2.0059	2.0017	−60.7	−60.7	121.4	520.7	(2)
2.004	2.003	2.0036	−12	−12	25	128	(11)
2.008	2.007	2.0076	−13	−13	26	128	(14)
2.0103	2.0069	2.0092	−17	−17	33	133	(2)
2.002	2.040	2.015	±7.3	±2.3	∓9.6	∓13.6	(46)

as might be expected, and no satisfactory interpretation has yet been put forward. It will probably be necessary to study these radicals in single crystals before their identity can be firmly established and structural implications exploited.

Another radical which should give interesting information from fluorine nuclei is NF_2, which is formed by dissociation of N_2F_4 at relatively low temperatures (37). The ESR spectrum for these radicals in the gas phase is very broad and structureless, either because of rotational interactions, or possibly because the rate of dimerization was sufficient, under the conditions used (37), to give uncertainty broadening. This radical should have a structure comparable with that of NO_2^{-2}, so that the spectrum from radicals randomly trapped may well be too complex for reliable interpretation, or the structure may be lost in the line-width.

Replacement by Hydrogen. This change is far more drastic than the previous one, since the π system, with respect to the X—H bond, is lost, and coupling to the proton must occur via σ-bonding electrons, or as an anisotropic contribution from orbitals on X. This situation has been extensively studied and discussed for ·CH$_3$ (16) and related alkyl radicals, with respect to coupling with both ^{13}C nuclei and α- and β-protons. These radicals, in contrast with comparable trioxides, are planar, or very nearly so. Similarly, it has been concluded that NH$_3^+$ is planar (14, 29). It would be interesting to study the radicals SiH$_3$ and PH$_3^+$, since, by comparison with NH$_3$ and PH$_3$, these radicals might be pyramidal. Results for SiH$_3$ have been reported (13), but unfortunately, only the isotropic proton coupling is given, which is insufficient to enable any firm conclusions about bond angles to be drawn. However, the isotropic proton coupling, which is only 7.6 gauss, is so small that it seems unlikely that this radical deviates much from planarity, since this would be expected to give rise to a large isotropic coupling. This is illustrated by our results for a radical thought to be HPO$_2^-$ (Table I). Here the isotropic proton coupling is very large, being comparable with that for the proton in HCO (8), and, in accord with the electron being in an s-p hybridized orbital directed away from the proton, the anisotropic contribution is very small. In this instance, replacing oxygen by hydrogen does not seem to have altered the bond angle very much.

Results for NH$_2$ (21) are in accord with expectation, although only the isotropic coupling constants are known. Thus the isotropic coupling to nitrogen is close to that for NO$_2^{-2}$ and that to the protons is similar to the coupling in NH$_3^+$, indicating that the structure is such that the unpaired electron is still largely in the p_x level.

Replacement by Nitrogen. Two interesting radicals have recently been detected in single crystals of KN$_3$ after exposure to ultraviolet light. One, which apparently contains four equivalent nitrogen atoms (41), does not fall into any of the categories of the present classification, and will be discussed elsewhere. The other, containing two equivalent nitrogen atoms (28), is probably N$_2^-$, and it will be shown that the results agree with this suggestion.

The radical N$_2^-$ is isoelectronic with NO, and thus the unpaired electron should be in the otherwise empty π^* level. However, since three principal

TABLE II. Calculated Spin

No. (Table I)	Radical	a^2_s	a^2_p
5	ClO	0.004	0.133
7	CO$_2^-$	0.14	0.08
8	NO$_2$	0.103	0.054
9	NO$_2^{-2}$	0.028	0.64
11	N(SO$_3$)$_2^{-2}$	0.025	0.87
16	ClO$_2$	0.01	0.69
18	NO$_3^{-2}$	0.077	—
22	$^-$O$_3$SNH$_2^+$	0.034	0.58
24	ON(SO$_3$)$_2^{-2}$	0.025	0.49
25	PO$_3^{-2}$	0.16	—
27	SO$_3^-$	0.13	—
28	ClO$_3$	0.076	—

a^2s, $a^2{_{Pi}}$, and b^2_0 give spin populations for appropriate s and p levels on X and total on g values have been found, and two of them are less than the free-spin value, it is necessary to postulate a large crystal-field splitting of the doublet π^* level, such that the electron is largely confined to one of these levels. The direction associated with $g = 2.0027$ (x) is then taken at the density axis of the $p\text{-}\pi$ level containing the unpaired electron. The very low g value of 1.983 is taken as g_z, along the molecular axis, and this leaves $g_y = 2.0008$ along the empty $p\text{-}\pi$ orbital. This assignment is in accord with the hyperfine coupling tensor, if the isotropic coupling is taken to be positive. Of the two alternative sets, we favor the one that gives $+10.7$ for the anisotropic coupling along x. Since the unpaired electron is approximately 50% on each nitrogen, this gives an equivalent coupling of 21.4, which compares favorably with other results given in Table I, and corresponds, in terms of the parameters used for our calculations of Table II, to about 0.8 of an electron in the p_x level.

An alternative interpretation to N_2^- is that radical 2 is N_3, formed by loss of an electron from an azide ion. This molecule, which corresponds to a 15-electron dioxide, would be linear, with a hole in the doubly degenerate πg level located on the outer nitrogens. Coupling to the central nitrogen would then be very small and might well be lost in the relatively broad lines. Once again, loss of axial symmetry must occur to explain the results, but, although the hyperfine interaction is reasonable for N_3, the g values are not, since one would anticipate that when the field is along the molecular axis the g value would be considerably greater than 2.0023, whereas the reverse is found. Description of this radical as N_2^- is therefore favored.

Replacement by SO_3 Groups. The radicals $N(SO_3)_2^{-2}$ and $ON(SO_3)_2^{-2}$ can be compared with NO_2^{-2} and NO_3^{-2}, respectively. The first radical has parameters (26) which are, indeed, comparable with those assigned to NO_2^{-2}, except that the electron seems to be more confined to nitrogen than in the dioxide (Table I).

The radical $ON(SO_3)_2^{-2}$ is remarkably stable, and was one of the first inorganic radicals to be studied by spin-resonance methods (45). The isotropic nitrogen coupling of 13 gauss is of the order to be expected for a π-electron radical, so that, although delocalization onto oxygen is unexpectedly large, the radical must be planar, in contrast with NO_3^{-2}.

Replacement by Alkyl or Aryl Groups. Radicals of the type R_2CO^- and R_2NO are very stable and have been studied extensively, especially when R is

Populations for Certain Radicals

$a^2_{p_y}$	$a^2_{p_z}$	b_0^2	p/s Ratio	$O\hat{X}O$	Ref.
0.133	—	0.734	—	—	(2)
—	0.66	0.2	4.71	134°	(36)
—	0.471	0.43	4.5	134°	(3)
—	—	0.185	—	—	(4)
—	—	0.1	—	—	(26)
—	0.031	0.31	—	—	(2)
—	0.737	0.186	9.57	116°	(4)
—	—	0.38	—	—	(—)
—	—	0.48	—	—	(—)
—	0.53	0.30	3.31	110°	(27)
—	0.49	0.39	3.77	111°	(11)
—	0.34	0.58	4.47	112°	(2)

oxygen or other ligands (b_0^2).

aryl (*1, 5, 24*). Again, although the analogous trioxide is apparently bent, these radicals are almost certainly planar. This suggests that the forces tending to constrain oxides such as NO_3^{-2} out of plane are relatively weak, or that our identification of radical 15 as NO_3^{-2} is incorrect. The *p:s* ratio for this radical is very large (9.5), so that, in fact, it is not far removed from planarity. It is hoped that further study of radicals in this class will help to shed light on the problem. Results for oxy radicals of second row elements such as PO_3^{-2} are unfortunately ambiguous, since bond angles have been estimated on the assumption that only 3*s* and 3*p* wave functions contribute: It is possible that inclusion of the correct admixture of the 3*d* level would greatly modify the estimated bond angle. An independent estimate of this angle for ClO_3 should be possible, and would be very helpful in this context.

Comparison of the radicals R_2CO^- and R_2NO shows that, as in other instances, the electron is more delocalized onto oxygen in the latter. This cannot be gaged by the relative reduction in *s* character for nitrogen, but is shown clearly by the marked decrease in coupling to β-protons in radicals where R is alkyl. Thus for the radical $Me_2\overset{\cdot}{C}OH$, a coupling constant of 18 gauss was estimated (*22*). This would be slightly reduced for the ketyl $Me_2\overset{\cdot}{C}O^-$, but not by more than 1 or 2 gauss (*43*). However, for the radical $(C_6H_{13})_2NO$, the coupling is reduced to 11 gauss (*5*). This reduction is in accord with the expected greater delocalization onto oxygen in the latter case.

Reactivity

Perhaps the most significant and at the same time the simplest reaction of the radicals under consideration is dimerization, and the following discussion is confined to this. Other reactions, such as electron or oxygen atom transfer, may be equally significant to their chemistry, but involve mechanistic factors extraneous to the present paper.

Two generalizations seem worth making.

a. That dimerization is facilitated for radicals whose unpaired electron is considerably localized on X.

b. That is also facilitated if the density axis of the X component of the orbital containing the unpaired electron has considerable extension in the -*z* direction—that is, away from the oxygens. This arises when there is considerable *s* contribution to this component.

These rather obvious qualitative generalizations are given a quantitative measure by the ESR results. They can be illustrated by comparing CO_2^- with NO_2, and the SO_2^- —ClO_2 pair with SO_3^- and ClO_3.

CO_2^- **and** NO_2. The results show that the unpaired electron is far more delocalized onto oxygen in NO_2, although the shape of the molecule is hardly altered. Thus factor *b* is constant, but factor *a* favors dimerization for CO_2^-. In fact, of course, in contrast with N_2O_4, there is no tendency for oxalate to dissociate into CO_2^-, even in water, where extra solvation would surely facilitate such a process.

SO_3^- **and** ClO_3. Again, it is clearly factor *a* which favors dimerization for SO_3^-, making $S_2O_6^{-2}$ extremely stable, but enabling Cl_2O_6 to dissociate readily at relatively low temperatures.

SO_2^- **and** ClO_2. It has recently been discovered that dithionite, $S_2O_4^{-2}$, dissociates slightly in aqueous solution (*25*). This was predicted by Dunitz (*19*), whose studies of the crystalline sodium salt revealed an unusually long S-S bond. It could also have been predicted by comparison with ClO_2, whose dimer is unknown even at very low temperatures (2). Again, presumably factor *a* is largely responsible for this difference.

However, the differences between dithionite and dithionate or ClO_2 and ClO_3 are dependent primarily upon factor *b*, since our results suggest that factor *a* would reverse the trends observed.

The results of Dunitz (19) are particularly significant and illustrate the sort of compromise involved for 19-electron dioxides. He found that the character of the monomer, SO_2^-, is retained to a considerable extent in the dimer, which is formed in such a manner that the oxygen atoms are eclipsed and the planes of the SO_2^- radicals are only 30° from parallel. The O-S-O angle is reduced to 109° in the dimer: This suggests that a rehybridization occurs, which serves to prevent the electron pairs originally in the $4a_1$ levels from interacting too strongly, by directing them out of the SO_2^- planes. Furthermore, in view of the very long S-S bond it is possible that a slight electron deficiency remains on the four oxygens, thus stablizing the cis-eclipsed configuration.

However, Dunitz has proposed a far more elegant explanation of the structure of dithionite in terms of hybridization of sulfur $3p_x$ and $3d_{xz}$ atomic orbitals (19). The arguments are not mutually exclusive, and our point of view has the advantage that it applies to all the elements under consideration. Unfortunately, although both O_3^- and NO_2^{-2} can be prepared very easily (12, 32), little is known about their tendency to dimerize, so that informative comparisons cannot yet be drawn.

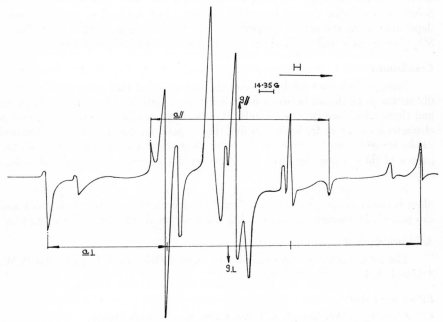

Figure 2.   ESR spectrum from γ-irradiated powdered $Mg(ClO_4)_2$

Lines from ^{35}Cl *and* ^{37}Cl *are resolved and derivation of hyperfine and g parameters is illustrated*

Interaction with Environment

Several interesting features of the ESR spectra of the radicals under consideration arise because of the way they interact with surrounding molecules. It is inappropriate in this discussion to do more than call attention to these phenomena, several of which have been discussed in detail elsewhere.

Sometimes interaction is so specific that new features, characteristic of one or more molecules in "contact" with the radical, are detected. Thus hyperfine coupling with the nuclei of neighboring alkali metal ions has been detected for certain ketyls in solution (1, 24) and for CO_2^- trapped in alkali metal formates (3, 36). This can be explained in terms of electron transfer to the outer s-orbital of the cation which is, nevertheless, so slight that the structure of the radicals is modified to only a minor extent. Less specific interactions can give rise to changes in hyperfine coupling and g tensors of the radicals concerned, the latter being the more sensitive, and the extent increasing as the symmetry and size of the radical decrease. These points are illustrated by the behavior of several of the radicals discussed above.

Also, line widths are an important function of the environment. In general, line widths are governed by interactions with magnetic nuclei of surrounding molecules, magnetic forces from nearby radicals, chemical changes such as dimerization or electron transfer, and spin-orbital-lattice relaxations.

It has been suggested that our inability to detect more than a very broad line from solutions of NO_2 in various solvents under a wide range of conditions is due to rapid dimerization (3). Weissman and coworkers have exploited this broadening effect, together with the specific coupling to sodium ions mentioned above, to study electron exchange between certain ketyls and their parent ketones (1). Solutions of chlorine dioxide have ESR spectra which are well or poorly resolved depending upon solvent or temperature (2) but, in contrast, that from ^{33}S in SO_2^- is extremely well resolved for aqueous solutions at room temperature (25).

Conclusions

Perhaps the most useful feature of the results is that they often enable a clear distinction to be drawn between orbitals having a considerable atomic s character and those which are pure π orbitals. Quantitative estimates of relative s and p character on an atom are limited in that they depend on the accuracy of calculated values for $\Psi^2(o)$ and $<r^{-3}>$ for the outer electrons of the neutral atom. Modifications of these values by intra- or intermolecular interactions are not taken into account.

Even though absolute values may be questionable, trends in hyperfine coupling parameters for given classes of radicals are more accurately monitored and can provide interesting and often subtle information about structural modification.

Acknowledgment

The author acknowledges his debt to many collaborators, in particular P. W. Atkins, J. A. Brivati, and N. Keen.

Literature Cited

(1) Adam, F. C., Weissman, S. I., *J. Am. Chem. Soc.* **80**, 1518 (1958).
(2) Atkins, P. W., Brivati, J. A., Keen, N., Symons, M. C. R., Trevalion, P. A., *J. Chem. Soc.*, in press.
(3) Atkins, P. W., Keen, N., Symons, M. C. R., *Ibid.*, in press.
(4) Atkins, P. W., Symons, M. C. R., *Ibid.*, in press.
(5) Baird, J. C., Thomas, J. R., *J. Chem. Phys.* **35**, 1507 (1961).
(6) Bennett, J. E., Ingram, D. J. E., Symons, M. C. R., George, P., Griffith, S., *Phil. Mag.* **46**, 443 (1955).
(7) Beringer, R., Castle, S. G., *Phys. Rev.* **78**, 581 (1950).
(8) Brivati, J. A., Keen, N., Symons, M. C. R., *J. Chem. Soc.* **1962**, 237.

(9) Carrington, A., Symons, M. C. R., *Ibid.*, **1960**, 889.

(10) Castner, T. G., Känzig, W., *Phys. Chem. Solids* **3**, 178 (1957).

(11) Chantry, G. W., Horsfield, A., Morton, J. R., Whiffen, D. H., *Mol. Phys.* **5**, 233 (1962).

(12) Clark, H. C., Horsfield, A., Symons, M. C. R., *J. Chem. Soc.* **1961**, 7.

(13) Cochran, E. L., Fourth International Symposium on Free Radicals, **D11** (1959).

(14) Cole, T., *J. Chem. Phys.* **35**, 1169 (1961).

(15) Cole, T., *Proc. Natl. Acad. Sci. U. S.* **46**, 506 (1960).

(16) Cole, T., Pritchard, H. O., Davidson, N. R., McConnell, H. M., *Mol. Phys.* **1**, 406 (1958).

(17) Coulson, C. A., *Victor Henri Volume Commemoratif, Contribution à l'Étude de la Structure Moléculaire*, 15 (1948).

(18) Cunningham, J., McMillan, J. A., Smaller, B. O., Yasaitis, E., *Phys. Chem. Solids* **23**, 167 (1962).

(19) Dunitz, J. D., *Acta Cryst.* **9**, 579 (1956).

(20) Florin, R. E., Brown, D. W., Wall, L. A., Fifth International Symposium on Free Radicals, **18-1** (1961).

(21) Foner, S. N., Cochran, E. L., Bowers, V. A., Jen, C. K., *Phys. Rev. Letters* **1**, 91 (1958).

(22) Gibson, J. F., Symons, M. C. R., Townsend, M. G., *J. Chem. Soc.* **1959**, 269.

(23) Henchman, N., Golding, R. N., unpublished results.

(24) Hirota, N., Weissman, S. I., *J. Am. Chem. Soc.* **82**, 4424 (1960).

(25) Horsfield, A., unpublished results.

(26) Horsfield, A., Morton, J. R., Rowlands, J. R., Whiffen, D. H., *Mol. Phys.* **5**, 241 (1962).

(27) Horsfield, A., Morton, J. R., Whiffen, D. H., *Ibid.*, **4**, 473 (1961).

(28) Horst, R. B., Anderson, J. H., Milligan, D. F., *Phys. Chem. Solids* **23**, 157 (1962).

(29) Hyde, J. S., Freeman, E. S., *J. Phys. Chem.* **65**, 1636 (1961).

(30) Jaccard, C., *Phys. Rev.* **124**, 1, 60 (1961).

(31) Jen, C. K., Foner, S. N., Cochran, E. L., Bowers, V. A., *Ibid.*, **112**, 1169 (1958).

(32) McLachlan, A. D., Symons, M. C. R., Townsend, M. G., *J. Chem. Soc.* **1959**, 952.

(33) McMillan, J. A., Matheson, M. S., Smaller, B., *J. Chem. Phys.* **33**, 609 (1960).

(34) Mulliken, R. S., *Revs. Mod. Phys.* **14**, 204 (1942).

(35) Ovenall, D. W., *Phys. Chem. Solids* **21**, 309 (1960).

(36) Ovenall, D. W., Whiffen, D. H., *Mol. Phys.* **4**, 135 (1961).

(37) Piette, L. H., Johnson, F. A., Booman, K. A., Colburn, C. B., *J. Chem. Phys.* **35**, 1481 (1961).

(38) Piette, J. H., Rempel, R. C., Weaver, H. E., Flournoy, J. M., *Ibid.*, **30**, 1623 (1959).

(39) Rowlands, J. R., Whiffen, D. H., *Nature* **193**, 61 (1962).

(40) Schonland, D. S., *Proc. Phys. Soc.* **73**, 788 (1959).

(41) Shuskus, A. J., Young, C. G., Gilliam, O. R., Levy, P. W., *J. Chem. Phys.* **33**, 622 (1960).

(42) Smith, R. C., Wyard, S. J., *Nature* **186**, 226 (1960).

(43) Symons, M. C. R., *J. Chem. Soc.* **1959**, 277.

(44) Walsh, A. D., *Ibid.*, **1953**, 2266.

(45) Weissman, S. I., Tuttle, T. R., de Boer, E., *J. Phys. Chem.* **61**, 28 (1957).

(46) Wigen, P. E., Cowen, J. A., *Phys. Chem. Solids* **17**, 26 (1960).

RECEIVED May 16, 1962.

8

The Nature of Peroxo-Bridged Dicobalt Complexes

G. L. GOODMAN, H. G. HECHT, and J. A. WEIL

Argonne National Laboratory, Argonne, Ill.

A literature survey of investigations of the peroxo-bridged dicobalt complexes is given, with primary interest devoted to the rather unusual, paramagnetic species. Chemical work relative to the composition, preparations, and reactions of these salts is briefly discussed. Recent investigations by optical, polarographic, and electron paramagnetic resonance techniques have shown that the electron hole characterizing the paramagnetic series of complexes is delocalized over both cobalt atoms and probably over the peroxo bridge and also, to some extent, over the other ligands. Possible structures proposed for this class of compounds are discussed in terms of the experimental results.

A considerable amount of attention has been directed in recent years to the compounds discussed here. The material reviewed does not constitute the last word relating to the peroxo-bridged dicobalt complexes; on the contrary, work on these compounds is actively in progress in a number of laboratories throughout the world. Interesting results have emerged, and it is hoped that this review will reliably summarize the present status of this field of research and serve as a guide to subsequent work.

Chemical Aspects of Complexes

There exists a series of diamagnetic complexes, typified by the dark brown decaammine-μ-peroxodicobalt(III) ion

$$[(NH_3)_5Co—O_2—Co(NH_3)_5]^{+4}$$

(*diamagnetic-1*)

obtainable by the oxidation of ammoniacal solutions of cobalt(II) salts. This salt has been known for a long time, having been first reported in 1852 by Fremy (*12*); it contains two cobalt atoms of valence +3. A related, paramagnetic series of compounds characterized by their green colors is now known to be derived from the compounds of the above type by further oxidation. The oxidized form of (*d-1*) was described by Maquenne (*23*) and by Vortmann (*38*), and its structure was formulated erroneously as a protonated version of (*d-1*). Subsequently, however,

Werner (*41, 43*) published the results of his work on these compounds and proposed the structure accepted today:

$$[(NH_3)_5Co\!-\!O_2\!-\!Co(NH_3)_5]^{+5}$$

(*paramagnetic*-1)

which differs from that of Maquenne and Vortmann just by removal of one proton. The complexes (*d*-1) and (*p*-1) are representative of a large class of compounds containing various ligands, some of which act as bridges between the cobalt atoms. Some examples of the paramagnetic series are:

$$\left[(NH_3)_4\ Co \underset{NH_2}{\overset{O_2}{\diamond}} Co(NH_3)_4 \right]^{+4}$$

(*p*-2)

$$\left[en_2\ Co \underset{NH_2}{\overset{O_2}{\diamond}} Co\ en_2 \right]^{+4}$$

(*p*-3)

$$\left[(NH_3)_3\ Co\!-\!OH\!-\!Co(NH_3)_3 \underset{NH_2}{\overset{O_2}{\diamond}} \right]^{+3}$$

(*p*-4)

$$\left[(NH_3)_3Cl\ Co \underset{NH_2}{\overset{O_2}{\diamond}} Co\ Cl(NH_3)_3 \right]^{+2}$$

(*p*-5)

Gmelin (*17*) gives a complete account of the early work, syntheses, and properties of these compounds. Numerous bridging groups are known, including not only O_2, OH, and NH_2, but also NO_2, SO_4, and CH_3CO_2 in the diamagnetic forms. Werner succeeded in resolving optical isomers of several dicobalt complexes, including (*p*-3) (*42*).

Additional studies (*1, 6, 20*) by chemical means have confirmed the composition and bond arrangement of (*p*-1) proposed by Werner, who had interpreted this formulation by assigning tri- and quadrivalencies, respectively, to the two cobalt atoms: $[(NH_3)_5Co^{III}(O_2)\ Co^{IV}(NH_3)_5]^{+5}$. The same electron structure was postulated for the other analogous complexes. Quadrivalent cobalt is not found in any other compound, and hence would be a feature peculiar to this class of complexes containing a peroxo bridge; it is this characteristic which accounts for the interest in these inorganic free radicals shown by a large number of workers.

An alternative interpretation of these results was first suggested by Gleu and Rehm (*16*) and supported by Jakób and Ogorzalek (*20*). These workers pointed out that on the basis of the available chemical evidence, one can interpret the results equally well by assuming that the two cobalt atoms are trivalent and joined by an O_2^- radical: $[(NH_3)_5Co^{III}(O_2^-)Co^{III}(NH_3)_5]^{+5}$. Another alternative, initially proposed by Malatesta (*22*), is essentially a modification of Werner's interpretation in terms of modern concepts of resonance. From this viewpoint, the two cobalt atoms are thought of as being equivalent and of valency intermediate between 3 and 4. Still other interpretations are possible.

It is doubtful that a distinction can be made between the various charge distributions proposed by purely chemical means, although this might be possible in principle. We thus rely on physical methods such as optical studies, x-ray analysis, polarography, magnetic susceptibility, and electron paramagnetic resonance (EPR) studies for a determination of the structure of these complex cations. This is not to say that the chemistry of these compounds is no longer of interest. Thompson and Wilmarth (35) have studied extensively the oxidation-reduction properties of several of these compounds and have cleared up a number of uncertainties concerning the structures reported in previous work.

In particular, the red diamagnetic peroxo complex assumed by Werner (41) to have the imido-bridged structure (d-2) was shown to be just the acid salt (d-3)

$$\left[en_2Co \overset{\displaystyle O_2}{\underset{\displaystyle NH}{\diagup\diagdown}} Co\ en_2 \right](NO_3)_3 \cdot HNO_3 \qquad \left[en_2Co \overset{\displaystyle O_2}{\underset{\displaystyle NH_2}{\diagup\diagdown}} Co\ en_2 \right](NO_3)_3 \cdot HNO_3$$

$$(d\text{-}2) \qquad\qquad\qquad\qquad\qquad (d\text{-}3)$$

of the reduced form of the amido-bridged dicobalt-peroxo complex (p-3). In later work (19), a new type of dicobalt-peroxo complexes, containing cyanide as ligands, has been reported. Both the diamagnetic form (d-4) and the paramagnetic oxidized form (p-6) were prepared.

$$[(CN)_5Co\text{—}O_2\text{—}Co(CN)_5]^{-6} \qquad\qquad [(CN)_5Co\text{—}O_2\text{—}Co(CN)_5]^{-5}$$

$$(d\text{-}4) \qquad\qquad\qquad\qquad\qquad\qquad (p\text{-}6)$$

Charles and Barnartt (7) have studied the reaction by which the rather unstable $[(NH_3)_5Co\text{—}O_2\text{—}Co(NH_3)_5]^{+4}$ ion is decomposed in dilute sulfuric acid solutions to form various products, including some $[(NH_3)_5Co\text{—}O_2\text{—}Co(NH_3)_5]^{+5}$. By contrast, the oxidized +5 ion is stable in acidic solution, although unstable in bases (32).

Recent work by Sykes (33) deals with the kinetics of the reduction of the complex (p-2) by ferrous ion in aqueous solution, and gives some evidence for the protonation of the peroxo bridge in acid solution. Other kinetic work, dealing with the oxidation of Co(III) perchlorate by H_2O_2, has been interpreted in terms of a dimeric cobalt complex species bridged by oxygen (1).

Several intermediates in the oxidation of certain cobalt chelates have been found, which are formed by the reversible absorption of oxygen (5, 15, 24, 34, 44, 45). These compounds are of interest to a large number of investigators because of their similarity to naturally occurring substances which act as oxygen carriers in biological systems. The intermediate formed in these reactions appears to be very similar to the diamagnetic peroxo-bridged ammine complexes—e.g., both are very unstable at low pH's, diamagnetic, and brown in color, and contain two cobalt complexes per oxygen molecule. The diamagnetic intermediate formed by treating the Co(II)-histidine complex with oxygen gas has recently been isolated in crystalline form and its properties have been studied by Sano and Tanabe (29). We have found no investigations of possible paramagnetic peroxo-bridged products obtained by further oxidation of the peroxodicobalt(III) complexes.

One factor which has probably been a deterrent to progress in the study of these compounds has been the long involved preparations used, which resulted in poor yields. Some improvements in these preparations have been made. A yield of about 30 to 50% of the monobridged peroxo +5 complex (p-1) can be obtained in the form of $[(NH_3)_5Co(O_2)Co(NH_3)_5](SO_4)_2HSO_4.3H_2O$ by the use of ammonium persulfate as an oxidizing agent (16, 21). A relatively short preparation which yields approximately the same quantity of the nitrate of this compound has been developed in this laboratory (39). The desired product is obtained by passing a 3% ozone in oxygen stream for about 30 minutes through an ammoniacal cobalt(II) nitrate solution containing ammonium ion. Ozone in oxygen has also been used instead of air in the conventional preparation (*41*) of [(NH$_3$)$_4$Co-(O$_2$,NH$_2$)Co(NH$_3$)$_4$](NO$_3$)$_4$. This technique reduces the time required for the preparation of this dibridged complex, although the yields are still rather poor (about 10 to 15%).

Physical and Theoretical Aspects of Complexes

We now turn to the electronic structures of these complex ions, relying chiefly on the physical methods mentioned above.

A number of investigations of the magnetic susceptibility of the peroxo compounds have been reported (*2, 11, 16, 22, 26*), which indicate the paramagnetic nature of the oxidized complexes in contrast to the diamagnetism of the reduced forms. Studies at various temperatures indicate that the paramagnetic compounds follow Curie's law closely and each possesses a permanent magnetic moment of about 1.7 Bohr magnetons, indicative of the presence of one unpaired electron.

Following the classic investigations of Werner and others, the first work dealing with optical properties of these compounds was that of Mathieu (*25*), who studied the absorption spectra, optical rotation, and circular dichroism (Cotton effect). The absorption spectra of aqueous solutions of some of these compounds have also been recorded by other workers (*7, 21, 31, 32, 33, 46*), several of whom included comparisons with spectra of more conventional cobaltic ammine complexes. A polarizing microscope has been used by Yamada, Shimura, and Tsuchida (*46*) to study the dichroism of small single crystals of the monobridged peroxo complexes (*d*-1) and (*p*-1). These workers discussed their results for the oxidized complex in terms of two cobalt atoms in different valence states with electrons moving through the peroxo radical so as to make the two cobalt atoms indistinguishable in the ground state. Unfortunately, however, no attempt to interpret these optical phenomena in terms of the details of any electronic structure has yet been published. The infrared spectrum of (*p*-2) is briefly mentioned by Chatt *et al.* (*8, 14*).

As a first step in any discussion of the electronic structure of the peroxo complexes, it is necessary to know or estimate the position of the nuclei of cobalt, oxygen, and other bridging atoms. Unfortunately, only rather sketchy, preliminary information is available from x-ray structural investigations. Okaya (*27*) has found a Co-Co distance of 4.51 A. for (*p*-1) pentanitrate, and very tentatively suggested a cis structure:

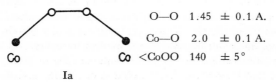

O—O   1.45   ± 0.1 A.

Co—O   2.0   ± 0.1 A.

<CoOO   140   ± 5°

Ia

On the other hand, Brosset and Vannerberg (*4*) found a Co—Co distance of 4.53 A. for this compound, and published a preliminary structure (*R* factor = 0.34):

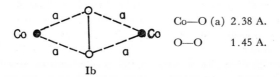

Co—O (a) 2.38 A.

O—O   1.45 A.

Ib

with oxygen atoms perpendicular to a line joining the cobalt atoms.

Even before x-ray data were available, Dunitz and Orgel (9) discussed the electronic structure for a linear grouping:

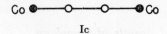

Ic

Assuming the ligands to be in octahedral positions about each cobalt atom, they classified the orbitals for this fragment according to transformation properties under symmetry group D_{4h} as well as with regard to bonding or antibonding character. In particular, they concluded that the highest filled orbital for the peroxodicobalt compounds is antibonding. They ascribed the differences between $(d\text{-}1)$ and $(p\text{-}1)$ to the removal of one electron from this orbital. In making up this molecular orbital, they considered as unimportant any mixing of cobalt orbitals of appropriate symmetry into the oxygen antibonding orbitals. Thus, considering the "frontier" electrons to be primarily near the oxygen atoms, Dunitz and Orgel favored the structure $Co^{+3}(O_2)^{-1}Co^{+3}$ for $(p\text{-}1)$.

The physical evidence for the antibonding nature of the orbital arises from the observation that the oxidized complexes are more stable than the reduced forms, despite the higher charge of the former. Some quantitative information about their relative stabilities has been furnished by the polarographic investigations of Gabovich and Reĭbel (6, 13, 28) and, particularly, of Vlček (36). Vlček also investigated the effect of structural changes on the electron affinities estimated from the half-wave potentials for a series of peroxodicobalt complexes with various bridging groups and ligands. Besides confirming the antibonding nature of the highest filled orbital, Vlček deduced that there must be appreciable contributions from cobalt orbitals to this molecular orbital.

Conclusive evidence concerning the importance of the cobalt atoms is available $(3, 10)$ from EPR studies of solutions of $(p\text{-}1)$, $(p\text{-}2)$, and $(p\text{-}3)$. Nuclear hyperfine structure in the spectra cannot arise from the oxygen (nuclear spin $I = 0$) but will arise from the cobalt nuclei (Co^{59}, 100% abundance, $I = 7/2$) if the unpaired electron exists in cobalt orbitals; no first-order contribution is expected from the other ligands. The observation of 15 hyperfine lines has made it clear that both cobalt atoms interact equally with the unpaired electron and hence that they are chemically equivalent. Accordingly, the formulation of the electronic structure as $Co^{+3} O_2^{-2} Co^{+4}$ has become unacceptable, and the postulate of quadrivalent cobalt in these complexes is incorrect. Furthermore, the magnitude of this hyperfine splitting, as well as the large deviation of the Zeeman splitting (g) factor from its free-electron value $(3, 10, 30, 40)$, makes it clear that the cobalt orbitals make relatively important contributions to the molecular orbital. Considerably more detailed information can be obtained from suitable EPR measurements (see above).

It follows that Dunitz and Orgel's picture of an unpaired electron placed primarily on the oxygen atoms is no longer tenable. Moreover, their symmetry classifications must also be altered because, while the exact oxygen positions are still uncertain, the x-ray information now available for $(p\text{-}1)$ does yield a reliable Co—Co distance, one which appears too short to hold the linear four-atom chain of structure Ic. Furthermore, as Vlcek (37) points out, the linearity of the CoO_2Co system in the polybridged complexes appears even more improbable simply from steric considerations.

In his modification of this theory of the electronic structure, Vlček (37) considered the oxygen atoms to be perpendicular to the Co—Co axis (as was subsequently actually reported for compound $(p\text{-}1)$ by Brosset and Vannerberg in their tentative structure Ib), in analogy with the situation in certain metal-olefin complexes. He succeeded, for both the monobridged and dibridged peroxo complexes, in constructing energy level diagrams yielding the correct antibonding character for the highest filled level, with appreciable contribution from both cobalt atoms. This formulation suffers from one major difficulty: It sacrifices the existence of any conventional σ-bonding system between the cobalt and oxygen atoms.

At the time of this writing, the structure for the nuclear geometry which appears most probable to us and which combines the strongest points of all these considerations is one of only C_2 symmetry (z-axis), in which the cobalt-cobalt direction is skewed to the oxygen-oxygen direction. The two important projections are:

Id

First of all, this structure allows us to retain a normal σ-bonding scheme—for instance, taking Co—O = 2 A., O—O = 1.5 A., and $<$CoOO = 110° allows the Co—Co distance to be 4.5 A. Furthermore, as is evident from Id, the structure comes close to reconciling the results of the available x-ray investigations, and provides an intermediate to the views of Dunitz and Orgel and of Vlček.

In a molecule with only C_2 symmetry, there are few restrictions on the construction of molecular orbitals. The principal question becomes the separation in energy for the basic atomic or group orbitals. In the peroxodicobalt compounds, it seems likely to us that the energy of separation between the cobalt d-orbitals and the antibonding peroxide π-orbitals is small in comparison to the interaction energy between these orbitals. If this is the case, the highest filled molecular orbital is formed from approximately equal contributions from each cobalt atom and each oxygen atom. The formal charges computed on the basis of this assumption are summarized by the formula (for the oxidized form of the complex) $Co^{+13/4} O_2^{-3/2} Co^{+13/4}$, where the somewhat strange formal charges arise because of the special juxtaposition of orbital energies that occurs for O_2^{-2} and Co^{+3}.

Of course, the final decision as to the correct structure will come from the x-ray work. However, detailed information about the nuclear positions and particularly about the electronic structure is obtainable from single crystal EPR measurements. We have made such measurements, have made a first-order analysis of the resulting data (40), and are now in the process of refining these results. The experiments were performed with single crystals containing a few per cent of complex (p-3) diluted with the diamagnetic complex

(*d*-5)

Such dilution is necessary to reduce magnetic interactions between the peroxo molecules in order to allow resolution of the cobalt hyperfine structure. Analysis of the highly anisotropic spectra is complicated by the multiplicity of lines and the overlapping between them. However, the analysis made by means of a curve-fitting procedure using high-speed computer techniques has led to the following tentative results. The principal values of the Zeeman (g) tensor are 2.079, 2.023, and 2.010. These values, all above the free electron g_e of 2.0023, confirm that the unpaired electron manifests itself as a hole in an otherwise filled molecular shell. The large deviations from g_e provide still further evidence that the unpaired electron orbital contains much cobalt admixture. The principal axis system, whose orientation is determined by the over-all symmetry of the molecule, appears to have one axis along the proposed twofold symmetry axis of the molecule, as postulated.

The cobalt hyperfine interaction tensors, $\bar{A}_a$ and $\bar{A}_b$, have identical sets of principal values, tentatively $|30.1|$, $|8.5|$, and $|1.1|$ oersteds. The magnitude is the best evidence of the cobalt contribution to the total orbital and the chemical equivalence of these two atoms. The principal axis system for each cobalt atom is determined by the local symmetry about that nucleus—i.e., the direction of the bonds. Thus determination of these two tensors can yield particularly valuable information about the nuclear geometry. Unfortunately, the principal axis directions are sensitive to small errors in the measured experimental components. However, our present data are consistent with a structure for (p-3) (analogous to structure Id):

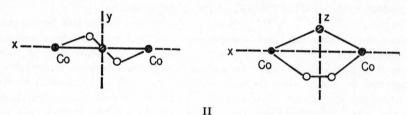

II

Again, this structure appears reasonable in that it makes use of accepted chemical bond lengths and angles: Co—O = 2.0 A., Co—N = 2.0 A., O—O = 1.5 A., <CoNCo = 109° 26′, <NCoO = 90°, and <CoOO = 110°; the Co—Co distance is then 3.2 A. This distance has just this value in the diamagnetic compound (d-5) as found by Goldstein and Jacobson (*18*).

Another interesting result is that the EPR line widths show marked anisotropy; we interpret this to mean that these widths result from unresolved hyperfine interactions between the unpaired electron and the ligand nitrogen atoms. Details of the nature of this dipolar interaction must await further, more elaborate analysis.

Literature Cited

(1) Baxendale, J. H., Wells, C. F., *Trans. Faraday Soc.* 53, 800 (1957).
(2) Belova, U. I., Syrkin, Y. K., *Izv. Sekt. Platiny i Drug. Blagorodn. Metal. Inst. Obshch. i Neorgan. Khim. Akad. Nauk SSSR* 30, 109 (1955).
(3) Bernal, I., Ebsworth, E. A. V., Weil, J. A., *Proc. Chem. Soc.* 1959, 57.
(4) Brosset, C., Vannerberg, N., *Nature* 190, 714 (1961).
(5) Cagliotti, V., Cilvestroni, P., Furlani, C., *J. Inorg. Nucl. Chem.* 13, 95 (1960).
(6) Chachan, I. B., Reibel, I. M., *Tr. Kishinevsk. s. Chem. Inst.* 10, 159 (1955).
(7) Charles, R. G., Barnartt, S., *J. Inorg. Nucl. Chem.* 22, 69 (1961).
(8) Chatt, J., Duncanson, L. A., Gatehouse, B. M., Lewis, J., Nyholm, R. S., Lobe, M. L., Todd, P. F., Venanzi, L. M., *J. Chem. Soc.* 1959, 4073.
(9) Dunitz, J. D., Orgel, L. E., *Ibid.*, 1953, 2594.

(10) Ebsworth, E. A. V., Weil, J. A., *J. Phys. Chem.* **63**, 1890 (1959).
(11) Feytis, E., *Compt. Rend.* **152**, 710 (1911).
(12) Fremy, E., *Liebigs Ann.* **83**, 240 (1852); *Ann. Chim. Phys.* (3) **35**, 271 (1852).
(13) Gabovich, A. A., Reĭbel, I. M., *Tr. Kishinevsk. Sel'skokhoz. Inst.* **9**, 185 (1956).
(14) Gatehouse, B. M., *J. Inorg. Nucl. Chem.* **8**, 79 (1958).
(15) Gilbert, J. B. Otey, M. C., Price, V. E., *J. Biol. Chem.* **190**, 377 (1951).
(16) Gleu, K., Rehm, K., *Z. anorg. Chem.* **237**, 79 (1938).
(17) "Gmelins Handbuch der anorganischen Chemie," 8th ed., System No. 58, Part B, pp. 332 ff., Verlag Chemie G.M.B.H., Berlin, Germany, 1932.
(18) Goldstein, P., Jacobson, R., unpublished work, still in progress.
(19) Haim, A., Wilmarth, W. K., *J. Am. Chem. Soc.* **83**, 509 (1961).
(20) Jakób, W., Ogorzalek. M., *Roczniki Chem.* **30**, 1055 (1956).
(21) Linhard, M., Weigel, M., *Z. anorg. Chem.* **308**, 1 (1961).
(22) Malatesta, L., *Gazz. Chim. Ital.* **72**, 287 (1942).
(23) Maquenne, L., *Compt. Rend.* **96**, 344 (1883).
(24) Martell, A. E., Calvin, M., "Chemistry of the Metal Chelate Compounds," pp. 337 ff., Prentice-Hall, New York, 1952.   Detailed discussion with references up to about 1950.
(25) Mathieu, J. P., *Bull. Soc. Chim.* **5**, 105, 771 (1938).
(26) Mathieu, J. P., *Compt. Rend.* **218**, 907 (1944).
(27) Okaya, Y., unpublished and preliminary results of experiments under Contract AF 1(600)-1556, Air Force Office of Scientific Research, ARDC-Chemistry Branch.
(28) Reĭbel, I. M., *Tr. Kishinevsk. s. Chem. Inst.* **11**, 169 (1956).
(29) Sano, Y., Tanabe, H., *J. Inorg. Nucl. Chem.*, to be published.
(30) Schneider, E. E., Weiss, J., *Proc. Chem. Soc.* **1959**, 130; *Arch. Sci.* (*Geneva*) **11**, Fascicule Special, 153 (1958).
(31) Servaud, J. P., *Compt. Rend.* **245**, 1632 (1957).
(32) Seufert, L. E., Liu, C. F., Masterson, W. L., Abstracts, 136th Meeting, ACS p. 37N, September 1959.
(33) Sykes, A. G., *Trans. Faraday Soc.* **58**, 543 (1962).
(34) Tanford, C., Kirk, D. C., Jr., Chantooni, M. K., Jr., *J. Am. Chem. Soc.* **76**, 5325 (1954).
(35) Thompson, L. R., Wilmarth, W. K., *J. Phys. Chem.* **56**, 5 (1952).
(36) Vlček, A. A., *Collection Czech. Chem. Commun.* **25**, 3036 (1960).
(37) Vlček, A. A., *Trans. Faraday Soc.* **56**, 1137 (1960).
(38) Vortmann, G., *Monatsh. Chem.* **6**, 404 (1885).
(39) Weil, J. A., unpublished manuscript.
(40) Weil, J. A., Goodman, G. L., *Bull. Am. Phys. Soc.*, Ser. II, **6**, 152 (March 1961).
(41) Werner, A., *Ann. Chem.* **375**, 9, 15, 61 (1910).
(42) Werner, A., *Ber.* **47**, 1961 (1914).
(43) Werner, A., Mylius, A., *Z. anorg. Chem.* **16**, 245 (1898).
(44) Yalman, R. G., *J. Phys. Chem.* **65**, 556 (1961).
(45) Yalman, R. G., Warga, M. B., *J. Am. Chem. Soc* **.80**, 1011 (1958).
(46) Yamada, S., Shimura, Y., Tsuchida, R., *Bull. Chem. Soc. Japan* **26**, 72, 533 (1953).

RECEIVED May 14, 1962.

9

Electron Paramagnetic Resonance Spectra of Halogen Atoms

N. VANDERKOOI, Jr., and J. S. MacKENZIE

*General Chemical Research Laboratory, Allied Chemical Corp.,
Morristown, N. J.*

The electron paramagnetic resonance spectra of fluorine, chlorine, and bromine atoms have been detected in the gas phase with a conventional X-band spectrometer. The atomic species were generated from the parent molecules in a flow system by microwave discharge and thermal dissociation techniques. An atomic g-factor of 4/3 was observed for all species (F[19], Cl[35], Cl[37], Br[79], and Br[81]) as required by Russell-Saunders coupling. In a general way, the hyperfine structure of the spectra could be predicted from a consideration of orbital and nuclear magnetic effects. Halogen atom concentrations were estimated using nitrogen dioxide as a reference compound. Virtually 100% dissociation of chlorine and bromine into the atomic species could be achieved by microwave methods. Attainable fluorine atom concentrations were relatively much lower, because of reaction with the vessel walls.

Recent studies have shown the feasibility of generating appreciable halogen atom concentrations in a vacuum flow system by the use of microwave discharge equipment (5, 6). Experimental success depends almost entirely upon treatment of the reaction vessel walls with suitable "poisons," found effective in preventing atom recombination. Oxy acids, such as sulfuric acid and phosphoric acid, provide a convenient and effective way of treating the walls of glass equipment.

The atom concentrations attainable with this technique make possible a number of interesting kinetic investigations, if convenient methods can be found to follow concentration changes. Chlorine and bromine atom concentrations can be determined calorimetrically and by chemical titration (5), both of which might serve to study reaction rates involving the atomic species. Rather strangely, however, the simple technique of measuring halogen atom concentration by means of their electron paramagnetic resonance (EPR) spectra seems to have been virtually ignored.

Indications of the feasibility of this approach are to be found in the work of Bowers *et al.* (*2, 3*) on the photolysis of iodine vapor in the cavity of an EPR spectrometer, and in the theoretical investigations of Beltran-Lopez *et al.* on the microwave Zeeman spectra of atomic fluorine and chlorine (*1, 8*). However, these studies were mainly concerned with the precise determination of atomic g factors to verify the Zeeman theory and involved specialized spectral equipment. The present investigation demonstrates that the spectra of atomic fluorine, chlorine, and bromine are readily observable in commercially available EPR equipment and that reasonable estimates may be made of their concentrations.

Experimental

All spectra were observed with a Varian 4500–10A EPR spectrometer using 100-kc. magnetic field modulation. Atomic species were generated from the appropriate halogen by either microwave or thermal dissociation techniques. In the former case the resonant cavity of a 125-watt Raytheon microwave power generator was placed around the quartz tube leading to the EPR cavity and as close as possible to the point of detection. When thermal dissociation was employed, a Nichrome heater was wrapped around the quartz tube leading to the EPR cavity. The distance between the heater and detection point was kept at a minimum. A fast-flow vacuum system (constructed of quartz in those parts exposed to the halogen atoms) operating in the range of 0.1 to 5 mm. of Hg pressure provided residence times of the order of a few milliseconds from time of generation to time of observation of the atomic EPR spectra.

The walls of the quartz tube leading from the generation source through the EPR cavity had to be washed with concentrated sulfuric acid or phosphoric acid, to obtain detectable quantities of atomic chlorine or bromine. No such treatment was necessary for fluorine.

Results and Discussion

The magnetic field values of the EPR spectra of atomic fluorine, chlorine, and bromine are recorded in Table 1. For the sake of completeness, the data of Bowers *et al.* (*2, 3*) on atomic iodine have also been included. Accuracy of these data is probably within ±2 gauss, as estimated from the atomic oxygen line in the fluorine spectra. A graphical representation of the spectral data is shown in Figure 1. The species giving rise to the various spectra was easily identified by determination of the atomic g factor and measurement of the number of lines observed. For atomic fluorine, chlorine, and bromine the observed g factor was $4/3$, in exact agreement with the value predicted by Russell-Saunders coupling. The atomic iodine g factor is uncertain, since the complete spectrum was not investigated.

Table I.   Magnetic Field Data for EPR Spectra of F, Cl, Br, and I Atoms

Species	F^{19}	Cl^{35}	Cl^{37}	$Br^{79} + Br^{81}$	I^{127a}
Resonant frequency, mc.	9249	9233	9233	9236	9330
Magnetic field values, gauss	5506	5115	5087	5848, 4750	6206.3
	5417	5106	5079	5792, 4730	5471.2
	5361	5095	5070	5666, 4662	4818.1
	4511	5012	5000	5608, 4628	4598.4
	4413	4995	4987	5549, 4512	4268.0
	4159	4980	4976	5490, 4472	3292.8
		4902	4910	5233, 4255	
		4889	4899	5222, 4173	
		4879	4892	5147, 4159	
		4800	4823	5099, 4152	
		4781	4809	4982, 4124	
		4759	4793	4960, 4116	

a (*2, 3*).

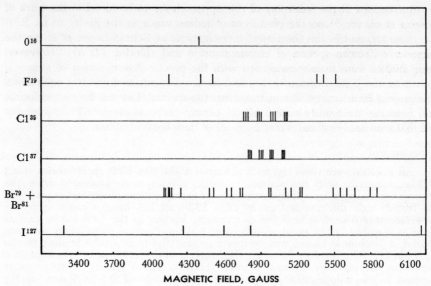

Figure 1. EPR spectra of halogen atoms

The number of spectral lines observable for an atomic species in a strong magnetic field is given by the expression $2J(2I + 1)$, where J is the total angular momentum quantum number and I is the nuclear spin quantum number. All halogen atoms have the same ground state, $^2P^3/_2$ ($J = {}^3/_2$), but differ in nuclear spin quantum number. The expected number of lines for the spectra of the halogen isotopes studied in this investigation are listed in Table II and are compared with our experimental observations. The agreement is excellent, except for atomic iodine, where the complete spectrum was not studied.

Table II. Observed Number of Lines in EPR Spectra

Halogen	I	$2J(2I + 1)$	No. of Lines
F[19]	1/2	6	6
Cl[35]	3/2	12	12
Cl[37]	3/2	12	12
Br[79], Br[81]	3/2	12	12
I[127a]	5/2	18	6

a (2, 3).

The position, number, and intensity of the spectral lines of atomic fluorine and chlorine observed in our work agree well with the published data of Beltran-Lopez *et al.* based on the microwave Zeeman spectra of these species (*1, 8*). Strong atomic fluorine lines were obtained in the microwave discharge of a 1 to 1 fluorine-nitrogen mixture at 2 mm. of Hg pressure, where the flow rate was such that the atoms took about 35 msec. to travel the 20 cm. from the discharge to the cavity. The data reported in Table I for atomic fluorine were obtained by using thermal dissociation. The heater temperature was set at about 1000°C. and the pressure adjusted to 0.4 mm. of Hg; less than 2 msec. was required for the atoms to travel the 2 cm. from the lower end of the heater and the center of the cavity. By using nitrogen dioxide as a concentration standard, the molecular fluorine was estimated to be approximately 10% dissociated in the cavity. Since a large atomic oxygen peak was also observed, considerable loss of fluorine atoms must have occurred by reaction with the quartz walls.

The atomic oxygen line observed in the fluorine spectra occurred at 4404.8 gauss at 9249 mc. per second. This gives a g value of 1.4998. Values of 1.500921 and 1.500905 have been reported by others (7, 9).

Both the chlorine and the bromine data were obtained with the microwave discharge. High concentrations of chlorine and bromine atoms were observed 20 cm. from the discharge after 90 msec. of travel at a pressure of 0.4 mm. of Hg. The chlorine and bromine were found to be almost 100% dissociated when compared to nitrogen dioxide as a quantitative reference. The first derivatives of the absorption curves of Cl^{35} plus Cl^{37} are shown in Figure 2. The spectra of the two isotopes are easily sorted out from the known natural abundances of Cl^{35} and Cl^{37}. The task of sorting out the Br^{79} and Br^{81} spectra was not attempted, since both isotopes are present to about the same extent in bromine and their hyperfine splitting constants are fairly similar.

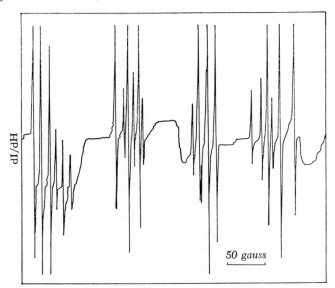

Figure 2. EPR derivative curve of atomic $Cl^{35} + Cl^{37}$

Precise determination of hyperfine constants for the halogen atoms was beyond the scope of the present investigation and, indeed, presents a problem of some magnitude (1, 4, 8). However, the major splitting in the spectra of F^{19}, Cl^{35}, Cl^{37}, Br^{79}, and Br^{81} roughly parallels the values of the nuclear magnetic moments.

Literature Cited

(1) Beltran-Lopez, V., Robinson, H. G., *Phys. Rev.* **123**, 161 (1961).
(2) Bowers, K. D., Kamper, R. A., Knight, R. B. D., *J. Sci. Instr.* **34**, 49 (1957).
(3) Bowers, K. D., Kamper, R. A., Lustig, G. D., *Proc. Phys. Soc. (London)* **70B**, 1176 (1957).
(4) Goodings, D. A., *Phys. Rev.* **123**, 1706 (1961).
(5) Ogryzlo, E. A., *Can. J. Chem.* **39**, 2556 (1961).
(6) Ogryzlo, E. A., *J. Phys. Chem.* **65**, 191 (1961).
(7) Radford, H. E., Hughes, V. W., *Phys. Rev.* **114**, 1274 (1959).
(8) Radford, H. E., Hughes, V. W., Beltran-Lopez, V., *Ibid.*, **123**, 153 (1961).
(9) Rawson, E. B., Beringer, R., *Ibid.*, **88**, 677 (1952).

RECEIVED May 16, 1962. Work supported by the Advanced Research Projects Agency (ARPA) under contract DA-30-069-ORD-2638.

10

Inorganic Free Radicals in Solution and Some Aspects of Autoxidation

N. URI

Explosives Research and Development Establishment,
Ministry of Aviation, Waltham Abbey, Essex, England

Emphasis is placed on evaluating thermodynamic quantities such as bond dissociation energies, ionization potentials, electron affinities, and heats of solvation. These are essential to understanding free radical reactions. The properties of simple radicals containing oxygen and hydrogen are summarized, together with their bearing on catalytic decomposition of hydrogen peroxide. The thermodynamic data are also applied to aspects of catalysis, photochemical formation of free radicals with special reference to photoexcited electron transfer, and photobiological systems. Other applications outlined include the basic concepts of inorganic photocatalysis, redox polymerization, and autoxidation. Evidence is presented to support the author's hypothesis that apparently uncatalyzed autoxidation is, as a rule, trace-metal catalyzed. The dependence of the rate of initiation on the polarity of the environment and its implications are illustrated by recent experimental observations.

The foundations for the edifice had been laid when I compiled my review on inorganic free radicals in solution ten years ago (23), in the sense that the basic concepts had been realized and kinetic studies based on sound energetics offered very great scope for further investigation in many fields: polymerization and autoxidation reactions, photochemistry and radiation chemistry of aqueous systems, and even reactions in biological systems.

Origins of Mechanisms Involving OH and HO₂ Radicals in Solution

Franck and Haber introduced radically new ideas into the field of inorganic kinetics (11). They postulated the formation of OH radicals in the course of the ultraviolet irradiation of aqueous solutions of halides and sulfites and also in the autoxidation of sulfites. At the same time OH radicals were postulated by Urey,

Dawsey, and Rice (*21*) in the study of the absorption spectrum of hydrogen peroxide.

The investigation of Haber and Weiss (*12*) concerning the reaction of ferrous ion and ferric ion with hydrogen peroxide can hardly be omitted from any review in this field. The decomposition of hydrogen peroxide was interpreted to proceed according to the scheme

$$Fe^{+2} + H_2O_2 \rightarrow Fe^{+3} + OH^- + OH \tag{1}$$

$$\rightarrow OH + H_2O_2 \rightarrow H_2O + HO_2 \tag{2}$$

$$HO_2 + H_2O_2 \rightarrow O_2\uparrow + H_2O + OH \tag{3}$$

$$Fe^{+2} + OH \rightarrow Fe^{+3} + OH^- \tag{4}$$

on the basis of which the authors explained the unusual phenomenon of the dependence of the stoichiometry of the reactions expressed by $\Delta H_2O_2/\Delta Fe^{+2}$ not only in the concentrations employed but also on the mixing conditions. The reaction of $Fe^{+3} + HO_2^- \rightarrow Fe^{+2} + HO_2$ was postulated as the primary step in the ferric-catalyzed reaction. A good deal of detail has been added and the mechanism had to be somewhat revised in subsequent work, but the aspect which has become the challenge in all kinetic investigations in inorganic chemistry was the reduction of complex stoichiometric relationships to simple steps involving only unimolecular or bimolecular reactions. The main achievement would have remained speculative and of only limited value if it had not been followed by a study of the energetics of free radicals, with which all the kinetic schemes could be brought into harmony.

Energetics of OH, HO₂, and Electron-
Transfer Reactions, Involving Metal Ions

The basic data which I compiled for the reactions involving these radicals are based partially on a critical appraisal of values reported in the literature and partially on my work. The tables given below are mainly taken from my published work. The important individual quantities which figure in these calculations are the bond dissociation energies, H...OH, H...O, H...O₂H, H...O₂, HO...OH, and the sum of the electron affinities of OH, HO₂, and O₂ in the gas phase and the hydration energies of the corresponding anions. The values which I have adopted are:

Bond Dissociation Energies

Reaction	*D, Kcal.*
$HOH \rightarrow H + OH$	121
$OH \rightarrow H + O$	100
$H_2O_2 \rightarrow 2OH$	56
$H_2O_2 \rightarrow H + HO_2$	102
$HO_2 \rightarrow H + O_2$	36

Electron Affinities in Aqueous Solution

	Heat, Kcal.
$OH(g) + e \rightarrow OH^-(aq)$	136
$HO_2(g) + e \rightarrow HO_2^-(aq)$	123
$O_2(g) + e \rightarrow O_2^-(aq)$	79

The most controversial and one of the most important quantities is the bond dissociation energy for the reaction $HO_2 \rightarrow H + O_2$. The understanding of autoxidation depends to some extent on this value. Much higher values have been postulated—e.g., 67 kcal. by Walsh (26). The evidence for the lower value of 36 kcal. is, apart from the agreement with kinetic data, based on the peaks of the electron transfer spectra of various ferric ion pair complexes. These allow an estimate of the electron affinity of the HO_2 radical in solution and consequently produce a value of 102 kcal. for $D_{H...O_2H}$ and 36 kcal. for $D_{H...O_2}$. This in turn leads to a dissociation constant of 10^{-2} for the HO_2 radical in aqueous solutions.

There is good agreement with the kinetic observations made by Barb, Baxendale, George, and Hargrave (2) and previously by Taube (19). With a value of $D_{H...O_2}$ in the range of 65 kcal., the dissociation of HO_2 in aqueous solution would be endothermic to an extent of 30 kcal. and the O_2^- ion would have negligible influence on the rates of the reaction. Further support for the low $H...O_2$ bond dissociation energy is obtained from the measurement of the activation energy of $Fe^{+3} + HO_2^- \rightarrow Fe^{+2} + HO_2$, which amounts to 28 kcal., thus confirming the value of 123 kcal. for the electron affinity of HO_2 in solution and indirectly the bond dissociation energy of $H...O_2$ as 36 kcal. The three thermodynamic cycles which are used to evaluate this quantity can be represented as follows (22):

Cycle 1

$$-D_{(HO_2...H)}$$

$$H_2O_2(g) \longrightarrow H(g) \quad + \quad HO_2(g)$$

$$-(\lambda + S)_{H_2O_2} \Big\uparrow \qquad\qquad -I_H + S_{H^+}\Big\uparrow \qquad\qquad \Big\downarrow E_{HO_2} + S_{HO_2^-}$$

$$H_2O_2(aq) \longrightarrow H^+(aq)^+ + HO_2^-(aq)$$

$$-Q$$

Hence $D_{(HO_2...H)} = Q - (\lambda + S)_{H_2O_2} + (-I_H + S_{H+}) + (E_{HO_2} + S_{HO_2^-})$. The analogous cycle involving H_2O and the OH radical instead of H_2O_2 and the HO_2 radical has been used to determine the electron affinity of OH in solution—i.e., the sum of $E_{HO} + S_{OH^-}$. In the case of water, however, a direct determination of $D_{(HO...H)}$ was available. With H_2O_2 it is necessary to determine the value of $E_{HO_2} + S_{HO_2^-}$ by other means, in order to obtain the value of $D_{(HO_2...H)}$. Fortunately, $E_{HO_2} + S_{HO_2^-}$ can be evaluated independently from a study of the electron transfer spectra of ferric ion pair complexes leading to the thermodynamic cycle (22) which involves the Franck-Condon principle.

Cycle 2

$$-Q^s_{Fe^{2+}X}$$

$$Fe^{+2}X(aq) \longrightarrow Fe^{+2}(aq) + X(aq)$$

$$-Nh\nu \Big\uparrow \qquad\qquad I^s_{Fe^{+2}}\Big\uparrow \qquad\qquad \Big\uparrow -(E^s_X + S_{X^-})$$

$$Fe^{+3}X^-(aq) \longrightarrow Fe^{+3}(aq) + X^-(aq)$$

$$-Q^s_{Fe_3^+X^-}$$

$Q^s_{Fe^{3+}X^-}$ is the heat of formation of the ion pair complex from the separate ions in solution. $Q^s_{Fe^{+2}X}$ is the heat of formation from $Fe^{+2}_{(aq)}$ and $X_{(aq)}$ of $Fe^{+2}X_{(aq)}$, which is of such configuration that its internuclear distances (including the hydration shell) are identical with those of $Fe^{+3}X^-_{(aq)}$. $I^s_{Fe^{+2}}$ is the ionization potential of ferrous ion in aqueous solution. $(E^s_X + S_{X^-})$ is the electron affinity of the free radical X in aqueous solution, including the hydration energy of X^-. Thus we obtain

$$Nh\nu = (E^s_X + S_{X^-}) - I_{Fe^{+2}} + Q^s_{Fe^{+3}X^-} - Q^s_{Fe^{+3}X}$$

The $[Fe^{+3}HO_2^-]^{+2}$ complex has an absorption spectrum of a type similar to that of $Fe^{+3}OH^-$, $Fe^{+3}Cl^-$, etc., and $Nh\nu$ is the photochemical energy corresponding to the peak of the electron transfer spectrum. While $Q^s_{Fe^{+3}X^-}$ can be measured, $Q^s_{Fe^{+2}X}$ does not vary significantly in the series with the changing monovalent anion and is ~ 40 kcal. This allowed the evaluation of $E_{HO_2} + S_{HO_2}$- as 136 kcal. When this value is used in the first thermodynamic cycle, one arrives at a value of 102 kcal. for the bond dissociation energy, $D_{(HO_2\ldots H)}$. Finally, the above value used in the third cycle (22):

Cycle 3

$$\text{H}_2\text{O}_2 \xrightarrow{\; -D_{(HO_2\ldots H)} = -102\,\text{kcal.}\;} \text{H} + \text{HO}_2$$

$Q_f = 34$ kcal.

$D_{(H\ldots O_2)}$

$$\text{H}_2 + \text{O}_2 \xrightarrow{\; -D_{H_2} = -104\,\text{kcal.}\;} \text{H} + \text{H} + \text{O}_2$$

leads to a value of 36 kcal. for the bond dissociation energy $D_{(H\ldots O_2)}$. On this basis initiation of the autoxidation by the reaction $RH + O_2 \rightarrow R\cdot + HO_2\cdot$ would be endothermic to an extent of 30 to 45 kcal. within the usual range of olefins and, therefore, practically negligible. This leads to the problem of alternative mechanisms for the initiation of autoxidation involving metal ions. As far as the catalytic decomposition of hydrogen peroxide is concerned, the values obtained fit in with the general experience of the ferrous- and ferric-catalyzed reactions. The energetics of the individual steps can be tabulated as follows (corrections for the heat of hydration of radicals have been allowed for) (23):

	Heat, Kcal.
$Fe^{+2} + H_2O_2 \rightarrow Fe^{+3}OH^- + OH$	-6
$OH + H_2O_2 \rightarrow H_2O + HO_2$	$+19$
$O_2^- + H_2O_2 \rightarrow O_2 + OH^- + OH$	$+14$
$Fe^{+2} + OH \rightarrow Fe^{+3} + OH^-$	$+42$
$Fe^{+3} + HO_2^- \rightarrow Fe^{+2} + HO_2$	-29
$Fe^{+3} + O_2^- \rightarrow Fe^{+2} + O_2$	$+20$
$Fe^{+2} + HO_2 \rightarrow Fe^{+3} + HO_2^-$	$+29$
$Fe^{+3}OH^- + OH \rightarrow Fe^{+2} + H_2O_2$	$+6$

The last reaction which I postulated in order to overcome difficulties in interpreting the ferric-catalyzed reaction, leads to the emphasis of the importance of ion pair complexes in the formation of free radicals by electron transfer, particularly in photochemical reactions, as discussed below.

The system $Fe^{+2} + H_2O_2$ has been generally used to determine the reactivity of OH radicals in relation to organic substrates with the $Fe^{+2} + OH$ reaction as the standard for comparison. In general, this means abstraction of hydrogen by the OH radical and an energy gain of 120 kcal. in the formation of water, so that for all practical purposes all $R\ldots H$ bonds would be sensitive to OH radical attack, since the over-all exothermicity will rarely be less than 20 kcal. It is rather interesting that it is possible to split the OH radical into O and H; this was reported by Dainton and Hardwick (8), who studied the system $Fe^{+2} - H_2O_2 - CO$ (in addition to the $Fe^{+2} - H_2O_2 - H_2$). While the rate constant for $OH + H_2 \rightarrow HOH + H$ was found to be only 0.15 times that of the reaction $Fe^{+2} + OH \rightarrow Fe^{+3} + OH^-$ at 20° C. in dilute perchloric acid), the rate constant for $OH + CO \rightarrow CO_2 + H$ was 2.6 times as large.

Photochemical Formation of Free Radicals in Solution and Their Subsequent Reaction

Apart from the thermal oxidation-reduction reactions involving metal ions in different valency states, discussed in detail in relation to the initiation of autoxidation, one of the most important modes of formation of free radicals is by photoexcitation. The modes of formation can be generally classified as (A) bond-breaking reactions, (B) electron transfer reactions, and (C) reactions which in general form an electronically excited state of the absorbing molecule which produces atoms or free radicals in subsequent bimolecular collisions with other species present.

Type A would include such reactions as the splitting of H_2O_2 into OH radicals or of the halogen molecules, Cl_2 and Br_2, into their respective atoms. These reactions have been investigated to a considerable extent in recent years. One of the most important features of these systems, as far as the solution phase is concerned, is the primary recombination effect first observed by Franck and Rabinowitch and sometimes called the "cage" effect of the solvent. It produces an upper limit for the primary quantum yield which is significantly below unity. If otherwise they are expected to be unity, in accordance with Einstein's law of photochemical equivalence, primary quantum efficiencies, in fact, vary, as a rule, between 0.2 and 0.6 and depend on the nature of the solvent environment. The other important feature is the Franck-Condon principle, which creates a large difference between the thermal and the photochemical energy required to rupture a chemical bond. While the thermal energy of the reaction $H_2O_2 \rightarrow 2OH$ is 47 kcal., the photochemical energy amounts to a minimum of 80 kcal. This is due to the fact that internuclear distances remain constant in the course of photoexcitation and the photochemical energy includes a term which accounts for the repulsion between the two OH radicals in the photoexcited state.

Type B, which comprises the various photoexcited electron transfer reactions leading to free radical formation, can be subdivided into those reactions which involve the solvent as electron acceptor or electron donor and those in which an ion pair complex is at the same time the species which absorbs the light and subject to internal electron transfer. Examples of the first kind, in which the solvent is the electron acceptor, include the irradiation of ferrous ion and many other reducing cations in aqueous solution, or reducing anions such as sulfite, formate, and the halides. This process generally leads to the formation of H atoms and is frequently accompanied by hydrogen evolution. As far as electron transfer in ionpair complexes is concerned, the systems which have been investigated in considerable detail are those involving the ferric complexes—e.g., $Fe^{+3}OH^-$, $Fe^{+3}Cl^-$, $Fe^{+3}F^-$, and $Fe^{+3}N_3^-$ and also others such as $Pb^{+2}Cl^-$ and $Ce^{+4}OH^-$. The light energy required for this type of photoexcited electron transfer is given by

$$h\nu = -\Delta H_{\text{ass.}} + E^s{}_X - I_{Fe^{+2}} + Q$$

where $\Delta H_{\text{ass.}}$ is the heat content change in the association of the ion pair $Fe^{+3}X^-$ from hydrated Fe^{+3} and X^- ions, $E^s{}_X$ is the electron affinity of X in aqueous solution, including the hydration energy of X^-, $I_{Fe}{}^{+2}$ is the ionization potential of ferrous ion in aqueous solution, and Q is the repulsion energy in the $Fe^{+2}\ldots X$ with an interatomic distance identical with that in the ion pair $Fe^{+3}X^-$ and the hydration shell in the corresponding nonequilibrium state (the origin of Q is readily understood on the basis of the Franck-Condon principle). Q was found to be ~40 kcal. and the remarkable fact is that this was almost independent of the nature of the anion, when X^- was F^-, Cl^-, OH^-, HO_2^-, or Br^-. These systems are particularly well suited for experiments where controlled production of free radicals is desired in order to study the initiation of polymerization, or reactions of free radicals with various organic substrates. Evans and Uri demonstrated the occurrence of free radicals in these systems and then used the irradiated $Fe^{+3}OH^-$ ion pair complex as a free radical "machine" to investigate various free radical reactions such as oxidation of organic substrates, polymerization of vinyl compounds, photo-oxidation of water, etc. As an example, the polymerization of methyl methacrylate or vinyl compounds induced by photoexcited electron transfer in a ferric ion pair complex could be explained fully by a stepwise reaction scheme (22).

Dainton and Tordoff (9) showed that in the case of acrylamide $Fe^{+3}OH^-$ is a significant terminator. I am not, however, convinced of the validity of their suggested extension of this mechanism to other vinyl monomers, and similar generalizations, particularly in view of the fact that under otherwise identical conditions in experiments concerning the oxidation of benzoic acid (4) a doubled maximum yield of ferrous ion formation was determined by straightforward analytical methods, indicating that in the latter case, but not in the former, $Fe^{+3}OH^-$ must be considered as a terminator. This is quite independent of the quantitative estimate of the $Fe^{+3}OH^-$ primary yield, which has become controversial. It is, however, feasible that $Fe^{+3}Br^-$ did not act as photoinitiator of the polymerization of methyl methacrylate or acrylonitrile because of efficient termination with $Fe^{+3}Br^-$, which would not be unexpected.

Photoexcitation of complex ions need not necessarily lead to electron transfer even as a secondary stage. In a recent study of the photochemistry of various cobaltic and chromic complex ions by Adamson and Sporer (1) it was shown that oxidation-reduction, apart from aquation, racemization, or exchange reactions, occurred not only by photoexcitation in the electron transfer band region but also in ligand field bands where electron transfer is out of the question. Very similar observations had been made by Copestake and Uri (7) in a detailed study of the photochemical and thermal decomposition of the trioxalatocobaltate(III) complex. In this case electron transfer was not postulated as the primary reaction. The suggested scheme was

$CoOx_3{}^{-3} \xrightarrow{h\nu} CoOx_3{}^{-3}$	Photoexcitation
$CoOx_3{}^{-3} \xrightarrow{kd} CoOx_3{}^{-3}$	Primary dark back-reaction
$CoOx_3{}^{-3} \xrightarrow{ks} CoOx_3{}^{-2} + Ox^-$	Dissociation of excited complex
$CoOx_3{}^{-3} + Ox^- \rightarrow Co^{+2} + 3\ Ox^{-2} + 2\ CO_2$	Reduction of cobaltic complex and oxidation of oxalate

The primary quantum efficiencies for cobaltous formation were evaluated as 0.73 for 313 mμ, 0.69 for 365 mμ (this is smaller than the value obtained by Adamson and Sporer for 370 mμ), 0.17 for 405 mμ, and 0.12 for 435 mμ. The interesting feature was the calculation that the quantum efficiencies at 405 and 435 mμ were too large to be accounted for if they were due to the tail end of the electron transfer absorption band in the near-ultraviolet. It was thus shown that absorption in the ligand field band led to the same over-all reaction. Independent evidence that the latter proceeds via the $C_2O_4^-$ radical ion was obtained by demonstrating its ability to lead to other reactions generally accepted as involving free radical mechanisms, including vinyl polymerization.

Type C comprises a large number of dye-photosensitized reactions and usually involves a radiationless transition from the excited singlet to a triplet state prior to free radical formation in subsequent reactions. They are not discussed in detail here, although the similarity of the dye-photosensitized reaction with the reactions photosensitized by uranyl ion is noteworthy. Attention must also be drawn to Simons' excellent review (18) of reactions of electronically excited molecules in solution, in which photochemical reactions of type C, including those involving energy transfer, are dealt with thoroughly.

Inorganic Photocatalysis

The study of the photochemical activity of $FeCl_4^-$ in alcohol by Brealey and Uri (6) revealed an interesting case of photocatalysis. The postulated mechanism is

Photoexcitation and primary dark back-reaction

$$\underset{\substack{|\\ \text{FeCl}_4^-(\text{H-CHOH})}}{\overset{\text{CH}_3}{\,}} \underset{k_d}{\overset{h\nu(k\varepsilon I)}{\rightleftharpoons}} \underset{\substack{|\\ \text{FeCl}_4^{-2}(\text{H}^+;\ \text{CHOH})}}{\overset{\text{CH}_3}{\,}}$$

Separation of primary product

$$\underset{\substack{|\\ \text{FeCl}_4^{-2}(\text{H}^+;\ \text{CHOH})}}{\overset{\text{CH}_3}{\,}} \overset{k_1}{\longrightarrow} \text{FeCl}_4^{-2} + \text{H}^+ + \underset{\substack{|\\ \cdot\text{CHOH}}}{\overset{\text{CH}_3}{\,}}$$

Reduction of $FeCl_4^-$

$$\underset{\substack{|\\ \text{CH}_3\text{C}\!-\!\text{OH}}}{\overset{\text{H}}{\,}} + \text{FeCl}_4^- \overset{k_2}{\longrightarrow} \underset{\substack{|\\ \text{CH}_3\text{C}\!=\!\text{O}}}{\overset{\text{H}}{\,}} + \text{H}^+ + \text{FeCl}_4^{-2}$$

In the presence of a dye such as thionine in 99.5% acidified alcohol, $FeCl_4^{-2}$ formed is instantaneously reoxidized to $FeCl_4^-$, the net reaction being the oxidation of alcohol by the dye with $FeCl_4^-$ as photocatalyst. Photocatalysis may be of considerable importance, when oxidation-reduction reactions are to be carried out which otherwise would not proceed as a result of too high an activation energy, as in the case of the direct oxidation of alcohol by thionine. In fact, this type of reaction may indicate the route to artificial photosynthesis. There are few other inorganic photocatalysts; one example is the oxidation of excess oxalate in a weakly acid solution photocatalyzed by ferric oxalate. The latter system has been studied in detail by Parker (16, 17). Systems resembling $FeCl_4^-$ are $CuCl_4^{-2}$ and $PbCl_4^{-2}$, also in ethyl alcohol. The latter is a particularly efficient photocatalyst and can cause the oxidation of ethyl alcohol by Janus Green, which is much more difficult to reduce than thionine. There would be no appreciable bleaching of the Janus Green in the absence of the catalyst. In principle, a system of this type bears some resemblance to the process of photosynthesis where, of course, the oxidation of water by carbon dioxide (or carboxylic acid) is photocatalyzed by chorophyll, but photosynthesis is energetically more difficult by a margin of approximately 0.8 volt than the oxidation of alcohol by Janus Green.

The most important process of photocatalysis in vivo—i.e., the process of photosynthesis—could well proceed via free radical intermediates. Experiments with photosynthesizing algae suspensions (25) indicated the likelihood of the formation of such radicals by the observation that methyl methacrylate was polymerizing, but under otherwise identical conditions no polymer could be detected in the dark, with irradiated dead algae, and in the absence of carbon dioxide. Chlorophyll in vitro was also found, under certain conditions, to act as photosensitizer of polymerization, indicating the likelihood of free radical intermediates; this was later confirmed by Krasnovsky and Umrikhina (15).

Trace Metals and Free Radical Intermediates in Autoxidation

Linoleic acid and its esters were frequently used in the study of autoxidation: Being a 1,4-diene, linoleic acid has one particularly weak α-methylenic C...H bond, so that, at least in the initial stages, the hydroperoxide which becomes conjugated is practically the only oxidation product. The generally accepted reaction mechanism is the chain reaction

$$\longrightarrow RO_2 + RH \xrightarrow{k_p} ROOH + R\cdot$$
$$R\cdot + O_2 \xrightarrow{\text{not rate-determining}} RO_2\cdot$$

and at oxygen saturation the termination is

$$RO_2 + RO_2 \xrightarrow{k_t} \text{products}$$

This mechanism illustrated by linoleic acid autoxidation is, however, typical for virtually all autoxidation processes. The general rate law based on stationary state kinetics is

$$\frac{-d(O_2)}{dt} = \frac{d[ROOH]}{dt} = \sqrt{r_i}\,\frac{k_p}{\sqrt{k_t}}\,(RH]$$

where r_i is the rate of initiation. One of the most difficult questions in this field is the one relating to the mode of initiation. In the studies carried out at the British Rubber Producers' Research Association [review by Bateman (18)], emphasis was placed on the formation of free radicals by bimolecular or unimolecular decomposition of the hydroperoxide itself. There are some difficult aspects in the energetics of the unimolecular decomposition, a detailed discussion of which has recently been presented (22). Moreover, one must not neglect the question of hydroperoxide formation prior to its decomposition, unless one is content to consider this as equivalent to the age-old question of the chicken and the egg. A good deal of kinetic research I carried out during the last few years indicated that the initial stage is intimately connected with trace metal catalysis (22).

First, it is necessary to explain why the direct interaction between olefins and oxygen should be ruled out. Abstraction of a hydrogen according to the reaction $RH + O_2 \rightarrow R + HO_2$ would be endothermic to an extent of 40 to 50 kcal., assuming the value of the bond dissociation energy of H...O_2 to be of the order of magnitude of 35 kcal. In view of this large endothermicity, this reaction could not be of any practical significance. From time to time various proposals have been made concerning the addition of oxygen across a double bond. The latest of these proposals was made by Khan (14): A cyclic transition state produced by the direct addition of oxygen to the olefin is postulated to be the initiation step in the autoxidation. This, however, is hardly acceptable, in view of the many observations indicating that the inhibitory effect of free radical acceptors is most marked during the induction period and the very early stages of autoxidation. It would be very surprising indeed if the initiation process did not involve free radicals from the beginning.

There is some difficulty with the energetics of unimolecular hydroperoxide decomposition. The endothermicity for the reaction $ROOH \rightarrow RO + OH$ is of the order of 50 kcal., whereas the observed activation energy is as low as 30 kcal. The question is, therefore, bound to arise: To what extent is decomposition trace metal–catalyzed? It can be demonstrated that ferrous phthalocyanine, even at concentrations below $10^{-6}M$, is a most powerful activator of hydroperoxides—e.g., in the oxidation of quercetin, rhamnetin, or β-carotene. The action of ferrous phthalocyanine is in principle similar to that of ferrous ion with hydrogen peroxide, already discussed. It may be described as reduction activation.

The heavy metal stearates most active in initiating autoxidation of methyl linoleate (Co^{+2}, Mn^{+2}, Ce^{+3}) (24) are those which can be oxidized by one-electron transfer, in accordance with

$$M^{n+} \rightarrow M^{(n+1)+} + e$$

Trace metals would be expected to produce free radicals by reduction of traces of hydroperoxide already present in the system according to

$$M^{n+} + ROOH \rightarrow M^{(n+1)+} + OH^- + RO\cdot$$

Heat and entropy changes in these systems have been evaluated for aqueous solutions, but it should be borne in mind that both complex formation and change of environment affect these significantly. Generally, a trace metal would be more powerful as a reduction activator in a less polar environment and hence will be frequently active in organic media but not in water. Cobaltous ion would be hardly reactive with hydrogen peroxide in aqueous solution, but various organic cobaltous complexes are among the most efficient reduction activators in olefinic autoxidation—e.g., cobaltous phthalocyanine. It is noteworthy that the thallous and stannous stearates were found to have no catalytic effect in the autoxidation of linoleic acid, while cupric stearate was active only in the presence of hydrogen peroxide or reducing substances (24). In view of the multiplicity of the initiation steps, it is significant that Heaton and Uri (13) devised experimental conditions in which the initiation reaction $Co^{+2} + ROOH \rightarrow Co^{+3} + OH^- + RO\cdot$ is isolated and the experimentally obtained steric factor and activation energy are in good agreement with theoretical expectation. However, the above-mentioned investigation also indicated the importance of the direct interaction between metal and oxygen in the early stages of autoxidation and there also appears to be free radical formation without the participation of a hydroperoxide. The first stage usually involves metal-oxygen formation.

Elvidge and Lever (10) have demonstrated that manganous phthalocyanine, which we found to be an efficient autoxidation catalyst, forms reversible oxygen complexes in pyridine. In collaboration with Hardy it was found that hemin formed a similar complex at 70° C. and that this equilibrium can be made reversible by passing oxygen and nitrogen successively through the solution. With ferrous phthalocyanine in benzene at room temperature the oxygen complex appears to be the stable form, but at the boiling point of benzene this complex can be dissociated with considerable loss of light absorption in the red band. The fact that on cooling, the original absorption spectrum can be repeated almost quantitatively substantiates the view that the observed change is a reversible equilibrium and not an oxidative degradation. One way to express the basic idea of the initiation process is to say that trace metals, by forming oxygen complexes, provide the labile energy-enriched oxygen for the otherwise inefficient reaction $RH + O_2 \rightarrow R\cdot + HO_2$, thus producing free radicals which lead ultimately to the chain reaction and to auto-catalysis by the hydroperoxide formed. There is no doubt that free radical formation occurs also by the reduction of the trace metal by either the hydroperoxide or the substrate itself (22) according to

$$M^{n+} + ROOH \rightarrow M^{(n-1)+} + H^+ + RO_2\cdot$$

$$M^{n+} + RH \rightarrow M^{(n-1)+} + H^+ + R\cdot$$

Thus in the system cobaltous stearate–linoleic acid cobaltic stearate is formed *in situ* and becomes a very efficient catalyst (13). Both the absolute and the relative rates of the above-mentioned hydroperoxide and substrate reactions depend on the nature of the substrate. With linoleic acid at a concentration ratio of [RH]/[ROOH] of about 50, the reaction with the substrate predominated over the one with the hydroperoxide.

The importance of complexing and the polarity of the environment has been emphasized. When metal phthalocyanines and metal stearates were compared in ethyl benzoate as solvent, their catalytic efficiencies in the autoxidation of $0.1M$ linoleic acid were of a comparable order of magnitude when the metal phthalocyanines and the metal stearates were present at concentrations of $2 \times 10^{-7}M$ and $2 \times 10^{-4}M$, respectively. These observations apply to ferrous, cobaltous, and manganous phthalocyanines, and it is noteworthy that the cupric, magnesium, and nickel phthalocyanines had no significant catalytic activity. It appears, therefore, that oxidation of the central metal ion by one-electron transfer plays an important role in initiating autoxidation.

The evidence for the hypothesis that initiation of autoxidation involves trace metal impurities and that autoxidation would in fact not occur in the absence of trace metals can be summarized as follows:

Trace metals in sufficient quantities to initiate autoxidation occur not only in crude hydrocarbons, fats, and oils, but also in highly purified materials—e.g., highly purified linoleic acid was found to contain 0.21 p.p.m. Cu and 0.0008 p.p.m. Co (results obtained by radioactivation analysis).

The autoxidation of these materials depend on the polarity of the environment; this is illustrated by the fact that the time taken for the conversion of 0.8% of linoleic acid into its hydroperoxide at 37° C. in cyclohexane, benzene, and 70 volume % aqueous ethyl alcohol was found to be 1, 2.5, and 20 days, respectively (22).

This dependence on the polarity of the environment is not experienced with free radical reactions in general, but it follows the same pattern as oxidation-reduction potentials of metal compounds in these solvents; a striking example is the case $FeCl_4^-/FeCl_4^{-2}$ where a jump of half a volt occurs in a very narrow range of ethyl alcohol–water mixtures (22).

Some new free radical acceptors which include pentahydroxyflavones and trihydroxypolyporic acids (5, 24) exhibit similar relative efficiencies in the apparently uncatalyzed autoxidation reaction and in systems into which metal catalysts were deliberately introduced.

It is my view that trace metals are responsible for the onset of autoxidation, and, apart from the reactions which involve formation of free radicals in reactions between metals and hydroperoxides, already present, there are two possibilities in which free radicals can be formed without the participation of hydroperoxides:

$$M^{n+} + RH \rightarrow M^{(n-1)+} + H^+ + R\cdot$$

$$M^{n+} \cdot O_2 + M^{n+}(XH) \rightarrow M^{(n+1)} + X^- + HO_2\cdot + M^{n+}$$

The latter appears to be preferred to the direct electron transfer between metal and oxygen. XH stands for either substrate or solvent.

As far as the general mechanism of electron transfer is concerned, there have been a number of important reviews in recent years (20, 27). This paper has dealt with the limited aspects which involves free radical formation and its consequences, while reviewing some of my work and placing particular emphasis on the importance of the role of trace metal impurities and of sound energetics in the analysis of reaction schemes.

Literature Cited

(1) Adamson, A. W., Sporer, A. H., *J. Am. Chem. Soc.* **80**, 3865 (1958).
(2) Barb, W. G., Baxendale, J. H., George, P., Hargrave, K. H., *Trans. Faraday Soc.* **47**, 462 (1951).
(3) Bateman, L., *Quart. Rev. (London)* **8**, 147 (1954).
(4) Bates, H. G. C., Uri, N., *J. Am. Chem. Soc.* **75**, 2754 (1953).
(5) Bennett, G. J., Uri, N., *Nature* **192**, 354 (1961); *J. Chem. Soc.*, in press.
(6) Brealey, G. J., Uri, N., *J. Chem. Phys.* **20**, 257 (1962).
(7) Copestake, T. B., Uri, N., *Proc. Roy. Soc. (London)* **A228**, 252 (1955).
(8) Dainton, F. S., Hardwick, T. J., *Trans. Faraday Soc.* **53**, 333 (1957).
(9) Dainton, F. S., Tordoff, M., *Ibid.*, **53**, 666 (1957).
(10) Elvidge, J. A., Lever, A. B. P., *Proc. Chem. Soc.*, **1959**, 195.
(11) Franck, J., Haber, F., *Sitzber. preuss, Akad. Wiss.* **1931**, 250.
(12) Haber, F., Weiss, J., *Proc. Roy. Soc. (London)* **A147**, 332 (1934).
(13) Heaton, F. W., Uri, N., *J. Lipid Research* **2**, 152 (1961).
(14) Khan, N. A., *Can. J. Chem.* **32**, 1149 (1954); **37**, 1029 (1959).
(15) Krasnovsky, A. A., Umrikhina, A. V., *Doklady Akad. Nauk S.S.S.R.* **104**, 822 (1955); *Biofizika* **3**, 547 (1958).
(16) Parker, C. A., *Trans. Faraday Soc.* **50**, 1213 (1954).
(17) Parker, C. A., Hatchard, C., *J. Phys. Chem.* **63**, 22 (1959).
(18) Simons, J. P., *Quart. Revs. (London)* **13**, 3 (1959).
(19) Taube, H., *J. Am. Chem. Soc.* **64**, 2468 (1942).
(20) Taube, H., "Recent Advances in Inorganic Chemistry and Radiochemistry," H. J. Emeleus and A. G. Sharpe, eds., Vol. 1, pp. 1–53, Academic Press, New York, 1959.
(21) Urey, H. C., Dawsey, L. H., Rice, F. O., *J. Am. Chem. Soc.* **51**, 1371 (1929).
(22) Uri, N., "Autoxidation and Antioxidants," Vol. 1, W. O. Lundberg, ed., pp. 55–106, 133–69, Interscience, New York, 1961.
(23) Uri, N., *Chem. Revs.* **50**, 375 (1952).
(24) Uri, N., IVth International Congress on Biochemical Problems of Lipids, p. 30, Butterworths, London, 1958; *Nature* **177**, 1177 (1956).
(25) Uri, N., *J. Am. Chem. Soc.* **74**, 5808 (1952); *Biochim. Biophys. Acta* **18**, 209 (1955).
(26) Walsh, A. D., *J. Chem. Soc.* **1948**, 331.
(27) Zwolinski, B. J., Marcus, R. J., Eyring, H., *Chem. Revs.* **55**, 157 (1955).

RECEIVED May 24, 1962.

11

Aqueous Chemistry of Inorganic Free Radicals

IV. Stoichiometry of the Reaction of Peroxydisulfate Ion with Hydrogen Peroxide and Evidence of Acidity Constant of the HO₂ Radical

MAAK-SANG TSAO[1] and W. K. WILMARTH

Department of Chemistry, University of Southern California, Los Angeles 7, Calif.

The reaction of H_2O_2 and $S_2O_8{}^{-2}$ has been used as a generating system for the HO_2 radical. By studying the relative competitive efficiencies of H_2O_2 and $S_2O_8{}^{-2}$ as scavengers for the HO_2 radical over a range of pH, it has been possible to gain information about the acidity of the HO_2 radical. In the present system, using these scavengers, ionization of HO_2 becomes important in the pH range from 4.5 to 6.5.

Earlier papers (*6, 13, 14*) in this series have dealt with various aspects of the aqueous chemistry of very reactive inorganic free radicals. In the present work our primary objective is to gain information about the acidity of the HO_2 radical.

This radical is an important reactive intermediate in many reactions including the one-electron oxidation of hydrogen peroxide and the one-electron reduction of molecular oxygen. It also plays an important role in aqueous systems undergoing high energy irradiation (*1*), particularly in aerobic conditions where it is formed by reaction of hydrogen atoms with molecular oxygen.

Appearance potential data (*5*) may be used to calculate a value of 5.0 ± 2.0 kcal. per mole for the heat of formation of gaseous HO_2. [The indicated uncertainty of ±2 kcal. is that estimated by the authors (*5*).] By estimating the entropy of gaseous HO_2 and the enthalpy and entropy of solution, we obtain the following approximate E values.

$$H_2O_2 \xrightarrow{-1.4} HO_2 \xrightarrow{0.1} O_2$$

Aqueous HO_2 is thus seen to be both a moderately strong reducing agent and a powerful oxidizing agent. Neutralization of HO_2 would stabilize the $O_2{}^-$ ion somewhat and reduce both the oxidizing and reducing strength of the radical.

The ΔH value for dehydration of HO_2 suggests that it is unstable with respect to formation of its anhydride, the O_3 molecule, except possibly in strongly alkaline solution. [In his estimation of $E°$ values Latimer (*9*) used data for the solution of O_3 in concentrated alkali reported by Weiss (*16*).]

---

[1]Present address, Chemistry Department, Chung Chi College, Hong Kong.

$$2HO_2 \longrightarrow H_2O + O_3$$

$$\Delta H = -16 \text{ kcal.}$$

Until very recently the evidence for the existence of the HO_2 radical in a condensed phase was based largely on kinetic measurements. However, recently it has been reported that the NMR spectrum of the HO_2 radical may be observed in ice irradiated at very low temperatures (8, 11) and at room temperature in an aqueous solution (10), where hydrogen peroxide is being oxidized by cerium(IV).

At present there are very few studies which yield information about the acidity constant of the HO_2 radical. However, in studies of the reaction of Fe^{+2} and H_2O_2 (2) and of the bromide ion catalysis of the reaction of O_3 and H_2O_2 (12) it has been suggested that ionization becomes important in the region above pH 2. These results are considered in more detail below.

Experimental

Materials. The method of purifying distilled water has been described (6, 13, 14). Except for Baker and Adamson's 70% perchloric acid and Baker's inhibitor-free hydrogen peroxide, all chemicals used in stoichiometric experiments were recrystallized at least once from purified water. Buffer solutions were prepared by adding purified KH_2PO_4 or $Na_4P_2O_7$ to solutions of $HClO_4$ in purified water.

Analytical Procedures. In the thermal experiments molecular oxygen was measured in a thermostated gas buret and manometer attached to an all-glass high-vacuum system made of capillary tubing to minimize the gas volume and increase the accuracy of the measurements. Persulfate was determined iodometrically after destruction of the hydrogen peroxide by catalytic decomposition caused by osmium tetroxide in alkaline solution (7). The change in hydrogen peroxide concentration could not be measured with the highest accuracy by direct analysis of H_2O_2 (or H_2O_2 plus $S_2O_8^{-2}$), since the percentage change during reaction was very small. Consequently, greater accuracy in changes of H_2O_2 concentration was obtained by measuring the volume of oxygen evolved and calculating the change in peroxide concentration from the relationship:

$$\Delta(H_2O_2) = 2(O_2) - \Delta(S_2O_8^{-2})$$

where (O_2) represents the number of moles of O_2 evolved per liter during the time interval under consideration. The solution was stirred magnetically to prevent supersaturation of oxygen. In calculating (O_2) using the ideal gas law, a correction was made for the vapor pressure of H_2O.

Co^{60} Irradiation Experiments. In some experiments the reaction of H_2O_2 and $S_2O_8^{-2}$ was induced by Co^{60} irradiation, using the source available at Cookridge Hospital near Leeds, England. The solutions were irradiated in glass-stoppered test tubes at a dose rate of approximately 10^{19} e.v. per liter per second. In these solutions the gas buret apparatus for analysis of molecular oxygen was not available. Iodometric analysis using aliquots of the solutions before and after carrying out the OsO_4-catalyzed destruction of H_2O_2 yielded values for the sum of H_2O_2 and $S_2O_8^{-2}$ concentrations and the $S_2O_8^{-2}$ concentration, respectively. The H_2O_2 concentration was then determined by difference.

Mechanistic Considerations

In a system as complex as the present one, it is possible to present the data efficiently only if the reader is familiar with the proposed reaction mechanism. For this reason we depart from the usual order and discuss the mechanism of reaction of H_2O_2 and $S_2O_8^{-2}$ before presenting the experimental results.

In the present study the reaction of H_2O_2 and $S_2O_8^{-2}$ is used as a generating system for the HO_2 radical. Our earlier detailed kinetic study provides strong evidence that HO_2 is generated in this system by the following series of reactions:

$$S_2O_8^{-2} \rightarrow 2\,SO_4^- \tag{1}$$

$$SO_4^- + H_2O \rightarrow HSO_4^- + OH \tag{2}$$

$$H_2O_2 + OH\ (\text{or}\ SO_4^-) \rightarrow H_2O\ (\text{or}\ HSO_4^-) + HO_2 \tag{3}$$

As the alternative forms given for Equation 3 imply, for our present purposes it does not matter whether the OH or SO_4^- radical reacts with the H_2O_2 molecule.

Let us first consider the fate of the HO_2 radical at an acidity great enough so that ionization of HO_2 may be neglected. Under these conditions the HO_2 radical is consumed in the two competitive pH-independent processes given by Equations 4 and 5.

$$HO_2 + S_2O_8^{-2} \xrightarrow{k_7} O_2 + HSO_4^- + SO_4^- \tag{4}$$
$$\Big\downarrow^{H_2O}$$
$$\longrightarrow OH$$

$$HO_2 + H_2O_2 \xrightarrow{k_8} O_2 + H_2O + OH \tag{5}$$

In these and in later equations the symbols placed over the arrows define the rate constants for the various reactions. Reactions 4 and 5 represent a pair of chain-carrying steps for two parallel chain reactions, each of which is initiated by Reactions 1 to 3. As the second chain-carrying step, the two chain reactions have a common link, since the OH radical generated in Reactions 4 and 5 can disappear only in Reaction 6 (or in chain-terminating steps which contribute negligibly to the over-all stoichiometry).

$$OH + H_2O_2 \rightarrow H_2O + HO_2 \tag{6}$$

Fortunately, it is possible by stoichiometric measurements alone to evaluate the competitive efficiences of $S_2O_8^{-2}$ and H_2O_2 as scavengers for the HO_2 radical in Reactions 4 and 5. In the limit when only Reaction 4 carries the chain, the above mechanism implies that the over-all stoichiometry will be given by Reaction 8; conversely, chain carrying by Reaction 5 alone would result in the stoichiometry of Equation 9.

$$H_2O_2 + S_2O_8^{-2} \rightarrow O_2 + 2\,HSO_4^- \tag{8}$$

$$2\,H_2O_2 \rightarrow O_2 + 2\,H_2O \tag{9}$$

In terms of experiment, the relative changes in concentration of $S_2O_8^{-2}$ and H_2O_2 may be used to calculate the relative contributions of Reactions 8 and 9, and these relative contributions, in turn, to identify the competitive efficiencies of $S_2O_8^{-2}$ and H_2O_2 for the HO_2 radical in Reactions 4 and 5. Since we are concerned only with conditions where the chains are long, important contributions to the stoichiometry are made only by the chain-carrying reactions, Equations 4, 5, and 6. The negligible chemical changes produced by Reactions 1 to 3 and the unspecified bimolecular radical termination reactions may be neglected.

Until now the discussion has been concerned only with the limiting region of pH where ionization of HO_2 may be neglected, where the chain-carrying Reactions 4 and 5 are assumed to be pH-independent, and where the competitive efficiencies of $S_2O_8^{-2}$ and H_2O_2 found by experiment should consequently be pH-independent. The experiments described below confirm the validity of these assumptions, since there is a stoichiometric, pH-independent "plateau" below pH3.

Let us next consider a second limiting region of pH at lower acidity, where ionization of HO_2 is assumed to be virtually complete. In this region chain carrying will be by O_2^- instead of HO_2 and Equations 10 and 11 will correspondingly replace Equations 4 and 5.

$$O_2^- + S_2O_8^{-2} \xrightarrow{k_9} O_2 + SO_4^{-2} + SO_4^- \tag{10}$$
$$\downarrow H_2O$$
$$\longrightarrow OH$$

$$O_2^- + H_2O_2 \xrightarrow{k_{10}} O_2 + OH^- + OH \tag{11}$$

To complete the mechanism here it is necessary only to add Reaction 12, a reaction which will be important, if at all, in the same region of pH as Reaction 11.

$$HO_2 + HO_2^- \xrightarrow{k_{10}} O_2 + OH^- + OH \tag{12}$$

At this point our presentation of the mechanism could be terminated, since it has already covered a range of pH greater than that found to be experimentally available. However, the later discussion will be simplified if we finally introduce Reaction 13, a process which would become important above pH 12 where neutralization of H_2O_2 occurs.

$$O_2^- + HO_2^- \xrightarrow{k_{12}} O_2 + OH^- + O^- \tag{13}$$

In Equation 13 we have neglected such pH-dependent phenomena (6, 14) as formation of O^- by neutralization of OH and acid or base catalysis of Reaction 2, because such considerations would not, so far as we are able to see, influence the validity of the conclusion to be drawn from our data. These conclusions seem to be based only upon the assumed form of Equations 4, 5, 10, 11, and 12.

It is now necessary to formulate the above arguments in quantitative terms. The following rate laws may be written merely from inspection of the mechanism proposed above.

$$-\frac{d(H_2O_2)}{dt} = \frac{d(S_2O_8^{-2})}{dt} +$$
$$2\left[\frac{k_8 + (k_{10}K + k_{11}K')(OH^-) + k_{12}KK'(OH^-)^2}{1 + K'(OH^-)}\right](H_2O_2)(HO_2) \tag{14}$$

$$-\frac{d(S_2O_8^{-2})}{dt} = [k_7 + k_9K(OH^-)](S_2O_8^{-2})(HO_2) \tag{15}$$

The rate constants refer to those placed above the arrows in the appropriate equations. The symbol (H_2O_2) refers to the total hydrogen peroxide present as either H_2O_2 or HO_2^-; K and K' are defined by Equations 16 and 17.

$$K = \frac{(O_2^-)}{(HO_2)(OH^-)} = K_{HO_2}/K_{H_2O} \tag{16}$$

$$K' = \frac{(HO_2^-)}{(H_2O_2)(OH^-)} = K_{H_2O_2}/K_{H_2O} \tag{17}$$

Equation 18 may be obtained merely by dividing Equation 14 by Equation 15 and integrating both numerator and denominator over the time interval from zero to time t.

$$\frac{\Delta(H_2O_2)}{\Delta(S_2O_8^{-2})} \equiv n = 1 + \left[\frac{k_8 + (k_{10}K + k_{11}K')(OH^-) + k_{12}KK'(OH^-)^2}{k_7 + (k_9K + k_7K')(OH^-) + k_9KK'(OH^-)^2}\right]\left[\frac{(H_2O_2)}{(S_2O_8^{-2})}\right]_{av.}$$
$$\tag{18}$$

The changes in H_2O_2 and $S_2O_8^{-2}$ concentration in a given time interval are given by $\Delta(H_2O_2)$ and $\Delta(S_2O_8^{-2})$. The quantity n, introduced for simplicity to represent $\Delta H_2O_2/\Delta S_2O_8^{-2}$ and defined by Equation 18, may be evaluated using the measured changes in concentrations of H_2O_2 and $S_2O_8^{-2}$ during a time interval under consideration. If the time interval is short enough so that the percentage changes in the H_2O_2 and $S_2O_8^{-2}$ concentrations are not too extreme, the value of $[(H_2O_2)/(S_2O_8^{-2})]_{av}$ represents the average value of the ratio of $(H_2O_2)/(S_2O_8^{-2})$ and is defined by Equation 19 in terms of the initial and final concentrations.

$$\left[\frac{(H_2O_2)}{(S_2O_8^{-2})_{av.}}\right] = \frac{1}{2}\left\{\left[\frac{(H_2O_2)}{(S_2O_8^{-2})}\right]_{init.} + \left[\frac{(H_2O_2)}{(S_2O_8^{-2})}\right]_{final}\right\} \tag{19}$$

To simplify the presentation we use R to represent the coefficient of $[(H_2O_2)/(S_2O_8^{-2})]_{av.}$ in Equation 18 and rewrite the equation in the form of Equation 21.

$$R = \left[\frac{k_8 + (k_{10}K + k_{11}K')(OH^-) + k_{12}KK'(OH^-)^2}{k_7 + (k_9K + k_7K')(OH^-) + k_9KK'(OH^-)^2}\right] \tag{20}$$

$$R = \frac{n-1}{2[(H_2O_2)/(S_2O_8^{-2})]_{av.}} \tag{21}$$

Before presenting the results it is useful to indicate the limiting, simplified forms of R which become very good approximations in various pH regions. To refer to these approximate forms we use R_1, R_2, and R_3, defined by the equations below. Inspection of Equation 20 indicates that at high acidity where terms in (OH^-) become negligible, $R_1 = k_8/k_7$. In the region where the first-power terms in (OH^-) are dominant R again becomes pH-independent, the approximate form being $R_2 = (k_{10}K + k_{11}K')/(k_9K + k_7K')$. Finally, at high alkalinity, a region we were not able to investigate, we have the approximation $R_3 = k_{12}/k_9$. The physical significance of these approximate forms may be seen by identifying the chain-carrying reactions which are characterized by the rate constants under consideration.

Of major interest in the present work is the hydrogen ion concentration at which R has a value midway between R_1 and R_2. This value of R and (H^+) will be designated as R_{m1} and $(H^+)_{m1}$, with R_{m1} being defined explicitly by the equation $R_{m1} = (R_1 + R_2)/2$. As Equation 22 indicates, $(H^+)_{m1}$ is a measure of the acidity constant of HO_2 multiplied by the factor k_9/k_7.

$$(H^+)_{m1} = \frac{k_9K_{HO}}{k_7} + K_{H_2O_2} \cong \frac{k_9K_{HO_2}}{k_7} \tag{22}$$

As the numerical data discussed below indicate, $k_9K_{HO_2}/k_7 \gg K_{H_2O_2}$ and the final simplified form of the equation is a very good approximation.

In the region of rapidly changing R between the R_2 and R_3 plateaus, there should be a hydrogen ion concentration, $(H^+)_{m2}$, which corresponds to a second midpoint value of R defined by the equation, $R_{m2} = (R_2 + R_3)/2$. This midpoint, which should occur at $pH = pK_{H_2O_2} = 12$, is of little physical interest, since it is merely associated with the ionization of H_2O_2.

$$(H^+)_{m2} = \frac{k_9KK_{H_2O_2}}{k_9K + k_7K'} \cong K_{H_2O_2} \tag{23}$$

Again the simplified form of the equation is a good approximation. By using the value of $R_2 = 0.055$, we obtain from Figure 1 the result $(H^+)_{m1} = k_9K_{HO_2}/k_7 = 3.8 \times 10^{-6}$.

Results

In Table I are listed the data obtained in solutions more acidic than pH 4.3, where variations in R are relatively small. The first six experiments are directly comparable, since they were all carried out at an ionic strength of 0.1. A comparison of the duplicate experiments indicates that the limit of reproducibility was approximately ±5%.

Table I. Stoichiometric Measurements at 30°

pH^a	$(H_2O_2)_0^b$	$(S_2O_8^{-2})_0^b$	(Na^+)	n	R	R_{calcd}^c
1.0	1.00	0.002	0.0^a	2.57	0.0014	0.0014
1.0	0.20	0.002	0.0^a	1.32	0.0013	
1.85	1.00	0.002	0.1	2.58	0.0014	0.0014
1.85	1.00	0.002	0.1	2.57	0.0013	
2.9	1.00	0.002	0.1	2.88	0.0017	0.0016
2.9	1.00	0.002	0.1	2.97	0.0017	
2.0	1.00	0.002	0.2	3.29	0.0021	
2.7	1.00	0.002	0.2	4.10	0.0027	
3.0	1.00	0.002	0.2	4.02	0.0026	
4.3	1.00	0.002	0.2	6.67	0.0053	

[a] pH maintained using phosphate or pyrophosphate buffers, except in first two experiments, which were carried out in $0.10N$ perchloric acid.
[b] Initial concentrations.
[c] Using Equation 21.

Experiments 1 to 4 show that R is pH-independent over the range 1.0 to 1.85, an indication that R has reached the limiting value designated above as R_1. In experiments 1 and 2 a fivefold variation in $(H_2O_2)/(S_2O_8^{-2})$ resulted in an approximate fivefold variation in $n - 1$ without producing a significant change in R, a verification of the applicability of Equation 21. In experiments 5 and 6 at pH 2.9 there is a small but detectable increase in R.

Experiments 7 to 10 were carried out at the higher ionic strength of 0.20 and in solutions containing sodium instead of potassium (or hydrogen) ion. A comparison of experiments 3, 4, and 7 indicates that somewhat higher values of R were obtained under these conditions. Higher ionic strength would be expected to result in enhanced dissociation of HO_2 and larger R values. Larger R values at the higher ionic strength might also be caused by formation of kinetically important concentrations of ion pairs having the formula $Na·S_2O_8^-$. Possibly such ion pairs would react less rapidly with O_2^- than $S_2O_8^{-2}$ does, a factor which would increase R.

The results obtained in less acidic solutions are presented in graphical form in Figure 1, to illustrate more clearly the drastic changes in R which occur in this region of acidity. Meaningful experiments could not be done in solutions less acidic than pH 6.1.

In studies carried out in the pH range of 3 to 6, it was necessary to buffer the solutions, since Reaction 8 tends to increase the acidity. Only phosphate and pyrophosphate buffers were used; almost all other buffer systems would be attacked by the OH or HO_2 radical. (Fluoride buffers could probably be used, although there are difficulties associated with the measurement of pH.) In addition, early exploratory experiments, not reported in detail here, indicated that spurious results would be obtained in buffers containing unpurified alkali. In these experiments the rate of reaction was much more rapid than in pyrophosphate buffers which did not contain alkali, and somewhat lower values of R were observed.

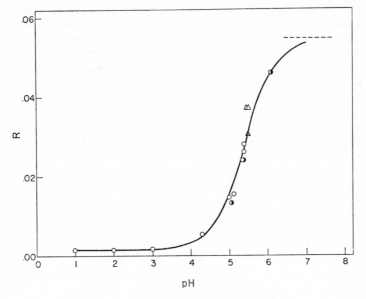

Figure 1.   Relation of R to pH at 30° K.

	H_2O_2	$S_2O_8^{-2}$
O	1.0	0.002
◑	1.0	0.010
▲	0.20	0.010
△	0.20	0.002

Both of these results suggest that use of unpurified alkali introduces heavy metal ion impurities which replace HO_2 and O_2^- in Reactions 5 and 11.

In solutions less acidic than pH 5, where R is changing rapidly with pH, the buffering capacity was inadequate, and R values measured in these solutions are less accurately known. For this reason it was difficult to provide further conclusive evidence that R was independent of $[(H_2O_2)/(S_2O_3^{-2})]_{av}$. However, the three experiments at pH 5.1 presented in Figure 1 constitute a reasonably convincing test of the theory. Further tests carried out at pH 5.4 provide points showing the random scatter which might be expected from the highly sensitive dependence of R upon pH.

In the later stages of this work, it was discovered that the decomposition of H_2O_2 in alkaline solution could be greatly reduced by coprecipitating the impurities in the alkali with barium phosphate. [At this time we were unaware of the work of D'Ans and Mattner (3) who used $Mg(OH)_2$ to coprecipitate traces of heavy metal ions.] The stabilization achieved with barium phosphate precipitation was not very reproducible, but in some experiments the rates of decomposition of H_2O_2 were as low as those recently reported by Duke and Hass (4). Unfortunately, this technique of alkali purification was discovered too late to use in the experiments carried out in solutions more alkaline than pH 6.1. However, the radiation experiments considered below suggest that the pH range beyond pH 6.1 would not have yielded meaningful results, even if purified alkali had been used.

In some studies the reaction of H_2O_2 and $S_2O_8^{-2}$ was induced by Co^{60} irradiation. These studies are not reported in detail, because the results are not as accurate as those obtained in the thermal system. However, a summary of the results is of interest. In the irradiated systems the maximum rate of generation of radicals was approximately 10^4 times that produced by Reaction 1. Studies in the pH range covered in Figure 1 gave results in good agreement with those obtained in the thermal system. It was hoped that the enhanced rate of initiation caused by the irradiation would enable us to measure R in slightly alkaline solutions, where the thermal studies were unsatisfactory because of the rapid thermal decomposition of H_2O_2. However, over the entire pH range from 6.5 to 14, the chain length was too short to yield meaningful values of R. This difficulty was not alleviated by the use of alkali purified in the manner indicated above.

For the theory developed above to be applicable it is necessary that the chain length be 10 or greater, so that the contributions to the net change by the chain initiation and termination may be ignored. The pH range over which these conditions are met may be understood by a consideration of Figure 2. The rate data presented here are not of the same order of accuracy as those presented earlier (13), since they were obtained as an incidental part of the stoichiometric measurements. For convenience the results have been tabulated as values of $-d \ln (S_2O_8^{-2})/t$, a formulation which is consistent with the first-order dependence of rate on $S_2O_8^{-2}$ concentration previously observed at pH 3 or less.

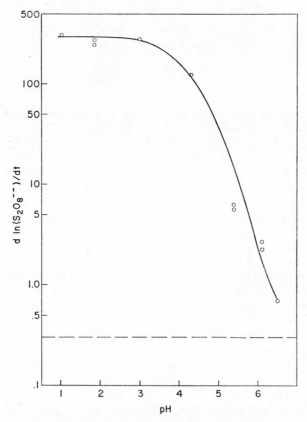

Figure 2. Relation of reaction rate to pH

$--- \quad -d \ln (S_2O_8^{-2}) \, dt \text{ in absence of } H_2O_2$

Since all rate measurements were based on initial rates and were carried out with the same concentration of reactants, this method of presentation is satisfactory, even if the assumed rate law is incorrect at the higher pH. As Figure 2 indicates, the reaction rate is pH-independent below pH 3. Under these conditions the chain length is approximately 1000. Above pH 3 the chain length rapidly decreases with decreasing acidity. At pH 6.1 the chain length is only 9, a value small enough so that neglect of chain initiation and termination may be producing errors comparable to the limit of error involved in evaluation of R. At pH 6.5 the chain length has decreased to 2, a value so small that an R value has not been calculated, since it would be seriously in error.

In the discussion of mechanism presented above it was assumed that chain initiation resulted only from the thermal decomposition of $S_2O_8^{-2}$, the rate-determining step being given by Equation 1. Evidence supporting this assumption was obtained by studying the reaction of $S_2O_8^{-2}$ and H_2O_2 in solutions containing allyl acetate, an efficient scavenger (17) for hydroxyl radicals. [The work of Volman and Chen (15) indicated that allyl alcohol might be used successfully as an OH scavenger in the photolysis of H_2O_2. However, in our system the presence of allyl alcohol did not completely suppress the chain reactions.] The presence of the allyl acetate reduced the first-order rate constant for disappearance of $S_2O_8^{-2}$ to a value within 20% of that observed for the thermal decomposition of $S_2O_8^{-2}$. Possibly the discrepancy of 20% represents the limit of error of the two experiments, since the accuracy of the iodometric analysis was rather low in solutions containing the allyl acetate polymer, and there was an unusually large scatter of points in the plot used to determine the first-order rate constants.

Discussion

Inspection of Figure 1 demonstrates that the numerical value of $R_1 = k_8/k_7 = 0.0014$ is well defined by the region of constancy of R in solutions more acidic than pH 3. In physical terms this result implies that $S_2O_8^{-2}$ is a better scavenger than H_2O_2 for HO_2 by a factor of approximately 700.

The solid line drawn through the points in Figure 1 is a theoretical one calculated using Equation 24.

$$R = \frac{0.0014 + 2.1 \times 10^7 \, (OH^-)}{1 + 3.8 \times 10^8 \, (OH^-)} \tag{24}$$

The physical significance of the numerical values of Equation 24 may be obtained by comparing it with Equation 20. (To obtain a value of unity for the first term in the denominator, it is necessary to divide both the numerator and denominator of Equation 20 by k_8.)

Equation 24 predicts that with increasing pH R should reach a second pH-independent value of $R_2 = 0.055$, the value indicated by the dashed line in the upper right-hand corner of Figure 1. In terms of experiment the value of R_2 is poorly defined, since the region of pH above 6 was inaccessible. Fortunately, the form of Equation 20 is such that the calculated value of $(H^+)_{m1} = 3.8 \times 10^{-6}$ is relatively insensitive to the choice of R_2.

The horizontal dashed line in Figure 2 represents the value of $-d \ln (S_2O_8^{-2}) / dt$ for solutions not containing H_2O_2. In any given experiment, the chain length may be obtained by comparing the ordinate value for a given point in the figure with that of the dashed line. The decrease in chain length with increasing pH observable in Figure 2 implies that the chain-carrying reactions given by Equations 10 and 11 are relatively inefficient compared to chain termination reaction.

Since the decrease in chain length may arise entirely from the efficiency of the termination reaction—i.e., $OH + O_2^- \rightarrow O_2 + OH^-$—it should not be concluded that the rate constants for Reactions 10 and 11 are necessarily smaller than those of Reactions 4 and 5.

For the system under consideration, the kinetic and stoichiometric behavior can be predicted without a knowledge of the quantity K_{HO_2}. As we have emphasized, in our system the important parameter is $k_9 K_{HO_2}/k_7$. The study of other systems where HO_2 appears under steady-state conditions can also yield only a value of K_{HO_2} multiplied by a coefficient consisting of a ratio of kinetic parameters. In short, the apparent region of neutralization of HO_2, as obtained in the kinetic analog of a titration curve, will differ somewhat, depending upon the system under consideration. As a general rule, it is probably safe to assume that the kinetic parameter which appears as a coefficient will not usually differ from unity by more than several powers of 10, since the coefficient represents the ratio of rate constants for a pair of very rapid reactions. The available data seem to support this assumption, since the region of neutralization reported in earlier studies (1, 2, 12) lies within a few pH units of that reported here.

Acknowledgment

W. K. Wilmarth expresses appreciation of the financial aid provided by a NATO postdoctoral research fellowship and thanks F. S. Dainton and other members of the Chemistry Department, and technical and administrative officials at Leeds University for their kindness and assistance during his sabbatical year spent at Leeds University.

Literature Cited

(1) Allen, A. O., "Radiation Chemistry of Water and Aqueous Solutions," Van Nostrand, New York, 1961.
(2) Barb, W. G., Baxendale, J. H., George, P., Hargrave, K. R., *Trans. Faraday Soc.* **47**, 462–500 (1951).
(3) D'Ans, J., Mattner, J., *Angew. Chem.* **64**, 448 (1952).
(4) Duke, F. R., Hass, T. W., *J. Phys. Chem.* **65**, 304 (1961).
(5) Foner, S. N., Hudson, R. L., *J. Chem. Phys.* **23**, 1364 (1955).
(6) Giuliano, C. R., Schwartz, N., Wilmarth, W. K., *J. Phys. Chem.* **63**, 353 (1959).
(7) Kolthoff, I. M., Belcher, R., "Volumetric Analysis," Vol. III, "Titration Methods. Oxidation-Reduction Reactions," 2nd ed., Interscience, New York, 1957.
(8) Kroh, J., Green, B. C., Spinks, J. W. T., *J. Am. Chem. Soc.* **83**, 2201 (1961).
(9) Latimer, W. M., "Oxidation Potentials," Prentice-Hall, New York, 1952.
(10) Saito, E., Bielski, B. H., *J. Am. Chem. Soc.* **83**, 4467 (1961).
(11) Siegel, S., Baum, L. H., Skolnik, S., Fluornoy, J. M., *J. Chem. Phys.* **32**, 1249 (1960).
(12) Taube, H., *J. Am. Chem. Soc.* **64**, 2469 (1942).
(13) Taso, M. S., Wilmarth, W. K., *Discussions Faraday Soc.* **1960**, 137.
(14) Tsao, M. S., Wilmarth, W. K., *J. Phys. Chem.* **63**, 346 (1959).
(15) Volman, D. H., Chen, J. C., *J. Am. Chem. Soc.* **81**, 4141 (1959).
(16) Weiss, J., *Trans. Faraday Soc.* **31**, 668 (1935).
(17) Wiberg, K. B., *J. Am. Chem. Soc.* **81**, 253 (1959).

RECEIVED April 30, 1962.

12

The Difluoramino Radical

FREDERIC A. JOHNSON

Redstone Arsenal Research Division, Rohm & Haas Co., Huntsville, Ala.

Results of studies of the tetrafluorohydrazine-difluoramino radical equilibrium ($N_2F_4 \rightleftarrows 2$ NF_2) are reviewed; good agreement of the four diverse methods indicates $\Delta H^{298} = 20.0 \pm 1.0$ kcal. A detailed analysis of the NF_2 infrared spectrum has established the F-N-F angle as about 104°. Various other properties of the difluoramino radical which have been studied include the mass spectrum and ionization potential, the broad unresolved EPR spectrum, and the ultraviolet spectrum. Reactions leading to the inorganic products HNF_2, $ClNF_2$, and $ONNF_2$ are summarized, with such discussion of the equilibria with Cl_2 and NO as the limited data permit.

During the past few years the dissociation of tetrafluorohydrazine (N_2F_4) into difluoramino free radicals (NF_2) has been studied intensively. Reactions of NF_2 have also been reported. A review of the published material on these subjects would appear to be in order.

The dissociation of N_2F_4 into NF_2 has been the subject of a number of recent papers (5, 9, 11, 19). Four independent methods of investigation were used; the summarized results are shown in Table I.

Table I. Dissociation of N_2F_4

Method	ΔH, Kcal.	ΔS, E.U.	K_p, 25°C.
Ultraviolet spectra (11)	21.8 ± 2	45 ± 5	8.8 × 10⁻⁷
$\left(\frac{\partial P}{\partial T}\right)_v$ (11)	19.9 ± 0.5	40 ± 2	1.2 × 10⁻⁶ (extrap.)
EPR (19)	19.3 ± 1	—	—
Mass spectra (9)	21.9 + 1.5	—	—
	20.0 ± 1		

The agreement of the enthalpy changes found by such diverse methods is gratifying and surely indicates that the true value is within the indicated range. The K_p values are also in good agreement, considering the extremes of pressure and temperature under which they were determined.

The figures given indicate that the radical is present at room temperature and 1-atm. pressure to the extent of only 0.05%. The radical concentration reaches 90% only at 300° C. and 1 atm., at 150° C. and 1 mm., or at 25° C. and 10^{-10} atm. It is not practical to obtain a large enough concentration of NF_2 for the usual methods of characterization. Modern methods of spectral investigation, however, are applicable and fruitful here.

Mass spectra of N_2F_4 (5, 9) show clearly that the main species present under ionizing chamber conditions—i.e., 10^{-8} mm. and 175° C.— is the radical (NF_2). The radical molecular weight of 52 is, of course, obtained directly in mass spectral work; the parent ion of N_2F_4 is observed only in molecular beams or with an unheated ionization section. The existence of this equilibrium ($N_2F_4 \rightleftarrows 2NF_2$) caused some initial misinterpretation of electron impact data, but good agreement now exists among the studies of Loughran and Mader (15), Herron and Dibeler (9), and Kennedy, Colburn, and Johnson (5, 11, 13). An ionization potential of 11.8 e.v. is found for NF_2 (11, 15). The average bond strengths of the two NF bonds in NF_2 is 70 kcal. from the heat of formation (1) of N_2F_4 and the N—N bond dissociation energy (11). In lieu of further experimental results, $D(F-NF)$ and $D(N-F)$ are now assumed (13) to be equal to the 70 kcal. average.

The electron paramagnetic resonance (EPR) spectra (19) indicate a single unpaired electron, as expected, in NF_2. The absorption band is broad and featureless, although fine structure might be expected from interaction with the N^{14} nuclei, as well as with molecular rotational levels. The cause of the lack of structure is found in the relatively high pressure and temperature of this study (40 mm. and above 80° C.). There would appear to be little hope of more detailed EPR data on this molecule except possibly in matrix studies, since good concentration necessitates either high pressure or high temperature, both of which are incompatible with maximum resolution. The fact that no signal is observed under conditions where sufficient numbers of radicals are present for studies of other species is due to the extreme broadness of the line (104 gauss), whereas many radicals have line widths of the order of 10 gauss. For NH_2 the coupling of 24 gauss to H^1 is about twice that to N^{14} (3). In other systems fluorine couplings are generally larger than those to hydrogen. The 104-gauss line width is reasonable, therefore, as is the large g value of 2.010 arising from the same strong interaction.

Investigation of the infrared spectra of NF_2 by Harmony, Meyers, Schoen, Lide, and Mann (8) and Johnson and Colburn (10) gives some details of the structure of the radical. Fundamental bands are found at 930 and 1074 cm.$^{-1}$; these are two of the three infrared active bands expected for the molecule. One of the reviewers kindly furnished the information that R. T. Myers has observed the third fundamental band recently at 575 cm.$^{-1}$ From the 4-cm.$^{-1}$ spacing of rotational levels in the 1074-cm.$^{-1}$ band (symmetric stretch) Harmony et al. (8) derive a bond angle of 104.2° using an assumed bond length of 1.37 A. (as found in NF_3). By analogy with OF_2, which has been extensively analyzed by Bernstein and Powling (2), a third fundamental at 510 cm.$^{-1}$ was estimated.

The ultraviolet spectrum (11) of NF_2 consists of a band at 260 mμ with a width of 20 mμ at half height. The poorly resolved vibrational spacing is approximately 370 cm.$^{-1}$, probably corresponding to the "scissors" frequency of the excited vibrational state. The lack of resolution is due in part to significant absorption by the first excited vibrational state of the ground electronic state—this participation of excited vibrational states is due to the low scissors frequency of NF_2, which requires some 9% of the molecules to be in vibrationally excited states at 25° C. From the band area an oscillator strength of 0.003 is calculated (16), indicating a forbidden transition. The generally symmetric shape of the band— i.e., with no band origin—is also indicative of a forbidden transition. The band is due without doubt to the nitrogen nonbonding pair or to the odd electron, rather than the N—F bonding electrons or fluorine nonbonding electrons. The band may be due to a n_N-σ^* transition such as appears from 200 to 250 mμ in amines, but the presence of the unpaired electron probably makes this assignment an over-simplification.

The reported reactions of NF$_2$ which yield inorganic products are few—three in fact. Of these, two are known to be equilibria: the reactions with NO and Cl$_2$. The third reaction to give HNF$_2$ will be discussed last.

Nitrosodifluoramine

Nitric oxide and tetrafluorohydrazine react to give nitrosodifluoramine (4). This blue-violet compound is responsible for the color of condensed N$_2$F$_4$ as handled by the usual vacuum techniques in glass systems. Its formation in the condensed state is favored by a high concentration of NF$_2$ radicals in the gas phase prior to condensation. If N$_2$F$_4$ is condensed from low pressures and temperatures near 25° C., as little as 0.1% of NO gives a deep color to the solid N$_2$F$_4$. However, if the same sample is chilled prior to condensation by passage through a cold coil or by the addition of helium which prevents rapid condensation, the NF$_2$ radicals recombine and only N$_2$F$_4$ and NO are deposited.

Nitrosodifluoramine is stable indefinitely at −160° C., but appears to decompose above −140° C. The mode of reaction appears to involve vaporization, then decomposition in the gas phase with subsequent recondensation of N$_2$F$_4$.

Relatively pure samples can be prepared by condensing at −196° C. a 10 to 1 mixture of NO and N$_2$F$_4$ which has been passed through a hot capillary. The combination of expansion and residual cold NO gas ensures that the gas mixture cools so rapidly that the weak NO—NF$_2$ bond persists when formed. The excess NO can then be pumped off at −183° C., leaving a nearly black solid. On warming, the NF$_2$ NO decomposes to a 2 to 1 mixture of NO and N$_2$F$_4$.

The F^{19} NMR spectrum of the black liquid at −140° C. shows two absorption peaks. The peak at −5736 cycles downfield from TFA is due to NF$_2$NO; the second peak is due to N$_2$F$_4$ (−5485 cycles from TFA). The initially greater NF$_2$NO peak decreases with time at −80° C., while the N$_2$F$_4$ peak increases.

The visible absorption spectrum of NF$_2$NO has been determined in liquid N$_2$F$_4$ and liquid NF$_3$ at −160° and −196° C., respectively. The absorbance at the 570-mμ maximum was found to be a linear function of nitric oxide concentration when the condensation conditions were such that the NF$_2$ concentration was many times the NO concentration. An absorptivity of NF$_2$NO of 110 liters per mole-cm. at 570 mμ was found. An oscillator strength of 0.001 is calculated for this band. The position of the absorption and the oscillator strength are typical of n_N-π^* nitroso group transitions, as shown by the following comparison.

	Solvent	λ_{max}, A.	ϵ
tert-BuNO	Ether	6650	20
CF$_3$—NO	Vapor	6925	24
(CH$_3$)$_2$N—NO	Ethyl alcohol	3610	125
F$_2$N—NO	N$_2$F$_4$, −160° C.	5700	(110)

The equilibrium 2 NO + N$_2$F$_4$ $\rightleftarrows$ 2 NF$_2$NO exists in the gas phase. At 25° C. and slightly elevated pressures, enough NF$_2$NO is present to color the mixture a pronounced blue. Higher pressures favor the formation of NF_2NO, but no quantitative data have appeared.

Chlorodifluoramine

This compound was first prepared by Petry (18), Redstone Research Division, Rohm and Haas Co. Impure $ClNF_2$ was obtained in fair yield by warming a condensed mixture of difluoramine (HNF_2) and boron trichloride. An addition compound stable at $-78°$ C. appears to be formed, which reacts on further warming to give a complicated gas mixture. Purified $ClNF_2$ has a melting point between $-196°$ and $-183°$, the boiling points of N_2 and O_2. The vapor pressure curve is described by the equation

$$\log P_{mm} = -950/T + 7.478$$

with an extrapolated boiling point of $-67°$ C. From the vapor pressure equation a heat of vaporization of 4350 cal. per mole is found; the related Trouton constant is 21.0.

The F^{19} nuclear magnetic resonance spectrum shows a single peak at 8685 cycles below TFA used as an external standard.

The ultraviolet spectrum exhibits absorption beginning at 3000 A. and increasing continuously to the limit of the instrument at 2000 A. The infrared shows bands at 10.5, 11.3, and 14.2 microns. The two strong bands at 10.5 and 11.3 microns probably represent the symmetric and asymmetric N—F stretching vibrations, although no definitive study has yet appeared.

The interesting equilibrium:

$$Cl_2 + N_2F_4 \underset{}{\overset{h\nu}{\rightleftharpoons}} 2\ NF_2Cl$$

is established photochemically at $25°$ C. The photoequilibrium constant is approximately 1×10^{-3}; however, this is not the true K_p, since Cl_2 and NF_2Cl are excited by the light used. At $25°$ C. the rates of reaction in the absence of light are slow and $ClNF_2$ can be stored in borosilicate glass; even at $120°$ C. little decomposition is noted over short periods. Presumably at higher temperatures the equilibrium exists as a consequence of faster formation and decomposition reactions, but no data are available on this point.

The only reported reactions of $ClNF_2$ are with Hg at $25°$ C. to give Hg_2Cl_2 and N_2F_2 quantitatively and with HgR_2 to give $RHgCl$, RCl, N_2F_4, and RNF_2.

Difluoramine

At room temperature and above, the difluoramino radical can abstract a hydrogen atom from hydrogen donors. The original preparation of difluoramine (12) was from arsine and tetrafluorohydrazine at $50°$ C. However, the reaction was treacherous, apparently as a result of catalysis by metallic arsenic. A much more satisfactory preparation, due to Freeman (6), from tetrafluorohydrazine and thiophenol at $50°$ C. gives a 75% yield of the difluoramine:

$$N_2F_4 + 2\ HS\varphi \rightarrow 2\ HNF_2 + \varphi SS\varphi$$

Aliphatic mercaptans also give HNF_2, but the reaction is not as clean and much N_2F_4 is reduced to N_2.

Recently an interesting route to HNF_2 has been given by Grakauskas (7). Fluorination of aqueous solutions of urea yields unsymmetrical difluorourea, which is hydrolyzed by sulfuric acid to give HNF_2 in very high yield.

Two fluorinations which produce HNF_2 directly are (1) the direct fluorination of urea at 0° C. and subsequent distillation of the corrosive liquid produced, which gives up to 15% yields of HNF_2 as reported by Lawton and Weber (*14*), and (2) the direct fluorination of excess ammonia with a packed reactor which gives complex mixture containing small amounts of HNF_2 as reported by Morrow (*17*) and coworkers.

The molecular weight of HNF_2 is 53 as established by mass spectral methods. The vapor pressures are described by the equation

$$\log P_{mm} = -1298/T + 8.072$$

The extrapolated boiling point is −23° C. The melting point has been given as −116° C. by Lawton and Weber (*14*). The critical temperature is 130° C.

The infrared spectrum of HNF_2 has strong bands at 7.0, 7.8, 10.2, and 11.2 microns. The bands at 10.2 and 11.2 microns appear to be the symmetric and asymmetric NF stretching vibrations. It is curious that the N−H stretching vibration which is expected near 4 microns does not appear in the spectra of HNF_2 gas.

The proton NMR (*12*) consists of a triplet, as expected for splitting by the sum of two identical fluorines. The band center is 6 cycles above benzene as external standard. The splitting is about 24 cycles. The F^{19} spectrum consists of a doublet which results from coupling with the hydrogen.

Literature Cited

(1) Armstrong, G. T., Marantz, S., Coyle, F., Natl. Bur. Standards Rept. **6584** (1959).
(2) Bernstein, H. J., Powling, J., *J. Chem. Phys.* **18**, 685 (1950).
(3) Cochran, E. L., Fourth International Symposium on Free Radical Stabilization, 1959 (**D-I-I**, Natl. Bur. Standards, Washington, D. C.).
(4) Colburn, C. B., *Advan. Fluorine Chem.* **3**, 88 (1962).
(5) Colburn, C. B., Johnson, F. A., *J. Chem. Phys.* **33**, 1869 (1960).
(6) Freeman, J. P., Kennedy, A., Colburn, C. B., *J. Am. Chem. Soc.* **82**, 5304 (1960).
(7) Grakauskas, V., Abstracts of Papers, 140th Meeting, ACS, Chicago, Ill., 1961, p. 23M.
(8) Harmony, M. D., Myers, R. J., Schoen, L. J., Lide, D. R., Jr., Mann, D. E., *J. Chem. Phys.* **35**, 1129 (1961).
(9) Herron, J. T., Dibeler, V. H., *Ibid.*, **35**, 747 (1961).
(10) Johnson, F. A., Colburn, C. B., *Inorg. Chem.*, in press.
(11) Johnson, F. A., Colburn, C. B., *J. Am. Chem. Soc.* **83**, 3043 (1961).
(12) Kennedy, A., Colburn, C. B., *Ibid.*, **82**, 2906 (1959).
(13) Kennedy, A., Colburn, C. B., *J. Chem. Phys.* **35**, 1892 (1961).
(14) Lawton, E. A., Weber, J. Q., *J. Am. Chem. Soc.* **81**, 4755 (1959).
(15) Loughran, E. D., Mader, C., *J. Chem. Phys.* **32**, 1578 (1960).
(16) Mason, S. F., *Quart. Rev.* **15**, 287 (1961).
(17) Morrow, S. I., Perry, D. D., Cohen, M. S., Schoenfelder, C., *J. Am. Chem. Soc.* **82**, 5301 (1960).
(18) Petry, R. C., *Ibid.*, **82**, 2400 (1960).
(19) Piette, L., Johnson, F. A., Booman, K. A., Colburn, C. B., *J. Chem. Phys.* **35**, 1481 (1961).

RECEIVED April 30, 1962. Work carried out under contract DA-01-021-ORD-11878.

13

Radical Reactions of Tetrafluorohydrazine

JEREMIAH P. FREEMAN

Redstone Arsenal Research Division, Rohm & Haas Co., Huntsville, Ala.

Tetrafluorohydrazine, N_2F_4, undergoes a variety of free radical reactions, including hydrogen abstraction to form difluoramine and coupling reactions to form inorganic and organic difluoramines. Nuclear magnetic resonance data on these difluoramines demonstrate the utility of this analytical tool in investigations in this field.

The remarkable stability of the difluoramino radical which has recently been established quantitatively (8, 14) was presaged by its early chemistry. In retrospect it is apparent that the formation of tetrafluorohydrazine from nitrogen trifluoride under hot tube conditions (4) involved the formation of the difluoramino radical, from which it is more difficult to remove another fluorine than from nitrogen trifluoride. At the time of the original synthesis, however, it could only be marveled at that N_2F_4, a compound much closer to nitrogen than NF_3, would survive conditions that decomposed the latter.

It was also observed that N_2F_4 decomposed in moist air to produce various nitrogen oxides. The origin of this reaction is undoubtedly the coupling of difluoramino radicals with oxygen, since undissociated N_2F_4 should be unaffected by air.

Finally, the remarkable conversion of "wet" nitrogen trifluoride to difluoramine (9) over hot arsenic, followed by the discovery that arsine was the hydrogen transfer agent (7), suggested that a radical abstraction reaction was occurring in the hot tube. In confirmation of this hypothesis a dependable method for the synthesis of difluoramine was found in the reaction of N_2F_4 with mercaptans (7), which are known to be good hydrogen atom sources.

$$2NF_2\cdot + 2RSH \rightarrow 2HNF_2 + 2RS\cdot$$
$$\downarrow RSSR$$

Difluoramino radicals also abstract hydrogen from aliphatic aldehydes to produce difluoramine. In addition, the acyl radical thus generated couples with an NF_2 radical to produce a new class of organic compounds, the N,N-difluoramides (13):

$$RCHO + \cdot NF_2 \rightarrow RCO\cdot + HNF_2$$

$$RCO\cdot + \cdot NF_2 \rightarrow RCONF_2$$

Difluoramino radicals combine with a variety of other radicals, with the product stability apparently directly related to the stability of the substrate radical. For instance, nitric oxide and NF_2 form a compound, difluoronitrosamine, only at low temperatures (3); at room temperature and atmospheric pressure the two radicals do not interact. Chlorine and N_2F_4 react under the influence of ultraviolet light to produce chlorodifluoramine, $ClNF_2$ (13). The equilibrium reaction is favored by high concentrations of chlorine and by high temperature (80° C). Because of this unfavorable equilibrium, the reaction of difluoramine and boron trichloride provides a more satisfactory route to chlorodifluoramine (11).

Alkyl radicals also react with N_2F_4. Methyl- and ethyldifluoramine have been prepared by the irradiation of the corresponding iodides with ultraviolet light in the presence of N_2F_4 (5). Similarly, thermal decomposition of azo compounds may be used as a source of alkyl radicals.

$$RI + NF_2 \rightarrow RNF_2 + I$$

α-Difluoraminoisobutyronitrile (I) and *tert*-butyldifluoramine (II) have been prepared from the corresponding azo compounds (13). Hexaphenylethane may be converted to trityldifluoramine with N_2F_4. These organodifluoramines show no tendency to dissociate to the parent radicals.

$$(CH_3)_2C(CN)NF_2 \qquad\qquad (CH_3)_3CNF_2$$
$$\text{I} \qquad\qquad\qquad\qquad \text{II}$$

A new class of organic NF compounds, N-fluoroazoxy compounds, has recently been reported. Trifluoronitrosomethane reacts with N_2F_4 under the influence of light or heat to form N-fluoro-N'-trifluoromethyldiazine-N'-oxide (III) (6). A free radical mechanism for the reaction was proposed and it was sug-

$$CF_3NO + NF_2 \rightarrow CF_3\overset{\displaystyle O}{\overset{\displaystyle \uparrow}{N}}{=}NF + [F]$$
$$\text{III}$$

gested that the reaction would be a general one. Considerable use of NMR spectroscopy was made to establish the structure of this unusual compound.

Additional chemical evidence for the free radical character of N_2F_4 is provided by the disclosure that it acts as an initiator in free radical chain reactions and may be used as a polymerization catalyst (1).

Table I. H[1] and F[19] NMR Spectra of Nitrogen-Fluorine Compounds

(40 mc.)

Compound	$F^{19}(C./S.)^a$	$H^1(C./S.)^b$
NF_3 (10)	-8760 (triplet, $J = 160$ c./s.)	
NF_2Cl (12)	-8685 (broad)	—
N_2F_4 (4)	-5360 (broad)	
HNF_2 (9)	-2900 (doublet, $J = 24$ c./s.)	$+6$ (triplet, $J = 24c/s.$)
$CH_3\overset{\displaystyle O}{\overset{\displaystyle \|}{C}}NF_2$ (13)	-4270 (broad)	$+190$ (triplet, $J = 2c./s.$)
$(CH_3)_3CNF_2$ (13)	-4220 (broad)	$+224$ (triplet, $J = 2c./s.$)
$(CH_3)_2C(CN)NF_2$ (13)	-4724 (broad)	$+204$ (triplet, $J = 2c./s.$)
$(C_6H_5)_3CNF_2$ (13)	-4432 (singlet)	-24 (singlet)
$CF_3CF_2CF_2NF_2$ (11)	-3680 (broad)	
$CF_3\overset{\displaystyle O}{\overset{\displaystyle \uparrow}{N}}{=}NF$	-4748 (broad)	

a Measured in cycles per second from trifluoroacetic acid standard.
b Measured in cycles per second from benzene standard.

Chlorodifluoramine reacts with organomercurials to produce organodifluoramines (2). The mechanism of these reactions is obscure but may involve free radicals—for example, treatment of diethyl- or di-*n*-butylmercury with chlorodifluoramine produces ethyl- and butyldifluoramine, respectively. These reactions were suggested by the reaction of NF_2Cl with mercury itself, which produces mercurous chloride and N_2F_4 (12).

The discovery of tetrafluorohydrazine and of its dissociation into difluoramino free radicals has opened a new area of both organic and inorganic chemistry. On the basis of the chemistry so far reported it may be assumed that a wide variety of fluoronitrogen compounds will soon be available for chemical investigation.

Since nuclear magnetic resonance spectroscopy has proved to be an almost indispensable tool in these investigations, some of the data so far accumulated are summarized in Table I.

Safety

The known instability of haloamines should urge caution in investigations in this field. Reference should be made to the warnings contained in the original articles to avoid unnecessary trouble.

Acknowledgment

We are indebted to the Ordnance Corps of the Army for support for this work. Inspiration to work in the general area of fluoronitrogen chemistry was provided by Warren D. Niederhauser.

Literature Cited

(1) Cleaver, C. S., U. S. Patent 2,963,468 (Dec. 6, 1960).
(2) Colburn, C. B., in "Advances in Fluorine Chemistry," by M. Stacey, J. C. Tatlow, and A. G. Sharpe, Vol. III, Butterworths, Washington, D. C., 1962.
(3) Colburn, C. B., Johnson, F. A., *Inorg. Chem.*, in press.
(4) Colburn, C. B., Kennedy, A., *J. Am. Chem. Soc.* **80**, 5004 (1958).
(5) Frazer, J. W., *J. Inorg. Nucl. Chem.* **16**, 23 (1960).
(6) Frazer, J. W., Holder, B. E., Worden, E. F., *Ibid.*, **24**, 45 (1962).
(7) Freeman, J. P., Kennedy, A., Colburn, C. B., *J. Am. Chem. Soc.* **82**, 5304 (1960).
(8) Johnson, F. A., Colburn, C. B., *Ibid.*, **83**, 3043 (1961).
(9) Kennedy, A., Colburn, C. B., *Ibid.*, **81**, 2906 (1959).
(10) Muetterties, E. L., Phillips, W. D., *Ibid.*, **81**, 1084 (1959).
(11) Muller, N., Lauterbur, P. C., Svatos, G. F., *Ibid.*, **79**, 1807 (1957).
(12) Petry, R. C., *Ibid.*, **82**, 2400 (1960).
(13) Petry, R. C., Freeman, J. P., *Ibid.*, **83**, 3912 (1961).
(14) Piette, L. H., Johnson, F. A., Booman, K. A., Colburn, C. B., *J. Chem. Phys.* **35**, 1481 (1961).

RECEIVED April 30, 1962.

The Significance of NO₂ Free Radicals in the Reactions of Dinitrogen Tetroxide and Metal Nitrates

C. C. ADDISON

Department of Chemistry, The University, Nottingham, England

The paper discusses two types of reaction involving metal complexes, and it is postulated that each proceeds by an initial free-radical step. In reactions between metal carbonyls and N_2O_4—NO_2 mixtures, the nature of the product depends upon the phase in which the reaction is carried out. In the liquid phase, where the predominant equilibrium is $N_2O_4 \rightleftarrows NO^+ + NO_3^-$, metal nitrates or carbonyl nitrates are formed; in the gas phase, where the equilibrium is $N_2O_4 \rightleftarrows 2NO_2$, metal nitrites or their derivatives are produced. Reactions of $Mn_2(CO)_{10}$, $Fe(CO)_5$, $Co_2(CO)_8$, and $Ni(CO)_4$ are discussed. Anhydrous metal nitrates in which the nitrate group is covalently bonded to the metal have enhanced reactivity. This is believed to result from the dissociation $M—O—NO_2 \rightarrow M—O•$ $+ NO_2•$. This can explain the solution properties of beryllium nitrates, and the vigorous (even explosive) reaction of anhydrous copper nitrate with diethyl ether.

Many of the published studies on the free-radical reactions of nitrogen dioxide have been concerned with its reactions with organic compounds. The nitrogen dioxide has normally been produced by heating the natural $N_2O_4 - NO_2$ mixtures to such a temperature that a high concentration of the NO_2 species is present.

This paper presents two different aspects of the chemistry of nitrogen dioxide. The first involves the differing products of reactions with metal complexes, depending on whether the reactions are conducted in the liquid or the gas phase. Over a period of several years, reactions of metals, metal oxides, carbonates, halides, and various complexes with liquid dinitrogen tetroxide (alone or diluted with organic solvents) have been studied in the author's laboratories. In all cases, the metal nitrate or some derivative is produced, and nitrites never occur as reaction products. In contrast, volatile metal complexes such as the carbonyls react in the gas phase to yield nitrites or their derivatives. These are believed to result from reaction with NO_2 free radicals. The second aspect involves the unexpectedly high reactivity of some simple metal nitrates in which the nitrate group is linked by strong covalent bonds to the metal. These can be interpreted on the assumption that NO_2 free radicals are produced by decomposition of the nitrate, though the mechanisms proposed are still largely speculative. Before the experimental evidence is presented, relevant aspects of the chemistry of nitrogen dioxide are discussed.

NO_2 Free Radical

The nitrogen dioxide molecule has 17 valency electrons, and its physical properties are consistent with those expected for an odd-electron molecule. It is paramagnetic, and a volume susceptibility of 3×10^{-15} c.g.s. unit (39) agrees with a predicted magnetic moment due to one electron only (54). NO_2 is a bent molecule, with bond length 1.188 A. and bond angle 134° (23, 46). Its dipole moment has been determined from measurements on N_2O_4 — NO_2 mixtures; assuming the tetroxide to have zero moment, the dipole moment of NO_2 depends on temperature, varying from 0.3 D at 125° to 0.58 D at 25° (9, 57). The odd electron is believed to be localized largely on the nitrogen atom, which has been related with its dimerization and its ability to add as a nitro group to unsaturated systems (55). A value of 9.91 e.v. has been quoted for the ionization potential (41); loss of one electron gives the linear NO_2^+ ion. The thermal dissociation

$$2NO_2 \rightarrow 2NO + O_2$$

begins at 150°, and is complete at 600°.

As an odd-electron molecule, many of the reactions of nitrogen dioxide are typical of free radicals. This applies particularly to its association with atoms such as, H, F, and Cl or other radicals such as, the OH, NO, alkyl, and alkoxy radicals; its addition reactions with unsaturated systems such as, olefins, acetylenes, and aromatic compounds, and its hydrogen abstraction reactions. The ability of the NO_2 free radical to abstract hydrogen from an organic molecule:

$$RH + NO_2 \rightarrow R\cdot + HONO$$

is the first step in many of its reactions with saturated organic compounds. This step may be succeeded by oxidation or nitration of the alkyl radical. The ease with which hydrogen abstraction occurs depends on the strength of the R-H bond; for paraffins and aldehydes this is represented by the series

$$-CH_3 \Big\rangle -CH_2- \Big\rangle -\overset{|}{\underset{|}{C}}H \Big\rangle R-\overset{H}{\underset{|}{C}} = O$$

It is therefore the strengths of the C — H bonds in the molecule which primarily determine the nature of the reaction product, and the temperature at which gas phase nitration or oxidation by NO_2 can be carried out. These reactions have been summarized in an excellent review by Gray and Yoffe (34).

Any study involving the reactivity, or mechanism of reaction, of NO_2 must of necessity take into account its possible conversion, before reaction, into any one of a number of closely related species such as N_2O_4, NO_2^+, or NO_2^-, and it is this feature which has rendered difficult the interpretation of its reactions. The investigation of the addition of dinitrogen tetroxide to olefinic double bonds gives a typical illustration of the difficulties encountered. In 1946 Levy and Scaife (43) observed that N_2O_4, in weakly basic solvents such as ether, reacted with olefins and that dinitroalkanes and nitronitrites were the main products. These reactions as they were developed between 1946 and 1949 (18) were interpreted on the basis that N_2O_4 suffers heterolytic dissociation to NO_2^+ and NO_2^- ions; the initial step was the attachment of NO_2^+ to the unsaturated center, the NO_2^- then attaching to the second carbon atom through an oxygen or a nitrogen atom. This proposal was based largely on the directive influence of unsymmetrical olefins, and the effect of solvents, and was supported by Ingold and Ingold in 1947 (40). In 1954, Addison (1) pointed out that the N_2O_4 molecule gives 1 to 1 addition compounds with aromatic hydrocarbons (11) in which partial electron transfer occurs by overlap of π orbitals. It was suggested that the formation of an olefin–N_2O_4 addition compound might be the initial step in the reaction, followed by fission of the $N - N$ bond in the tetroxide. In 1953, Shechter and Conrad (48) found that the products of the dinitrogen tetroxide–methyl acrylate reaction could not be explained on the basis of heterolytic addition, and postulated that initial attack was by the neutral NO_2 radical. In work extending until 1958, this has been shown to be the correct mechanism. Reactions have been carried out in the presence of nitryl chloride (49), nitrosyl chloride, chlorine, bromotrichloromethane (21), and iodine (53); the intermediate nitroalkyl radical is trapped, and nitro-halides are produced. There is now little doubt that the active species in this reaction is the NO_2 free radical, but the experiments on which this final conclusion is now based extended over a period of 12 years!

Associated Species

The over-all equilibrium is expressed by the equations

$$N_2O_4 \rightleftharpoons NO_2\cdot + NO_2\cdot \tag{1}$$

$$N_2O_4 \rightleftharpoons NO_2^+ + NO_2^- \tag{2}$$

$$N_2O_4 \rightleftharpoons NO^+ + NO_3^- \tag{3}$$

Added to this, there is the dissociation

$$2NO_2 \rightarrow 2NO + O_2 \tag{4}$$

at higher temperatures, which introduces the closely related free radical NO into the system, so that there are altogether seven nitrogen-containing species to be taken into consideration. The position is less complicated, however, than would appear from these equations, since the number of available species is limited by experimental conditions. The solid consists of N_2O_4 molecules only, and is color-less and diamagnetic.

Liquid State. Liquid dinitrogen tetroxide is complex in character. The pale yellow liquid at the freezing point ($-11.2°$ C.) contains 0.01% of nitrogen dioxide; this increases with temperature, and the deep red-brown liquid at the boiling point ($21.15°$ C.) contains 0.1% of nitrogen dioxide (33, 52, 56). The position of the equilibrium (Equation 1) is influenced by solvents used to dilute the tetroxide, and electron-donor solvents which form addition compounds with dinitrogen tetroxide move the equilibrium towards the undissociated tetroxide (12). Thus, for a given concentration of tetroxide, nitrogen dioxide coloration is strongest in paraffins, carbon tetrachloride, and chloroform, whereas ethyl acetate and dioxane solutions are only faintly colored. It is reasonable to assume that the partial electron transfer to the tetroxide which occurs in these mixtures, and which is known to influence its chemical reactions (13), should also restrict its homolytic dissociation.

The actual mode of dimerization of the NO_2 radical is an unsolved problem which continues to attract attention. In both the solid (22) and vapor (50) states, the dimer N_2O_4 is found to be planar, and the entropy and free energy functions are not compatible with free rotation (*20, 25, 31*). The fact that the two NO_2 units do not rotate with respect to one another, in spite of the long $N - N$ bond (1.75 A.), indicates that this bond is of a very unusual type. It cannot be regarded as a simple σ-bond, and must have some multiple-bond character. An attractive concept has recently been developed which considers the $N - N$ bond as a new type of "π-only" bond, or a fractional π-bond, possessing no sigma character (*24, 26, 35*).

It is a surprising fact that the species NO_2^+ and NO_2^- (Equation 2) have never been recognized as free ions in liquid dinitrogen tetroxide, although the latter would appear to dissociate heterolytically in its addition compounds with strong electron acceptors. The 1 to 1 addition compound with boron trifluoride has been shown to have the structure $NO_2^+[BF_3.NO_2]^-$, and its powerful nitrating properties are consistent with the presence of the NO_2^+ ion (*17, 51*).

Dissociation into NO^+ and NO_3^- ions (Equation 3) is well established, and explains the reactions of liquid $N_2O_4 - NO_2$ mixtures with metals, salts, complexes, etc., and solvolysis also occurs on this basis. The extent of dissociation increases with the dielectric constant of the medium, and is complete in solutions in pure nitric acid (*32*). In the liquid tetroxide alone, the difference between the molar polarization and molar reactivity is greater than can be accounted for by the NO_2 present, and the presence of a small concentration of $[NO^+][NO_3^-]$ ion pairs has been suggested (*2*). These species cannot be produced in a single step, and there are two theories as to how they might be formed. The first involves heterolytic dissociation to NO_2^+ and NO_2^-, followed by oxygen atom transfer. The second (and perhaps the more feasible) involves the NO_2 radical. These dimerize, in the main, to give a dimer having structure I. However, they may also dimerize to a very small degree to a dimer having structure II (*44*), or structure III which has been observed in nitrogen dioxide trapped at liquid helium temperatures (*27*); structures II and III can then dissociate directly to NO^+ and NO_3^-.

It will be clear from the above that in the liquid state there exists the greatest number of closely related species, and reactions in the liquid state are consequently the most difficult to interpret. The particular species which reacts is determined by the chemical nature of the reactant concerned.

Vapor State. Here the situation is much simpler. Ionic species are no longer present, and in the absence of nitric oxide the choice lies merely between nitrogen dioxide and dinitrogen tetroxide. The proportions vary very much with temperature; at 21.15° C., the tetroxide is 15.9% dissociated, whereas dissociation to NO_2 is complete at 140°. It does not necessarily follow, however, that reaction at low temperatures involves dinitrogen tetroxide, as reaction with olefins clearly shows.

Reactions with Metal Carbonyls

Dimanganese Decacarbonyl. This reaction should be described first, since no replacement of carbonyl groups is involved. When solutions of dimanganese decacarbonyl and of dinitrogen tetroxide in light petroleum at 0° C. are mixed, the solution becomes deep orange. Within 30 minutes precipitation begins, and continues for 30 to 40 hours. The product is a yellow powder, and its infrared spectrum shows it to consist of the nitratocarbonyl, $Mn(CO)_5NO_3$, the nitro-carbonyl, $Mn(CO)_5NO_2$, with a trace of the nitritocarbonyl, $Mn(CO)_5ONO$. The nitrato and nitro compounds were isolated by extraction into chloroform, in which the nitro compound is less soluble, and are obtained in similar amounts by this method (8). The first step in this reaction must involve the fission of the Mn-Mn bond in $Mn_2(CO)_{10}$, and there is every reason for believing that the nitro compound is formed by direct attachment of the NO_2 free radical—i.e.,

$$Mn_2(CO)_{10} \rightarrow 2(CO)_5Mn\cdot$$

$$(CO)_5Mn\cdot + NO_2\cdot \rightarrow (CO)_5MnNO_2$$

By analogy with its reactions with organic compounds, the NO_2 radical would be expected to add as a nitro group forming the Mn-N rather than the Mn-O bond. The remaining $(CO)_5Mn\cdot$ radical should react with NO_2 to give predominantly the nitro compound also; in fact, only a trace of the nitrite $Mn(CO)_5$-ONO is observed.

The nitrato product can be formed by one of two routes. One possibility is the oxidation of $Mn(CO_5)NO_2$ by excess N_2O_4. In this case, however, the green color of N_2O_3 should be observed in the liquid at 0°, and this was not the case. It is assumed therefore that the formation of the nitrate is the result of heterolytic dissociation of the tetroxide,

$$Mn_2(CO)_{10} + NO^+NO_3^- \rightarrow Mn(CO)_5NO_3 + Mn(CO)_x(NO)_y$$

The nitrosyl carbonyl has not been identified, but crude products contain infrared absorption bands which have been attributed to such a compound.

To obtain further evidence for the reaction scheme outlined above, the reaction has been carried out in the gas phase (7). Dimanganese decacarbonyl vapor and dinitrogen tetroxide were mixed at 60° C. A smoke was formed immediately the gases came into contact, which settled to a very pale yellow powder. This was the nitro compound, $Mn(CO)_5NO_2$, containing only a trace of the nitrate, which may well have been formed by oxidation of the nitro compound under these conditions. The increased yield of $Mn(CO)_5NO_2$ in the gas as compared with the liquid state is consistent with the free-radical interpretation, since heterolytic dissociation of the tetroxide is no longer possible.

Detailed discussion of the properties of $Mn(CO)_5NO_2$ is outside the scope of this paper. It is of interest, however, that when heated at 65° under a vacuum, the compound sublimes, and the product appears from its infrared spectrum to be a mixture of nitro and nitrito complexes. Some conversion of the Mn-NO₂ bond to Mn-ONO therefore occurs during the process of vaporization and condensation.

Dicobalt Octacarbonyl. In its reactions with N_2O_4–NO_2, this compound differs from manganese carbonyl in two respects:

At room temperature, all carbonyl groups are removed as carbon monoxide during the course of the reaction.
Products of reaction in the solution and in the vapor state are different.

When $Co_2(CO)_8$ is added to liquid dinitrogen tetroxide, either as the pure liquid or diluted with organic solvents, a slow reaction occurs and the addition compound $Co(NO_3)_2 \cdot 2N_2O_4$ is precipitated; warming to 100° C. gives the anhydrous nitrate, $Co(NO_3)_2$, and no nitrite has been observed in any product obtained from reactions in the liquid state. In contrast, cobalt carbonyl and dinitrogen tetroxide vapors react on contact to give a gray-brown powder, which is found to be pure cobalt nitrite (*14*).

$$Co_2(CO)_8 + 4NO_2 \rightarrow 2Co(NO_2)_2 + 8CO$$

Again, this reaction would appear to involve attack by the NO_2 free radical. Following the example of manganese carbonyl, the stages in the reaction may well be

$$Co_2(CO)_8 + 2NO_2 \cdot \rightarrow 2Co(CO)_4NO_2$$

$$\downarrow NO_2 \cdot$$

$$Co(CO)_x(NO_2)_2 \xrightarrow{-CO} Co(NO_2)_2$$

This scheme implies addition reactions followed by substitution reactions, but the intermediate stages have not been identified. The NO_2 substitution reactions are no doubt similar in principle to, but rather more complicated than, the reaction between nickel carbonyl and nitrogen dioxide (see below). The structure of the product, and the bonding of the NO_2 groups to the metal, are discussed in connection with the nickel compound, which has been more fully investigated.

Whether or not the nitro or nitrito groups, once introduced into the complex, are compatible with the carbonyl groups appears to depend very much on the transition metal concerned. These reactions provide a route for the preparation of transition metal nitrites; hitherto, silver nitrite has been the only example of this class of compound.

Nickel Carbonyl. Reaction of nickel carbonyl with dinitrogen tetroxide in the liquid state follows that outlined for cobalt carbonyl. No nitrite is observed in the product, which is pure $Ni(NO_3)_2 \cdot 2N_2O_4$; heating gives the anhydrous nitrate. It has been customary to attribute the production of nitrate in this way to the heterolytic dissociation of the tetroxide which is possible in the liquid state. This is certainly true of solvolytic processes—e.g.,

$$NiCl_2 + 2NO^+ \cdot NO_3^- \rightarrow Ni(NO_3)_2 + 2NOCl$$

but the reaction of carbonyls may not necessarily follow this pattern. Anhydrous nickel nitrite, $Ni(NO_2)_2$, is not soluble in liquid dinitrogen tetroxide, but is slowly converted to nickel nitrate in the liquid. In solution in solvents of high dielectric constant (such as dimethylsulfoxide) nickel nitrite is converted immediately to the nitrate. Whether this is a true oxidation

$$Ni(NO_2) + 2N_2O_4 \rightarrow Ni(NO_3)_2 + 2N_2O_3$$

or an anion exchange

$$Ni(NO_2)_2 + 2NO^+ \cdot NO_3^- \rightarrow Ni(NO_3)_2 + 2NO^+ + 2NO_2^-$$

is immaterial, since the existence of the rapid forward reaction means that $Ni(NO_2)_2$ may well be an initial product in the liquid phase reaction. This, therefore, keeps open the possibility that the reaction of nickel carbonyl with dinitrogen tetroxide in the liquid state may be initiated by the NO_2 free radical, as in the case of manganese carbonyl.

No such alternatives exist in the case of the gas phase reaction. All the carbonyl groups are displaced when the gases are mixed at room temperature, and the smoke which is formed settles to a pale green deposit of pure nickel nitrite (*6*). The over-all reaction is therefore

$$Ni(CO)_4 + 2NO_2 \rightarrow Ni(NO_2)_2 + 4CO$$

Kinetic studies on the exchange of radioactive carbon monoxide with nickel carbonyl have shown that the first step in the dissociation may be represented by

$$Ni(CO)_4 \rightarrow Ni(CO)_3 + CO$$

for reactions in solution (*19*), and this is the case in the gas phase also (*29*). Reaction of nickel phosphine carbonyls also involves a similar dissociation mechanism (*45*). The stabilization of the sp^2 triangular plane intermediate, $Ni(CO)_3$, has been attributed to the three strong π orbitals which are available for overlap with the ligand orbitals, as compared with two in the tetrahedral $Ni(CO)_4$ (*42*). This indicates that substitution reactions will occur by an S_{N1} mechanism, and we can envisage the NO_2 radical adding to the three-coordinate intermediate—i.e.,

$$Ni(CO)_3 + NO_2 \cdot \rightarrow Ni(CO)_3NO_2$$

This product will presumably dissociate in the same way as the tetracarbonyl—i.e.,

$$Ni(CO)_3NO_2 \rightarrow Ni(CO)_2NO_2 + CO$$

and further radical addition will occur:

$$Ni(CO)_2NO_2 + NO_2 \cdot \rightarrow Ni(CO)_2(NO_2)_2$$

We may compare this product with the highly unstable nickel carbonyl halides—e.g., $Ni(CO)_2Cl_2$—and it is reasonable to expect that it will decompose:

$$Ni(CO)_2(NO_2)_2 \rightarrow Ni(NO_2)_2 + 2CO$$

The way in which the NO_2 groups are bonded to the metal is now of interest. Although the nickel compound has been referred to above as a nitrite, this is not strictly true. The infrared spectrum of the solid shows NO_2^- bands at 1388, 1333, 1240, and 830 cm.$^{-1}$ In addition, there are strong bands at 1575 cm.$^{-1}$ (as observed for organic nitro compounds, $R-NO_2$) and at 1080 cm.$^{-1}$ (observed only in the case of nitrito-metal bonding $M-O-N=O$). The NO_2 groups are therefore covalently bonded to the metal; the compound is readily soluble in a number of organic solvents, and should be represented formally as nitronitrito-nickel, $Ni(NO_2)(ONO)$.

Iron Pentacarbonyl. In its reactions with liquid dinitrogen tetroxide this compound follows the pattern outlined above, and the remarks on reactions of nickel carbonyl probably apply here also. The solvate, $Fe(NO_3)_3 \cdot N_2O_4$, is produced (*4*). This has the structure $NO^+[Fe(NO_3)_4]^-$ in the solid state; it is volatile without decomposition, and is believed to be a five-coordinate complex, $Fe(NO)(NO_3)_4$, in the vapor state. We have not yet succeeded in isolating the simple trinitrate, $Fe(NO_3)_3$, by removal of N_2O_4.

The gas phase reaction proceeds very much as described for nickel carbonyl, but the product does not contain the nitrite group (*10*). A smoke is formed immediately the gases come into contact, but the analysis and infrared spectrum of the solid formed show it to be the oxide-nitrate $FeO(NO_3)$. It seems likely that initial reaction involves the NO_2 radical, and an iron nitrite such as $Fe(NO_2)_3$ may be produced initially. The oxidation-reduction properties of the ferric and nitrite ions may render them incompatible; $FeO(NO_3)$ would then be left as a decomposition product. So little is known about transition metal nitrites that this must remain conjecture at present, but it may be relevant to recall that it has not yet been possible to isolate pure samples of $Fe(NO_3)_3$, $Al(NO_3)_3$, or $Cr(NO_3)_3$.

Reactions of Covalent Metal Nitrates

Covalent bonding of the nitrate group to a metal atom normally occurs only in the absence of water. Recent work on anhydrous metal nitrates has been concerned with both structure and chemical reactivity and it is now coming to be realized that these two aspects are closely interlinked. Generalizing, we may say that the stronger the covalent bond, the more reactive is the metal nitrate. Furthermore, extreme covalency leads to volatility (as with the volatile copper nitrate) and those nitrates which display volatility are also the most reactive chemically.

Strong covalent bonding of the nitrate group occurs, of course, in the alkyl nitrates, and the dissociation

$$R—O—NO_2 \rightarrow R—O· + NO_2·$$

is an important step in the chemistry (and pyrolysis) of alkyl nitrates. In principle, this dissociation may also occur in a nitrate group covalently bonded to a metal

$$M^{(a)}O^{(b)}NO_2 \rightarrow M—O· + NO_2·$$

Dissociation will occur at bond (a), or bond (b) or at both bonds, depending on the relative strengths of the two bonds. The first indication of dissociation by breaking the O—N bond was obtained with anhydrous beryllium nitrate (16). Anhydrous (ionic) nitrates of barium, strontium, calcium, and magnesium dissolve in pure water to give metal and nitrate ions only. On adding beryllium nitrate to water, brown fumes are evolved and a slight turbidity remains which is clarified by acid. When hydrolyzed in sodium hydroxide solution in a closed system, both nitrate and nitrite ions are produced. Expressed as a percentage of the original beryllium nitrate, the amount of nitrite found in solution was 5%, and this was largely independent of the concentration of sodium hydroxide. The hydrolysis is therefore expressed as follows:

$$Be(NO_3)_2 + H_2O \begin{cases} [BeO_2··] + 2NO_2· \quad (10\%) \\ Be^{2+} + 2NO_3^- \quad (90\%) \end{cases}$$

The NO_2 thus produced will hydrolyze to give equal quantities of nitrate and nitrite. The nature of the beryllium species remaining after fission of the O—N bond has not been investigated; it seems unlikely that both of the NO_3 groups in any one molecule will undergo fission at the O—N bond. The ratio of nitrate to nitrite would indicate, however, that the Be—O and O—N bonds in the unit Be—O—NO_2 must be of comparable strength. In nonaqueous media, such as in ethyl acetate, anhydrous beryllium nitrate dissolves and gives a pale yellow color to the solution. The absorption spectrum of the solution shows this to be nitrogen dioxide.

It is of particular interest to compare the hydrolytic behavior of basic beryllium nitrate, $Be_4O(NO_3)_6$. This compound (15) has the structure which is already well known for basic beryllium acetate; each nitrate group is part of a six-membered ring

The NO_2 group can no longer break away as in the simple nitrate, since two of its oxygen atoms are now bonded to beryllium atoms. This compound hydrolyzes slowly in water, to give nitrate ions only.

It is likely that as further anhydrous nitrates are prepared, further examples of such behavior will be found. Certain ruthenium nitrates also give nitrite on hydrolysis (28). All metal nitrates which by their covalent bonding can release NO_2 radicals during reaction need not necessarily give nitrite on hydrolysis; the latter is a complicated process which involves the coordination chemistry of the metal. For example, copper nitrate gives only nitrate ions in aqueous solution, but its reactions with ethers are at present interpreted on a free-radical basis.

Reaction of Copper Nitrate with Diethyl Ether. When a small amount of anhydrous copper nitrate is added to dry diethyl ether at room temperature, a green solution is obtained. No brown fumes are observed, but an apple-green solid is slowly deposited. However, if a small amount of ether is added to an excess of copper nitrate, reaction is very vigorous. Nitrogen dioxide and acetaldehyde are evolved, and a green solid is again formed which no longer reacts with ether. On one occasion, ether was slowly evaporated from a dilute solution of copper nitrate at 50°. Brown fumes suddenly appeared when the solution became viscous, and this was followed by a violent explosion (16).

This reaction occurs only under conditions in which the strong covalent bonds between copper and the nitrate groups are maintained. Copper nitrate is a covalent monomer in the gas phase (3, 47) and in solution in nonaqueous solvents (5). However, it retains its reactivity towards ether only in those solvents which are weak ligands to the copper atom. If we say for the sake of discussion that copper nitrate dissolves in basic solvents to give a complex of the type

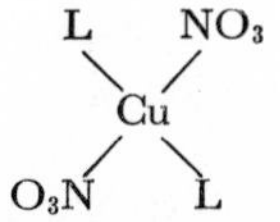

$$
\begin{array}{ccc}
L & & NO_3 \\
 \diagdown & & \diagup \\
 & Cu & \\
 \diagup & & \diagdown \\
O_3N & & L
\end{array}
$$

then the strength of the $Cu-NO_3$ bonds will vary with the solvent, L. When ether vapor is passed into copper nitrate in nitrobenzene, reaction occurs as described above, but when ethyl acetate or methyl cyanide is used as solvent, no reaction occurs. These solvents solvate the copper atom more strongly, and in consequence weaken the $Cu-NO_3$ bond to such a degree that reaction with ether is no longer possible (16). The position is summarized as follows:

$$(NO_3)Cu-O-NO_2 \rightarrow (NO_3)Cu^+ + NO_3^-$$
(in basic solvents; no attack on ether)

$$(NO_3)Cu-O-NO_2 \rightarrow (NO_3)CuO\cdot + NO_2\cdot$$
(the nitrate alone, or in very weakly basic
solvents; ether attacked by $NO_2\cdot$)

The anhydrous nitrate is therefore regarded as a low-temperature source of NO_2 radicals, and it follows, as observed, that the greater the nitrate-ether ratio, the more vigorous should the reaction become. The reaction of NO_2 on the ether is complex, but will include reactions of the type set out in the following scheme:

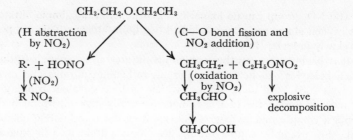

$$CH_3.CH_2.O.CH_2CH_3$$

(H abstraction   (C—O bond fission and
  by NO_2) NO_2 addition)

R· + HONO $CH_3CH_2·$ + $C_2H_5ONO_2$
$\downarrow$ (NO_2) $\downarrow$ (oxidation
R NO_2 $\downarrow$ by NO_2)   explosive
                                   CH_3CHO decomposition

$$CH_3COOH$$

The products of reaction are consistent with this mechanism. The presence of the copper salts has certain advantages so far as interpretation is concerned, since some of the species formed can be trapped out in the insoluble copper compound formed.

The gaseous products have not yet been systematically analyzed. Nitrogen dioxide and acetaldehyde are evolved and nitroalkanes may also be present. The green solid product has a remarkably consistent analysis, corresponding to $Cu_2(OH)(CH_3COO)(NO_3)(NO_2)$, and nuclear magnetic resonance confirms that all the carbon present is in the form of the acetate ion. The decomposition schemes given above indicate that NO_3^- and OH^- ions may result from the $NO_3.Cu.O·$ radical originally produced; nitrite is formed in the course of hydrogen abstraction, and acetate as a result of oxidation.

Reaction of Copper Nitrate with Dimethyl Ether. In sharp contrast to the behavior of diethyl ether, dimethyl ether shows little reactivity with copper nitrate. Dimethyl ether was condensed onto copper nitrate at $-70°$ C.; on warming to $-20°$ C. ether evaporated to leave a pale blue solid which melted to a green oil at $-12°$. This oil was stable up to $50°$ C., and analysis showed it to be a molecular addition compound, $Cu(NO_3)_2.1.5$ Me_2O; on treatment with water the dimethyl ether was evolved. Some decomposition of the addition compound does occur on long standing under vacuum (*16*).

This contrast in behavior can be explained by reference to the high temperature nitration of paraffins and ethers by nitrogen dioxide. With the paraffins, the lowest members are the least reactive of the series (*30, 37*); the higher aliphatic ethers give higher yields of nitro compounds (*38*) and the α-hydrogen atoms are attacked only with difficulty. Therefore if we interpret these copper nitrate reactions on the basis of attack by NO_2 on the ether, there is an obvious difference between the diethyl and dimethyl ethers. On any other mechanism it is difficult to explain the wide difference in reactivity. For example, if dimethyl ether acted as a strong ligand to copper it could prevent reaction by weakening the $Cu-NO_3$ bond, but there is no evidence that its coordinating powers should differ so greatly from those of diethyl ether.

Reaction of Copper Nitrate with Nitromethane. This is the most surprising property so far observed for an anhydrous metal nitrate, especially as nitromethane had previously been regarded as a very satisfactory inert medium for reactions of dinitrogen tetroxide. Solutions of copper nitrate in nitromethane are stable indefinitely at room temperature, but reaction occurs if the solution is kept at the boiling point ($101°$ C.) for some time. On boiling a 0.135M solution for two minutes, the solution suddenly evolves nitrogen dioxide copiously, and a green copper salt is deposited. Molecular weight measurements indicate that the copper nitrate is present as the undissociated monomer at this concentration (*5*). Nitromethane is a good solvent for copper nitrate because of its high dielectric constant, but as a very weak ligand it will not decrease the strength of the $Cu-NO_3$ bond. Conditions are therefore ideal for the dissociation of the nitrate to nitrogen dioxide, and the reaction can also be interpreted on this basis. In the direct gas phase reaction (36) nitromethane is attacked by nitrogen dioxide at 400° to

$$CH_3NO_2 + NO_2 \rightarrow HCHO + HONO + NO$$

500° C. and its reaction with copper nitrate probably proceeds by the same mechanism.

Acknowledgment

The author is indebted to the U. S. Department of the Army for financial assistance for part of the work described in this paper.

Literature Cited

(1) Addison, C. C., Gordon Conference on Inorganic Chemistry, New Hampton, N. H., June 1954.
(2) Addison, C. C., Bolton, H. C., Lewis, J., *J. Chem. Soc.* **1951**, 1294.
(3) Addison, C. C., Hathaway, B. J., *Ibid.*, **1958**, 3099.
(4) Addison, C. C., Hathaway, B. J., Logan, N., *Proc. Chem. Soc.* **1958**, 51.
(5) Addison, C. C., Hathaway, B. J., Logan, N., Walker, A., *J. Chem. Soc.* **1960**, 4308.
(6) Addison, C. C., Johnson, B. F. G., Logan, N., Wojcicki, A., *Proc. Chem. Soc.* **1961**, 306.
(7) Addison, C. C., Kilner, M., unpublished results.
(8) Addison, C. C., Kilner, M., Wojcicki, A., *J. Chem. Soc.* **1961**, 4839.
(9) Addison, C. C., Lewis, J., *Ibid.*, **1953**, 1837.
(10) Addison, C. C., Logan, N., unpublished results.
(11) Addison, C. C., Sheldon, J. C., *J. Chem. Soc.* **1956**, 1941.
(12) *Ibid.*, **1958**, 3142.
(13) Addison, C. C., Sheldon, J. C., Hodge, N., *Ibid.* **1956**, 3900.
(14) Addison, C. C., Sutton, D., unpublished results.
(15) Addison, C. C., Walker, A., *Proc. Chem. Soc.* **1961**, 242.
(16) Addison, C. C., Walker, A., unpublished results.
(17) Bachman, G. B., Feuer, H., Bluestein, B. R., Vogt, C. M., *J. Am. Chem. Soc.* **77**, 6188 (1955).
(18) Baldock, H., Levy, N., Scaife, C. W., *J. Chem. Soc.* **1949**, 2627.
(19) Basolo, F., Wojcicki, A., *J. Am. Chem. Soc.* **83**, 520 (1961).
(20) Bernstein, H. J., Burns, W. G., *Nature* **166**, 1039 (1950).
(21) Brand, J. C. D., Stevens, I. D. R., *J. Chem. Soc.* **1958**, 629.
(22) Broadley, J. S., Robertson, J. M., *Nature* **164**, 915 (1949).
(23) Brown, M., Wilson, M. K., *J. Chem. Phys.* **22**, 955 (1954).
(24) Brown, R. D., Harcourt, R. D., *Proc. Chem. Soc.* **1961**, 216.
(25) Chalvet, O., Daudel, R., *J. Chim. Phys.* **49**, 77 (1952).
(26) Coulson, C. A., Duchesne, J., *Bull. Classe Sci., Acad. Roy. Belg.* **43**, 522 (1957).
(27) Fateley, W. G., Bent, H. A., Crawford, B., *J. Chem. Phys.* **31**, 204 (1959).
(28) Fletcher, J. M., private communication.
(29) Garrett, A. P., Thompson, H. W., *J. Chem. Soc.* **1934**, 1822.
(30) Geiseler, G., *Angew. Chem.* **67**, 270 (1955).
(31) Giauque, W. F., Kemp, J. D., *J. Chem. Phys.* **6**, 40 (1938).
(32) Goulden, J. D. S., Millen, D. J., *J. Chem. Soc.* **1950**, 2620.
(33) Gray, P., Rathbone, P., *Ibid.*, **1958**, 3550.
(34) Gray, P., Yoffe, A. D., *Chem. Revs.* **55**, 1069 (1955).
(35) Green, M., Linnett, J. W., *J. Chem. Soc.* **1960**, 4959; *Trans. Faraday Soc.* **57**, 10 (1961).
(36) Harnsberger, H. F., thesis, University of California, Berkeley, 1951.
(37) Hass, H. B., Dorsky, J., Hodge, E. B., *Ind. Eng. Chem.* **33**, 1138 (1941).
(38) Hass, H. B., Hudgin, D. E., *J. Am. Chem. Soc.* **76**, 2692 (1954).
(39) Havens, G. G., *Phys. Rev.* [2] **41**, 337 (1932).
(40) Ingold, C. K., Ingold, E. H., *Nature* **159**, 743 (1947).
(41) Kandel, R. J., *J. Chem. Phys.* **23**, 84 (1955).
(42) Kimball, G. E., *Ibid.*, **8**, 188 (1940).
(43) Levy, N., Scaife, C. W., *J. Chem. Soc.* **1946**, 1093, 1096, 1100.
(44) Longuet-Higgins, H. C., *Nature* **153**, 408 (1944).
(45) Meriwether, L. S., Fiene, M. L., *J. Am. Chem. Soc.* **81**, 4200 (1959).
(46) Moore, G. E., *J. Opt. Soc. Am.* **43**, 1045 (1953).
(47) Porter, R. F., Schoonmaker, R. C., Addison, C. C., *Proc. Chem. Soc.* **1959**, 11.

(48) Shechter, H., Conrad, F., *J. Am. Chem. Soc.* **75**, 5610 (1953).
(49) Shechter, H., Conrad, F., Dualton, A. L., Kaplan, R. B., *Ibid.*, 74, 3052 (1952).
(50) Smith, D. W., Hedberg, K., *J. Chem. Phys.* **25**, 1282 (1956).
(51) Sprague, R. W., Garrett, A. B., Sisler, H. H., *J. Am. Chem. Soc.* 82, 1059 (1960).
(52) Steese, C. M., Whittaker, H. G., *J. Chem. Phys.* **24**, 776 (1956).
(53) Stevens, T. E., Emmons, W. D., *J. Am. Chem. Soc.* 80, 338 (1958).
(54) Vleck, J. H. Van, "Theory of Electric and Magnetic Susceptibility," p. 275, Oxford Univ. Press, London, 1932.
(55) Walsh, A. D., *J. Chem. Soc.* **1953**, 2266.
(56) Whittaker, A. G., *J. Chem. Phys.* **24**, 780 (1956).
(57) Williams, I. W., Schwingle, C. H., Winning, C. H., *J. Am. Chem. Soc.* **56**, 1427 (1934); **58**, 197 (1936).

RECEIVED May 3, 1962.

15

Reactions of Nitrogen(II) Oxide

RUSSELL S. DRAGO

Chemistry Department, University of Illinois, Urbana, Ill.

The structure, properties, and familiar reactions of nitrogen(II) oxide are reviewed briefly. The discussion is mainly concerned with reactions of basic molecules with NO that give rise to products containing the N_2O_2 group. The reactions of nitric oxide with sulfite ion, ethyl alcohol, amines, and oximes are discussed. These reactions are correlated through a generalized reaction scheme that involves formation of the reactive free radical intermediate BNO, where B is a base. In addition, reactions that involve base attack on nitric oxide but lead to other products are reviewed. These include nitric oxide reactions with phosphorus and sulfur donors and with organic nitrites.

Much of the chemistry of nitrogen(II) oxide, NO, is treated in standard inorganic reference texts or in review articles (*1, 24*). After briefly reviewing this material, our main concern will be with a newly recognized reaction type (*12, 13*) and the application of this concept to the correlation of some interesting reactions.

The various classes of reactions that are commonly treated can be rationalized by a consideration of the structure of nitric oxide which is represented in molecular orbital terminology as:

$$KK\sigma 2s^2\, \sigma^* 2s^2\, \sigma 2p_x^2\, [\pi 2p_y = \pi 2p_z]^4 [\pi 2p_y^* = \pi 2p_z^*]^1$$

The odd electron is in a molecular orbital consisting of both the nitrogen and oxygen atoms and hence is delocalized over these atoms. The following three general categories of reactions are recognized for NO:

1. Reactions with other radicals which involve pairing of the odd, π electron to form a polar covalent bond. Examples include:

$$2NO + Cl_2 \rightarrow 2NOCl$$

and

$$CF_3I + NO \xrightarrow[h]{Hg} CF_3NO^{(4)} + I_2$$

In some instances an ionic nitrosyl cation is believed to exist in products of this type—i.e., in $NO^+ClO_4^-$.

2. Reactions which involve addition of an electron to produce NO^-. This species is produced when nitric oxide is bubbled into a solution of potassium in liquid ammonia (*15*). Although on the basis of molecular orbital theory a para-

$$K + NO \xrightarrow[NH_3(l)]{} KNO$$

magnetic species should result from the addition of one electron to the π^* orbital, the product is diamagnetic. This could result from a breakdown in the sequence of molecular orbitals obtained for homonuclear diatomics when applied to NO^- or to a more complex structure for KNO than one containing monomeric NO^-.

3. Reactions in which nitric oxide behaves as a ligand toward transition metal ions. In many of these complexes, a lone pair of electrons on NO forms a weak sigma bond with the metal ion and the odd electron in the nitric oxide molecule pairs with an electron of the metal ion in d_{xy}, d_{xz}, or d_{yz} to form a pi bond. The infrared spectra of several of these complexes have been reported (*20*).

Since the various aspects of the above reactions have been reviewed in detail, the main concern of this article is with reactions of nitrogen(II) oxide that do not fall into the above categories.

Lewis Acid Behavior of NO

There is considerable evidence that nitric oxide is a Lewis acid. In this type of interaction electron density is accepted into the π-antibonding molecular orbital. The structure of the adduct can be represented as $B \mid \overset{x}{N} - \overline{O} \mid$. The following reactions may involve a species BNO, as a transition state or intermediate.

Alkyl Nitrites. An exchange reaction (*19*) between ^{14}NO and $EtO^{15}NO$ proceeds through a BNO intermediate or transition state. The exchange is first-order in nitric oxide and first-order in alkyl nitrite. Two possible mechanisms were proposed (*19*), both of which involve NO behaving as a Lewis acid:

$$RO\ ^{15}NO + ^{14}NO \rightarrow [O - \overset{R}{^{14}N} .... O ..... \,^{15}NO] \rightarrow RO\ ^{14}NO + ^{15}NO$$

or

$$RO\ ^{15}NO + ^{14}NO \rightarrow \left[RO - ^{15}N \underset{^{14}N}{\overset{\overset{O}{\diagup}}{\diagdown}} \underset{O}{} \right] \rightarrow RO\ ^{14}NO + ^{15}NO$$

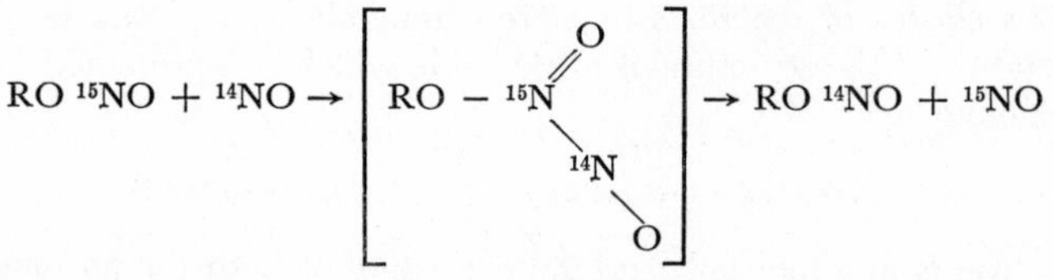

In the latter mechanism it was proposed (*19*) that the intermediate rearranges to yield products. Both mechanisms support the proposal that NO is a Lewis acid.

Sulfite Ion. The reaction of NO with sulfite ion and several of the reactions discussed subsequently can be explained by a reaction sequence in which a base attacks NO to form BNO in the first step, followed by a rapid reaction of the BNO radical with a second molecule of NO. In several of these reactions the dimer BN_2O_2 is formed, although NO does not dimerize to a measurable extent at room temperature (*17*). The reaction of sulfite ion with NO is an example of this reaction type. When nitric oxide is bubbled into a cooled (0° C.) basic aqueous solution of potassium sulfite, a white solid which has the empirical formula $K_2SO_3N_2O_2$ precipitates (*10*).

$$SO_3^{-2} + 2NO \rightarrow SO_3N_2O_2^{-2}$$

A single-crystal x-ray examination (7) of the solid potassium salt indicates that the anion contains the N_2O_2 group and has the structure:

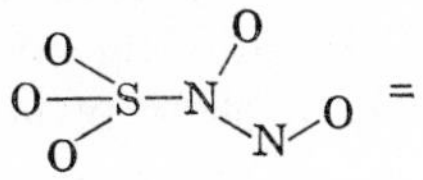

An infrared study indicates (11) that electrons are completely delocalized in the N_2O_2 group. This delocalization is described in valence bond theory as a hybrid structure of the primary structures:

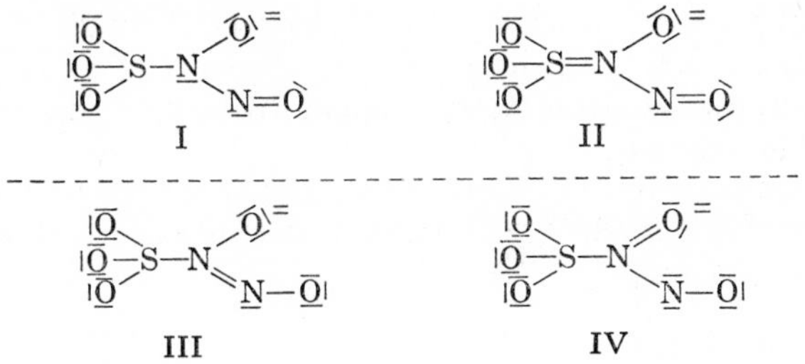

I

II

III

IV

Resonance forms for the sulfite ion have not been included. There has been discussion concerning whether the compound should be considered a sulfonated hyponitrite (16) or a nitrosated hydroxylamine sulfonate (9). The compound can be prepared by nitrosating a sulfonated hydroxylamine (9). There is little to be gained by this dispute, for the structure is best described as in the above diagrams or in molecular orbital terminology. The reaction of sulfite ion and nitric oxide is best considered as a Lewis acid–base reaction in which nitric oxide behaves as the acid and sulfite ion as the donor. A reaction sequence can be formulated with the following equations:

$$SO_3{}^{-2} + NO \rightarrow [SO_3NO{}^{-2}] \text{ (BNO)}$$

$$[SO_3NO{}^{-2}] + NO \rightarrow SO_3N_2O_2{}^{-2}$$

In the absence of adequate kinetic data, these proposed reaction sequences are speculative in nature and will not be dignified by the term "reaction mechanism." The sequences proposed will be found valuable in both correlating many nitric oxide reactions and in suggesting additional experiments.

Primary, Secondary, and Tertiary Amines. It has been demonstrated (12, 13) that nitric oxide behaves as a Lewis acid toward a large number of primary and secondary amines. The reactions with primary and secondary amines can be generalized by the following scheme:

$$R_2NH + NO \rightarrow [R_2NHNO] \text{ (BNO)}$$

$$[R_2NHNO] + NO \rightarrow [R_2NHN_2O_2]$$

$$[R_2NHN_2O_2] + R_2NH \rightarrow R_2NH^+R_2NN_2O_2{}^-$$

For primary amines RNH_2 is substituted for R_2NH, RNH for R_2N, and $RNH_3{}^+$ for $R_2NH_2{}^+$ in the above scheme. The reaction is carried out by bubbling nitric oxide into a cold ($-78°$) ether solution of the amine. Pure solid products precipitate, many of which can be reprecipitated from chloroform solution with ether. Very high yields (70 to 80%) are obtained for many products by a high pressure procedure (12).

The diethylamine product has a slight dissociation pressure of amine and NO at room temperature. It will slowly disappear if allowed to stand overnight on a desk top, but will keep for weeks at room temperature in a sealed container and indefinitely if stored at $-78°$. The products are diamagnetic and their infrared and NMR spectra (12, 13) support the formulation $R_2NH_2^+ R_2NN_2O_2^-$ for secondary amines, and $RNH_3^+RNHN_2O_2^-$ for primary amines. The sodium salt derivatives of the anion, $R_2NN_2O_2^-$, can be prepared by the following reaction:

$$R_2NH_2^+ + R_2NN_2O_2^- + Na^+ + OEt^- \rightarrow R_2NH + EtOH + Na^+ + R_2NN_2O_2^-$$

An analogous reaction can be effected for primary amine products. The similarities in the infrared spectra of the anions in the sodium and alkylammonium salts support the structures proposed for these products. The stabilities and properties of the products obtained from various amines have been described (12). When hindered amines are employed, no product is obtained, presumably because of a steric effect. By analogy with the structure of $SO_3N_2O_2^{-2}$, the following structure is proposed for the anion.

$$\begin{array}{c} C_2H_5 \\ \diagdown \\ \diagup \\ C_2H_5 \end{array} N \diagdown N \diagup \overset{\overset{\textstyle O}{|}}{N} \diagdown N-O \quad ^-$$

If this is the correct structure, the two oxygens are cis to one another and should be capable of forming neutral chelate complexes with metal ions, similar to those formed by acetylacetonate. These considerations led to the study of some metallic derivatives of the ligand $Et_2NN_2O_2^-$ (21). Neutral complexes form with several metal ions and appear to be solvent-stabilized, since they form readily in solution but decompose upon removal of the solvent. Elemental analysis and molecular weight data on a stable copper(II) complex indicate that the Et_2NN_2-O_2^- ion behaves as a bidentate ligand (21). Comparison of the infrared spectra of the copper, sodium, potassium, and calcium salts as well as that of an alkylated product, $Et_2NN_2O_2Et$ (26), further supports chelation by the anion (21).

The mechanism of the reaction between nitric oxide and the amines is not known at present. In a reported (14) kinetic study low concentrations of NO were utilized. Reaction of NO with trace impurities in the solvent gave rise to a species whose spectrum was mistakenly assumed to be that of nitric oxide. The three-step scheme presented above is favored, with the first step probably being rate-controlling.

Both piperazine and N,N'-dimethylethylenediamine form salts with nitrogen (II) oxide (22). The product of the piperazine reaction can be formulated as either

$$H_2\overset{+}{N}\diagdown\diagup NN_2O_2^- \quad \text{or} \quad H_2\overset{+}{N}\diagdown\diagup \overset{+}{N}H_2 \quad O_2^-N_2N\diagdown\diagup NN_2O_2^-$$
$$\qquad \text{I} \qquad\qquad\qquad\qquad\qquad \text{II}$$

A sodium salt derivative was prepared, with the empirical formula $Na_2O_2N_2N\diagdown\diagup NN_2O.2H_2O$, supporting structure II. Attempts to prepare a sodium salt for the product of the N,N'-dimethylethylenediamine reaction were not successful, so analogy with the formulation of the piperazine product could not be confirmed. Nitric oxide underwent reaction with trimethylamine to produce the very unstable compound $(CH_3)_3NN_2O_2$ (22).

Oxygen Donors. The phase diagram of the binary system dimethyl ether–nitric oxide indicates (5) the formation of the very unstable addition compound,

$(CH_3)_2ON_2O_2$. The acid $H_2N_2O_3$, the existence of which has been suggested (*25*), is another example of a donor combined with N_2O_2. Salts of this acid have been isolated (*2*).

Alcohol. Traube Reaction. The Traube reaction (*23, 28, 29*) involves the conversion of ethyl alcohol, in the presence of added base, to methylenediisonitramine by nitric oxide. The structure of the product has been established by a single-crystal x-ray study.

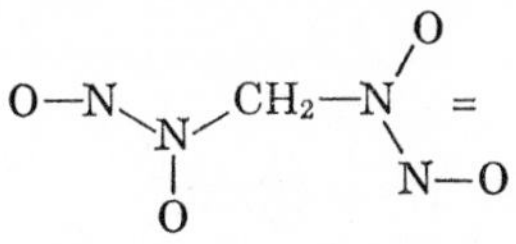

The first step in the reaction is reported to involve the conversion of ethyl alcohol to acetaldehyde:

$$EtOH + 2NO \rightarrow CH_3CHO + H_2O + N_2O$$

The subsequent steps can now be fitted into the BNO scheme. As in an aldol condensation reaction, the aldehyde is converted to a carbanion which acts as the donor; in this case toward NO, forming BNO. The second step involves formation of BN_2O_2. The following sequence of reactions is proposed:

The hydroxide required for the last step is formed in the alcohol oxidation and formate is recovered as one of the products.

Oximes. The reaction of *p*-benzoquinone dioxime, $HON = \langle \_\_\_ \rangle = NOH$, with nitric oxide in basic methanol solution is reported (*8*) to produce $_2O_2N - \langle \_\_\_ \rangle - N_2O_2{}^{-2}$. The sodium salt of *n*-butylaldoxime, $RCH = NONa$,

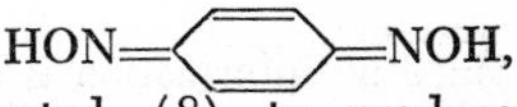

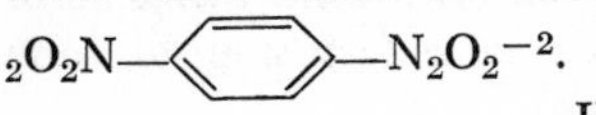

yields $RC \begin{smallmatrix} \nearrow NOH \\ \searrow N_2O_2 \end{smallmatrix}$ — and $R\overset{H}{\underset{|}{C}} - (N_2O_2)_2.H_2O^{-2}$. Delocalization occurs in the N_2O_2 groups. It is tempting to speculate and incorporate these reactions into our BNO scheme. For the *p*-benzoquinone reaction the first step involves BNO formation:

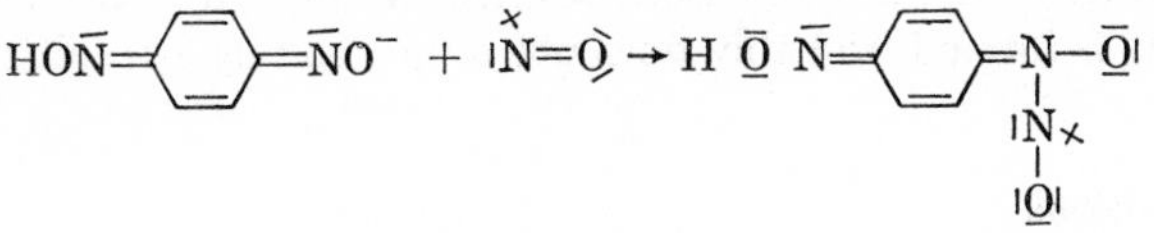

The odd electron in this BNO radical is very probably delocalized over the entire molecule. Attack of the second NO molecule occurs on the oxime nitrogen, for this leads to a stable product:

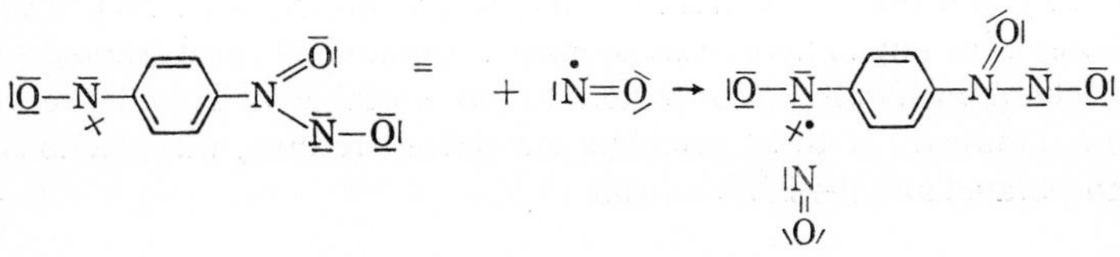

The reaction sequence is similar to that for the amine, except that the radical coupling (second step) occurs at a different atom in the oxime. The place of attack is probably determined by product stability. Electron delocalization occurs in the equivalent N_2O_2 groups in the product. The structure of the product is not known for certain, but other possible structures would simply require a different position of attack by the NO molecule.

The following scheme accounts for the product proposed for the n-butyl-aldoxine reaction:

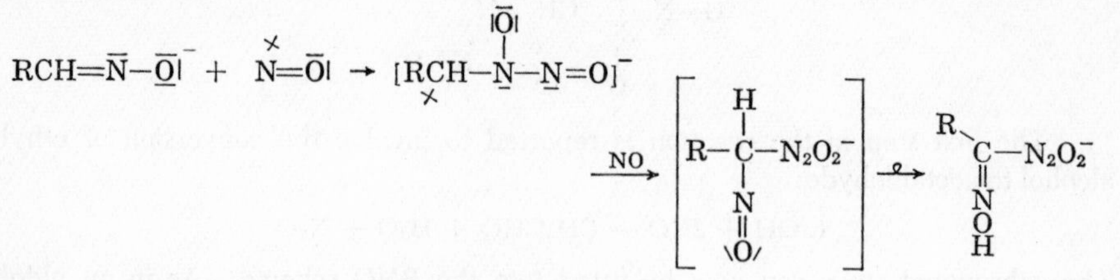

$$RCH{=}\bar{N}{-}\bar{O}|^- + \overset{x}{N}{=}\bar{O}| \rightarrow [RCH{-}\underset{x}{N}{-}N{=}O]^-$$

$$\xrightarrow{NO} \left[\begin{array}{c} H \\ | \\ R-C-N_2O_2^- \\ | \\ N \\ \| \\ \backslash O \diagup \end{array} \right] \xrightarrow{\quad} \begin{array}{c} R \\ \diagdown \\ C-N_2O_2^- \\ \| \\ N \\ | \\ O \\ | \\ H \end{array}$$

Reactions of Group V and Sulfur Donors

There are several oxidation reactions effected by NO that can be incorporated into the BNO scheme. Mercaptans are oxidized to symmetrical disulfides (22), triphenylphosphine to triphenylphosphine oxide, and phosphites to phosphates (18, 22). A kinetic study (18) of the reaction of alkyl phosphites with nitric oxide indicates that the reaction is first-order in phosphite and first-order in nitric oxide. This indicates initial formation of a species, BNO:

$$(RO)_3P + NO \rightarrow (RO)_3 PNO$$

Since no information is obtained from kinetics about subsequent steps, these can only be proposed. The adduct $(RO)_3PN_2O_2$ could form. A second molecule of phosphite could abstract an oxygen from the adduct in a fast step to form $(RO)_3PO$, $(RO)_3P$, and N_2O. An alternate mechanism,

$$(RO)_3PN_2O_2 + (RO)_3P \rightarrow (RO)_3PO + (RO)_3P + N_2O$$

in which oxygen transfer occurs from the N_2O_2 group to the phosphorus in the intermediate, $(RO)_3PN_2O_2$, is possible.

Triphenyl phosphite, triphenylarsine, and triphenylstibine are not oxidized by NO (22). Because of the decreased basicity of these materials, the initial step in which BNO is formed probably does not occur, and as a result there is no oxidation.

Miscellaneous Reactions

Several brief preliminary reports in the literature indicate the formation of products from nitric oxide containing nitrogen-nitrogen bonds. Lithium aluminum hydride plus nitric oxide is reported to give rise to hyponitrite ion (17). Grignard reagents (27) and aluminum triethyl (3), when reacted with NO, give rise to intermediates which upon hydrolysis produce nitrosated alkyl-substituted hydroxylamines. These materials are reported to be unstable and evidence for their existence is indirect. If these products are indeed formed, the reactions can be easily incorporated into the BNO scheme.

Literature Cited

(1) Addison, C. C., Lewis, J., *Quart. Revs.* **9,** 115 (1955).
(2) Angeli, A., *et al., Gazz. Chim. Ital.* **33II,** 245 (1903), and references contained therein.
(3) Baker, E. B., Sisler, H. H., *J. Am. Chem. Soc.* **75,** 5193 (1953).
(4) Barr, D. A., Haszeldine, R. N., *J. Chem. Soc.* **1955,** 1881, and references contained therein.
(5) Baume, G., Germann, A. F. G., *J. Chim. Phys.* **12,** 244 (1914).
(6) Bryden, J. H., *Acta Cryst.* **12,** 581 (1959).
(7) Cox, E. G., Jeffrey, G. A., Stadler, H. P., *J. Chem. Soc.* **1951,** 1467, and references contained therein.
(8) Danzig, M. J., Martel, R. F., Riccitiello, *J. Org. Chem.* **25,** 1071 (1960); **26,** 3327 (1961).
(9) Degener, E., Seel, F., *Z. anorg. allgem. Chem.* **280,** 143 (1955).
(10) Drago, R. S., *Inorg. Synth.* **5,** 120 (1957). References to original work contained in this reference.
(11) Drago, R. S., *J. Am. Chem. Soc.* **79,** 2049 (1957).
(12) Drago, R. S., Karstetter, B. R., *Ibid.,* **83,** 1819 (1961).
(13) Drago, R. S., Paulik, F. E., *Ibid.,* **82,** 96 (1960).
(14) Drago, R. S., Ragsdale, R. O., Eyman, D. P., *Ibid.,* **83,** 4337 (1961).
(15) Frazer, J. H., Long, N. O., *J. Chem. Phys.* **6,** 462 (1938).
(16) Gehring, M. R., Otto, R. *Z. anorg. allgem. Chem.,* **280,** 143 (1955).
(17) Karrer, P., Schwyzer, R., *Rec. Trav. Chim.* **69,** 474 (1950).
(18) Kuhn, L. P., Doali, J. O., Wellman, C., *J. Am. Chem. Soc.* **82,** 4792 (1960).
(19) Kuhn, L. P., Günthard, H. H., *Helv. Chim. Acta* **43,** 607 (1960).
(20) Lewis, J., Irving, R. J., Wilkinson, G., *J. Inorg. Nuclear Chem.* **7,** 32 (1958).
(21) Longhi, R., Drago, R. S., *Inorg. Chem.,* in press.
(22) Longhi, R., Ragsdale, R. O., Drago, R. S., *Ibid.,* in press.
(23) MacDonald, G. W., Masson, O., *J. Chem. Soc.* **65,** 944 (1894).
(24) Moeller, T., *J. Chem. Educ.* **23,** 441, 542 (1946); **24,** 149 (1947).
(25) Nichols, M. L., Morse, C. W., *J. Phys. Chem.* **35,** 1239 (1931).
(26) Reilly, E. L. (to E. I. du Pont de Nemours & Co.), French Patent **1,171,532** (Jan. 27, 1959).
(27) Sand, J., Singer, F., *Ber.* **35,** 3186 (1902); *Ann.* **239,** 190 (1903).
(28) Traube, W., *Ber.* **27,** 1507 (1894).
(29) Wieland, H., Chavan, J., Klages, F., *Ibid.,* **61B,** 2382 (1928).

RECEIVED May 8, 1962.

16

The Reactions of Alkyl-Substituted Amino Radicals

BRIAN G. GOWENLOCK and DAVID R. SNELLING

Department of Chemistry, University of Birmingham, Birmingham 15, England

Literature on the preparation and reactions of alkyl-substituted amino radicals and thermochemical information is reviewed. This survey and experimental work presented here demonstrate that our knowledge of the chemistry of alkyl-substituted amino radicals is small. Further studies using a variety of radical sources and techniques are being developed. It is hoped that the nature of the surface-promoted reactions of dimethylamino radicals may be further elucidated.

From the time of Paneth's discovery of the lower alkyl free radicals (23) there has been a continuous and growing interest in the hydrocarbon free radicals. This has embraced reactions in the gaseous, liquid, and solid states. The field has progressed from an early qualitative mapping of the characteristic reactions of these radicals to semiquantitative and then accurate quantitative studies of the kinetics of reaction of hydrocarbon free radicals. In addition, our knowledge of the thermochemistry of hydrocarbon free radicals has grown (6), and the many self-consistent pieces of evidence confirm the detailed trustworthiness of the pattern of heats of formation of the gaseous radicals. However, comparison of our knowledge of hydrocarbon free radicals with that of many other free radicals reveals that our knowledge of the latter is often fragmentary. Apart from alkoxyl free radicals, which participate in many important reactions, our knowledge of many other simple alkyl-substituted nonhydrocarbon free radicals is rudimentary and mainly qualitative. This is particularly true for alkyl-substituted amino radicals, and if we consider the two isoelectronic series—RCH_2, RNH, RO and R_2CH, R_2N—it is immediately obvious that we lack detailed knowledge of the nitrogen-containing radicals. The work described here is part of a systematic program designed to alter this situation.

Thermochemistry of Substituted Amino Radicals

The thermochemistry of substituted amino radicals may best be determined by the method employed for alkyl radicals—namely, measurement of the activation energy, E_1, for the forward Reaction 1, the enthalpy increase being ΔH. If we

$$R{-}H \underset{E_2}{\overset{E_1}{\rightleftarrows}} R + H \quad \Delta H \qquad (1)$$

150

assume that the energy of activation for the reverse reaction, E_2, is equal to zero (a very plausible assumption for the reaction between two free radicals), we can relate the enthalpies of formation of the gaseous species by Equation 2

$$\Delta H(R) = \Delta H(RH) - \Delta H(H) + \Delta H \tag{2}$$

or, as $E_1 = \Delta H$, by Equation 3

$$\Delta H(R) = \Delta H(RH) - \Delta H(H) + E_1 \tag{3}$$

This method can then be extended to the case of substituted hydrocarbons, RX. By these techniques Szwarc (27) developed our knowledge of the thermochemistry of alkyl radicals and the technique has been extended (18) to alkoxyl radicals, using known activation energies and heats of formation of the necessary ROX molecules. This method could, in theory, be extended to the case of alkyl-substituted amino radicals by utilizing known heats of formation of molecules RNHX and R_2NX and activation energies for the thermal decomposition of such molecules. However, this approach is limited by the fact that these activation energies have never been measured. Thus the only use of this technique must be to make an intelligent guess at the activation energy. At first sight this appears impossible, but, if we remember that such activation energies are bond dissociation energies, then it is possible to assume smooth trends in bond dissociation energies within isoelectronic families of molecules and therefore calculate values for the enthalpies of formation of alkyl-substituted amino radicals. This method is based upon the known smooth trend in bond dissociation energies in the series CH_3-CH_3, NH_2-NH_2, $HO-OH$ discussed by Evans, Warhurst, and Whittle (12), and the isoelectronic series argument developed by Gray and Williams (18). If the method is a sound one, enthalpies of formation of substituted amino radicals which have been derived from different isoelectronic families should be in close agreement. Gowenlock, Jones, and Majer (17) have used this method to obtain the enthalpies of formation of CH_3NH, C_2H_5NH, and $(CH_3)_2N$ and we can extend the technique to cover other examples. The values so obtained in kilocalories per mole are:

Radical	CH_3NH	C_2H_5NH	$(CH_3)_2N$	$(C_2H_5)_2N$	C_6H_5NH	$(C_6H_5)_2N$
ΔH (radical)	37 ± 3	33 ± 3	34 ± 3	22 ± 3	54 ± 3	83 ± 3

It is obviously necessary to free such values from the charge of being purely subjective, and electron impact studies have been used (17) to confirm these values for CH_3NH and $(CH_3)_2N$. The respective values of 32 ± 5 and 32.2 ± 5 kcal. per mole are in reasonable agreement with the estimates. Confirmation by direct determination of ionization potentials of the radicals and by kinetic measurements of bond dissociation energies is in progress in our laboratories.

Sources of Substituted Amino Radicals

These radicals may be generated by a variety of methods and we may compare these methods with those that are well established for alkyl (30) and alkoxyl (18) radicals. Thus, there is an essential similarity between the three sources of azo compounds $R-N=N-R$, hyponitrites $RO-N=N-OR$, and tetrazenes $R_2N-N=N-NR_2$, all of which would be expected to produce the appropriate radicals (either photolytically or pyrolytically). The literature evidence for the four simplest radicals is summarized here.

Methylamino. It has been suggested (5) that the initial step in the thermal decomposition of methylamine is

$$CH_3NH_2 \rightarrow CH_3NH + H \tag{4}$$

but this is highly improbable, for the C—N bond dissociation energy is about 20 kcal. per mole lower than the N—H bond dissociation energy and consequently Reaction 5 will be the primary radical-producing reaction.

$$CH_3NH_2 \rightarrow CH_3 + NH_2 \tag{5}$$

Hence, the variety of products formed in the pyrolysis of methylamine (22) are due to attack by amino radicals (and not methylamino radicals) on the methylamine, followed by subsequent reactions. In contrast to this, photolysis of methylamine (9, 10) does yield methylamino radicals by Reaction 6

$$CH_3NH_2 + h\nu \rightarrow CH_3NH + H \tag{6}$$

and photosensitized decomposition (32, 35) also yields methylamino radicals.

$$CH_3NH_2 + Hg\ (^3P_1) \rightarrow CH_3NH + H + Hg\ (^1S_0) \tag{7}$$

The only other recorded source is the thermal decomposition of 1,3-dimethyltriazene (24)

$$CH_3—N\!\!=\!\!N—NHCH_3 \rightarrow CH_3 + N_2 + CH_3NH \tag{8}$$

Reaction 8 is the obvious primary reaction and is entirely analogous to the known decomposition of aryl triazenes.

Ethylamino. It appears that the photolysis of ethylamine (9, 10) proceeds by a similar mechanism to methylamine:

$$C_2H_5NH_2 + h\nu \rightarrow C_2H_5NH + H \tag{9}$$

Dimethylamino. There are many more known sources of this radical than of the methylamino radical. Photolysis of dimethyl- and trimethylamine yields the radical by Reactions 10 and 11

$$(CH_3)_2NH + h\nu \rightarrow (CH_3)_2N + H \tag{10}$$

$$(CH_3)_3N + h\nu \rightarrow (CH_3)_2N + CH_3 \tag{11}$$

Further photolytic sources are dimethylnitrosamine (1), for which the initial reaction is probably

$$(CH_3)_2N—NO + h\nu \rightarrow (CH_3)_2N + NO \tag{12}$$

and tetramethyltetrazene (31), which gives only the required radicals and nitrogen

$$(CH_3)_2N—N\!\!=\!\!N—N(CH_3)_2 + h\nu \rightarrow 2(CH_3)_2N + N_2 \tag{13}$$

Pyrolytic sources are trimethylamine (22), dimethylnitrosamine (16), dimethylnitramine (14), and tetramethyltetrazene (25, 31, 33), the pyrolyses proceeding according to the thermal analogs of Reactions 11, 12, and 13. A further probable source of these radicals is provided by the reaction between dimethylchloramine and copper-bronze in ether at 40° (19).

$$(CH_3)_2NCl + Cu \rightarrow (CH_3)_2N + CuCl \tag{14}$$

Diethylamino. The known sources of this radical are analogous to the dimethylamino sources—namely, photolyses of triethylamine (20) and diethylnitrosamine (1) and pyrolyses of triethylamine (29), tetraethyltetrazene (36), and tetraethylhydrazine (34).

Reactions of Substituted Amino Radicals

These would be expected to be similar to the reactions of alkyl and alkyloxy free radicals and the reaction may be classified as follows.

Association with Radicals, Including Dimerization. Little evidence exists for the monoalkyl-substituted amino radicals, although this would be expected by analogy with alkyl radicals. In the pyrolysis of dimethyltriazene the two association reactions

$$2CH_3NH \rightarrow CH_3NHNHCH_3 \tag{15}$$

$$CH_3NH + CH_3 \rightarrow (CH_3)_2NH \tag{16}$$

must be the precursors of the products suggested to fit the stoichiometric equation assumed on the basis of the degree of pressure rise on decomposition. However, analyses are absent.

There is good evidence (*25, 31*) for the dimerization of dimethylamino radicals, and an excellent preparative route to tetramethylhydrazine is provided thereby.

$$2(CH_3)_2N \rightarrow (CH_3)_2NN(CH_3)_2 \tag{17}$$

Disproportionation. Again there is little evidence for the disproportionation of the monoalkyl-substituted amino radicals, although this reaction would be expected

$$2CH_3NH \rightarrow CH_3NH_2 + CH_2NH \tag{18}$$

the methyleneimine product probably undergoing several self-addition reactions. However, for dialkylamino radicals more evidence is available and it is reported that disproportionation of dimethylamino (*1, 31*) and diethylamino radicals (*34, 36*) occurs.

$$2(CH_3)_2N \rightarrow (CH_3)_2NH + CH_3-N=CH_2 \tag{19}$$

$$2(C_2H_5)_2N \rightarrow (C_2H_5)_2NH + C_2H_5-N=CH-CH_3 \tag{20}$$

The methylmethyleneimine formed in Reaction 19 can either polymerize

$$n\text{-}CH_3-N=CH_2 \rightarrow \left[\begin{array}{c} -N-CH_2- \\ | \\ CH_3 \end{array} \right]_n \tag{21}$$

or form the ring trimer, 1,3,5-tri-*N*-methylhexahydro-*s*-triazine

$$3\ CH_3-N=CH_2 \rightarrow \tag{22}$$

Decomposition. Just as alkyl and alkyloxy radicals can decompose to give a stable double-bonded molecule and either a hydrogen atom or methyl radical—Reactions 23 and 24—so we would expect decomposition of alkyl-substituted amino radicals to take place.

$$C_2H_5 \rightarrow H + C_2H_4 \tag{23}$$

$$C_2H_5O \rightarrow CH_3 + CH_2O \tag{24}$$

Reaction 25

$$CH_3NH \rightarrow CH_2=NH + H \qquad (25)$$

has been proposed as a step in the photolysis of methylamine (*35*), though probably of similar endothermicity as Reactions 23 and 26.

$$CH_3O \rightarrow CH_2O + H \qquad (26)$$

This reaction has not been confirmed. For dialkylamino radicals, reactions such as 27 and 28 would be expected.

$$(CH_3)_2N \rightarrow CH_3-N=CH_2 + H \qquad (27)$$

$$(CH_3)_2N \rightarrow CH_2=NH + CH_3 \qquad (28)$$

Again, direct evidence is lacking. However, the occurrence of monomethylamine (*31*) in the products of pyrolysis of tetramethyltetrazene and of tetramethylmethylenediamine both in the same pyrolysis products and in the reaction products of dimethylchloramine and copper (*19*) argues that there must be some decomposition reactions of these radicals. Gesser, Mullhaupt, and Griffiths (*15*) have also argued for the occurrence of Reactions 29 and 30 among the possible reactions of dimethylamino radicals at $-75°$:

$$(CH_3)_2N \Big\langle \begin{array}{l} H_2 + X \qquad\qquad (29) \\ CH_4 + Y \qquad\qquad (30) \end{array}$$

The unknown products, X and Y, are nonvolatile at these temperatures.

Reaction with Molecules. As is to be expected, we have only speculation for the reactions of monomethylamino radicals, whereas for dimethylamino and diethylamino radicals some reliable information is available. Thus reaction with nitric oxide can occur (*36*).

$$(C_2H_5)_2N + NO \rightarrow (C_2H_5)_2N-NO \qquad (31)$$

Abstraction of hydrogen atoms can occur in the liquid phase, these being of the general type

$$(CH_3)_2N + H-R \rightarrow (CH_3)_2NH + R \qquad (32)$$

where the substrate is cumene (*11*), non-1-ene (*7*), cyclohexanol (*7*), and benzyl alcohol (*7*). Similarly, addition to double bonds may occur as with α-methylstyrene (*7*).

$$(CH_3)_2N + CH_2{=}\underset{\underset{C_6H_5}{|}}{C}{-}CH_3 \rightarrow (CH_3)_2N-CH_2-\underset{\underset{C_6H_5}{|}}{C}{-}CH_3 \qquad (33)$$

In addition to these typical free radical reactions, it has also been reported that tetramethyltetrazene and hence possibly the dimethylamino radical react with aluminum alkyls and hydrides (*13*).

It is possible that dialkylamino radicals participate in the oxidation reactions of some tertiary aliphatic amines (*8*), but such reactions are mainly speculative.

Thus we may summarize our knowledge of the reactions of these radicals as fragmentary and incomplete. The only well established features mirror those of alkyl and alkyloxy radicals and further information should be obtained from experimental studies of a character similar to those well established in these fields.

Our Investigation

The thermal decompositions of tetramethyltetrazene (TMT) and tetraethyltetrazene (TET) have been studied in flow systems using the following conditions.

A. TMT. Temperature of reaction vessel, 195° to 300° C. Borosilicate glass reaction vessel, the surface-volume ratio of which could be altered by a factor of up to 7.5 by packing with either borosilicate glass or silica glass wool. Reaction time, 0.7 to 3.0 seconds. Total pressure in reaction vessel 4 to 10 mm. Carrier gases, nitrogen, carbon dioxide, sulfur hexafluoride, and carbon dioxide–nitric oxide.

B. TET. Temperature of reaction vessel, 195° to 250° C. Reaction time, 0.7 to 3.0 seconds. Total pressure in reaction vessel, 10 to 30 mm. Carrier gases, carbon dioxide and sulfur hexafluoride.

The pyrolysis products were separated by trapping in various low temperature baths and the residual noncondensable gases were pumped into a known volume where the pressure was measured and samples were taken for mass spectrometric analysis. Samples of the liquid products could be taken for analysis by both mass spectrometry and gas liquid chromatography (GLC). Samples of materials for identification of products were obtained as follows:

Dimethylamine and trimethylamine (commercially available), 1,3,5-tri-N-methyl hexahydro-s-triazine (from reaction of formaldehyde and methylamine), tetramethylhydrazine (gift of B. J. Aylett), tetramethylmethylenediamine (from reaction of formaldehyde with dimethylamine), dimethyl- and diethylnitrosamine (from reaction of nitrous acid with the appropriate dialkylamine), diethylmethylamine (from reductive methylation of diethylamine), ethylethylideneamine (from reaction of ethylamine and acetaldehyde), and TMT and TET (from oxidation of the appropriate *unsym*-dialkylhydrazine).

Cracking patterns and GLC retention times of these materials were measured as aids to identification of pyrolysis samples. Three GLC columns were employed at different phases of this work:

A. 10% (by weight) polyethylene glycol suspended on 44/60 mesh firebrick used at a temperature of 55° and a nitrogen flow rate of 50 cc. per minute. Column length was 12 feet, the diameter 4 mm., and the material coiled copper tubing.

B. 10% (by weight) Apiezon grease M, suspended on 60/80 mesh firebrick, used at a temperature of 80° and a nitrogen flow rate of 20 cc. per minute. Column length was 6 feet, diameter and materials as in A.

C. 10% (by weight) silicone gum. Other details as in B.

Results

TMT. The pyrolysis of TMT in the temperature range 190° to 250° C. yields only two products—tetramethylhydrazine (TMH) and nitrogen. At temperatures of 255° C. and above other products are formed—tetramethylmethylenediamine (TMMD), trimethylamine (TMA), dimethylamine (DMA), and 1,3,5-tri-N-methylhexahydro-s-triazine (ring trimer). The first investigation of relative product yields was made using column A and revealed that the yields of some of the products formed are increased by packing of the reaction vessel. Thus without packing TMMD:TMH = 0.25 and DMA:TMH = 0.01 to 0.05 at 300° C. With silica packing these ratios are greater and in contrast to the previous results are markedly temperature-dependent, at 300° C. the major products being TMMD and DMA. The following ratios (reaction conditions 267° C., pressure 8 mm., reaction time 1.5 seconds) show the effect of altering surface-volume ratio by a factor of 6.

Without packing	TMMD:TMH = 0.20	DMA–TMH = 0.02
With packing (silica)	TMMD:TMH = 0.90	DMA–TMH = 0.08

The effect of borosilicate glass packing is to give an intermediate increase in product ratios: Thus TMMD:TMH = 0.31 at 259°, 0.40 at 272°—i.e., the increase is less than for the silica surface. Packing of the reaction vessel (either silica or borosilicate glass) also produced small quantities of TMA (of the same order of magnitude as DMA). The ring trimer has been identified, using columns B and C, in the products from the pyrolysis of TMT (packed reaction vessel) at 285° C. This product occurs in only small quantity.

TET. The products from the pyrolysis of TET were always more varied than from TMT and comprised nitrogen, methane, ethane, diethylamine (DEA), diethylmethylamine (DEMA), ethylethylideneamine (EEA), tetraethylhydrazine (TEH), and two other products, one of which is possibly ethylamine. The dimerization-disproportionation ratio for the diethylamine radicals is approximately 1 to 1 at 250° C. and the other products are produced only in the upper region of temperatures employed by us. Thus at 240° the major products were the dimerization and disproportionation products (TEH, DEA, EEA), and the occurrence of DEMA at the higher temperatures was always accompanied by methane and ethane production.

Discussion

The virtual absence of disproportionation in the reactions of the dimethylamine radical is a surprising feature of this work, and contrasts with the results of previous workers (1, 31). However, previous work was carried out at much longer reaction times than those employed by us. This suggests that if Bradley's linear correlation (3, 21) of entropy difference between the products ($S_{disp}-S_{comb}$) with difference between the apparent entropies of activation ($S_{comb}^{\pm}-S_{disp}^{\pm}$) holds, then $S_{comb}^{\pm}-S_{disp}^{\pm}$ is about 6 to 7 e.u., and $S_{disp}-S_{comb}$ is about 28 to 32 e.u. This implies that the same activated complex is required for the two reactions—i.e.,

$$CH_3 \diagdown \underset{CH_3 \diagup}{N} \cdots \overset{\textstyle H}{\cdots} \diagdown \underset{\underset{\diagup}{\underset{CH_3}{N}}}{\diagup} CH_2$$

However, this is probably an oversimplification, as the disproportionation reaction is surface-catalyzed and the two reactions must have different energies of activation. This behavior of dimethylamino radicals is in marked contrast to the isoelectronic isopropyl radicals, the disproportionation-combination ratio of which is unaltered by temperature and surface (2, 30). The surface-promoted radical decomposition is also in marked contrast to the absence of such effects in the isopropyl radical reactions (2) and must be attributed to the presence of the nitrogen atom. Amino radicals also undergo surface reactions (28). The occurrence of TMA suggests the participation of methyl radicals in the reactions, and a possible route is provided by Reactions 28 and 34.

$$(CH_3)_2N \rightarrow CH_2=NH + CH_3 \tag{28}$$

$$(CH_3)_2N + CH_3 \rightarrow (CH_3)_3N \tag{34}$$

However, the methyleneimine (or some polymer thereof) has not yet been detected, and some ethane also must presumably result, although in much smaller quantities than TMA. In addition to the above, the production of TMMD is best explained by the participation of methyl radicals following either route A or B.

A.
$$CH_3 + (CH_3)_3N \rightarrow CH_4 + (CH_3)_2N-CH_2 \tag{35}$$

$$(CH_3)_2N-CH_2 + (CH_3)_2N \rightarrow (CH_3)_2N-CH_2-N(CH_3)_2 \tag{36}$$

B.
$$CH_3 + CH_3-N=CH_2 \rightarrow (CH_3)_2N-CH_2 \tag{37}$$

Both of these suggestions are defective because of the absence of methane (route A) and the much greater quantities of TMMD produced compared with DMA (route B with Reaction 19 as the precursor of methylmethylene imine). A further route to TMMD could be provided by methylene insertion into the NN bond of TMH. This, though theoretically feasible, seems unlikely and requires the production of methylene from dimethylamino radicals by a surface reaction. The radical decomposition reactions (29 and 30) proposed by Gesser, Mullhaupt, and Griffiths (*15*) are not confirmed by our results.

The behavior of diethylamino radicals is akin to that of alkyl radicals, in that both dimerization and disproportionation occur and at approximately equal rates. However we have no accurate numerical data for the corresponding *sec*-pentyl radical which may be used to provide the required contrast. The occurrence of DEMA, methane, and ethane in the reaction products suggests that the methyl radical is an essential precursor and the decomposition of diethylamino radicals

$$(C_2H_5)_2N \rightarrow C_2H_5-N=CH_2 + CH_3 \tag{38}$$

would provide a rational basis for this. Our study of diethylamino radicals is less complete than for dimethylamino radicals. In particular, surface effects have yet to be investigated.

Both dimethylamino and diethylamino radicals react with nitric oxide to form the corresponding nitrosamine, by Reactions 31 and 39.

$$(CH_3)_2N + NO \rightarrow (CH_3)_2N-NO \tag{39}$$

With TMT the sole products are TMH and dimethylnitrosamine (DMNA) and from the product ratio DMNA:TMH, which is in the region of 20 to 1 under our flow conditions at about $250°$, the relative k_{39}/k_{17} ratios can be determined. Assuming that $k_{17} = 10^{14}$ cc. mole^{-1} sec.$^{-1}$, then $k_{39} \approx 10^{11}$ cc. mole^{-1} sec.$^{-1}$–i.e., a P factor of $\approx 10^{-3}$. This is comparable with the value for Reaction 40

$$CH_3 + NO \rightarrow CH_3-NO \tag{40}$$

given as $\approx 10^{-4}$ (*4, 26*). Reaction 40 has third-body restrictions and so, presumably, has Reaction 39. The agreement between the two collision yields is enheartening in view of the assumptions involved, which make the value of k_{39} only approximate.

Acknowledgment

D. R. Snelling thanks the University of Birmingham and British Nylon Spinners, Ltd., for research grants. The authors thank J. R. Majer for mass spectrometric analyses.

Literature Cited

(1) Bamford, C. H., *J. Chem. Soc.* **1939**, 12.
(2) Billinge, B. H. M., Gowenlock, B. G., unpublished work.
(3) Bradley, J. N., *J. Chem. Phys.* **35**, 748 (1961).
(4) Bryce, W. A., Ingold, K. U., *Ibid.*, **23**, 1968 (1955).
(5) Carter, A. G., Bosanquet, P. A., Silcocks, C. G., Travers, M. W., Wilshire, A., *J. Chem. Soc.* **1939**, 495.
(6) Cottrell, T. S., "The Strengths of Chemical Bonds," Butterworths, London, 1958.
(7) Cowley, B. R., Waters, W. A., *J. Chem. Soc.* **1961**, 1228.
(8) Cullis, C. F., Waddington, D. J., *Proc. Roy. Soc. (London)* **A244**, 110 (1958); **A246**, 91 (1958).
(9) Eméléus, H. J., Jolley, L. J., *J. Chem. Soc.* **1935**, 929, 1612.
(10) Eméléus, H. J., Taylor, H. S., *J. Am. Chem. Soc.* **53**, 3370 (1931).
(11) Erusalimskiĭ, B. L., Dolgoplosk, B. A., Kavuchenko, A. P., *Zhur. Obscheĭ Khim.* **27**, 267 (1957).
(12) Evans, M. G., Warhurst, E., Whittle, E., *J. Chem. Soc.* **1950**, 1524.
(13) Fetter, N. R., Bartocha, B., *Can. J. Chem.* **40**, 342 (1962).
(14) Flournoy, J. M., *J. Chem. Phys.* **36**, 1106 (1962).
(15) Gesser, H., Mullhaupt, J. T., Griffiths, J. E., *J. Am. Chem. Soc.* **79**, 4834 (1957).
(16) Gowenlock, B. G., Haynes, R. M., unpublished work.
(17) Gowenlock, B. G., Jones, P. P., Majer, J. R., *Trans. Faraday Soc.* **57**, 23 (1961).
(18) Gray, P., Williams, A., *Chem. Revs.* **59**, 239 (1959).
(19) Klages, F., Nober, G., Kircher, F., Bock, M., *Ann.* **547**, 1 (1941).
(20) Kozac, P. J., Gesser, H., *J. Chem. Soc.* **1960**, 448.
(21) Laidler, K. J., Wojciechowski, B. W., "The Transition State," Chemical Society Special Publication, London, 1962.
(22) Meadows, G. W., Kirkland, J. J., *J. Phys. Chem.* **65**, 2139 (1961).
(23) Paneth, F. A., Hofeditz, W., *Ber.* **62B**, 1335 (1929).
(24) Ramsperger, H. C., Leermakers, J. A., *J. Am. Chem. Soc.* **53**, 2061 (1931).
(25) Rice, F. O., Grelecki, C. G., *Ibid.*, **79**, 2679 (1957).
(26) Steacie, E. W. R., "Atomic and Free Radical Reactions," p. 646, Reinhold, New York, 1954.
(27) Szwarc, M., *Chem. Revs.* **47**, 76 (1950).
(28) Szwarc, M., *Proc. Roy. Soc. (London)* **A198**, 267 (1949).
(29) Taylor, H. A., Jutterbock, E. E., *J. Phys. Chem.* **39**, 1103 (1935).
(30) Trotman-Dickenson, A. F., "Free Radicals," Methuen and Co., London, 1959.
(31) Watson, J. S., *J. Chem. Soc.* **1956**, 3677.
(32) Watson, J. S., Darwent, B. de B., *J. Chem. Phys.* **20**, 1041 (1952).
(33) Watson, J. S., Waring, A. J., *Can. J. Chem.* **38**, 298 (1960).
(34) Westphal, O., Eucken, M., *Ber.* **76**, 1137 (1943).
(35) Wetmore, O. C., Taylor, H. A., *J. Chem. Phys.* **12**, 61 (1944).
(36) Wieland, H., Fressel, H., *Ann.* **392**, 133 (1912).

RECEIVED April 30, 1962.

17

A New Deep Violet Compound, $(O_2ClF_3)_n$, Dioxygen Chlorine Trifluoride

A. G. STRENG and A. V. GROSSE

Research Institute, Temple University, Philadelphia 44, Pa.

A new deep violet compound, $(O_2ClF_3)_n$, was discovered by reacting O_2F_2 with ClF at 119° to 140° K. It is thermally stable up to 195° K. for over a year. The stability of its concentrated deep violet solution in anhydrous HF depends on the oxygen pressure. This solution has practically the same conductivity as HF and thus the compound is not an electrolyte. The compound is a very strong oxidizing substance, and reacts with NH_3, various hydrocarbons, and even ice at low temperatures. It seems to surpass even ozone as an oxidizer.

The colored polyoxygen difluorides—O_2F_2, O_3F_2 (3, 4), and O_4F_2 (2)—represent the most potent oxidizers known, since they are endothermic compounds of oxygen and fluorine.

O_3F_2 decomposes into O_2F_2 and O_2 at $\simeq$ 120° K.; O_4F_2 into O_3F_2 and O_2 at about 100° K. In the decomposition reaction, regardless whether it proceeds with the formation of free O-F radicals or atomic oxygen, highly reactive species are formed. For this reason the addition of only 0.1 weight % O_3F_2 to liquid O_2 makes the mixture hypergolic with a wide variety of fuels, including H_2, at low temperatures (5).

Higher members of this series, such as O_5F_2 and O_6F_2, may exist (2) and thus the abstraction of fluorine from the lower members by means of a suitable reaction is of particular interest. The view has been expressed (2) that in such an abstraction reaction cyclic polymers of oxygen—i.e., O_5 and O_6—may form, since the strengths of O-O and O-F bonds are similar. The red color of the polyoxygen fluorides is due to the O-O bonds, since the O-F bond in OF_2 does not give rise to any significant absorption in the visible spectrum. In this respect the colored O-O bonds in the fluorides are different from the O-O bonds in the colorless H_2O_2, or H_2O_4 and alkyl peroxides.

In our studies (6) attempting fluorine abstraction, O_2F_2 was reacted with ClF. If the reaction is carried out without special precautions, the two substances readily react following the stoichiometric equation:

$$O_2F_2 + ClF \rightarrow O_2 + ClF_3 \qquad (1)$$

with $\Delta H_{298} = -30.1$ kcal. per mole.

However, if the reaction is carried out under mild conditions, from just above the melting point of ClF (119° K.) up to 130° K., an intense violet colored intermediate compound of the elementary composition $(O_2ClF_3)_n$ (referred to simply as O_2ClF_3) is formed, in line with the scheme:

$$O_2F_2 + ClF \rightarrow O_2ClF_3$$

Its color and hue are very similar to those of the organic dye methyl violet.

At the beginning it was thought that the intense violet color may be due to the formation of blue ozone mixed with some unreacted red-orange O_2F_2,:

$$3 O_2F_2 + 3 ClF \rightarrow 2 O_3 + 3 ClF_3$$

It could be readily shown that no ozone formed, since the latter can be easily vacuum-distilled out of such a mixture.

The O_2ClF_3 was obtained in a purity of 81%, the other 19% being the nearly colorless ClF_3. O_2ClF_3 is a solid, thermally stable up to 195° K. At this temperature it can be kept for over a year. It has a vapor pressure of less than 12 microns at 158° K.; at this pressure and temperature it dissociates into its components, which can be collected on a liquid nitrogen finger (77° K.). If the finger is warmed up to 119° to 140° K., the violet compound forms again.

The compound is insoluble in liquid O_2 and O_3 at 90° K., in liquid ClO_3F and C_3F_8 at $\simeq$ 140° K., and in liquid NF_3, CCl_2F_2, and $CClF_3$ at $\simeq$ 160° K. It is soluble in ClF at 125° K., O_2F_2 at 140° K., and ClF_3 at 190° K.

It is readily soluble in anhydrous HF at 190° K., forming a deep violet solution. The solubility is high and a 65 weight % or 23 mole % O_2ClF_3 solution is not saturated at 190° K.

This solution is not an electrolyte. A $0.5M$ solution of O_2ClF_3 in HF had specific conductivity of 3.57×10^{-3} ohm^{-1} cm.$^{-1}$ at 195° K., while the pure anhydrous HF used had the same conductivity. After decomposition the residual clear and colorless solution of ClF_3 in HF also had the conductivity of 3.57×10^{-3} ohm^{-1} cm.$^{-1}$

In contrast, a $0.5M$ solution of a typical electrolyte, KF in HF, has a specific conductivity of 86.0 ohm^{-1} cm.$^{-1}$, or approximately 25,000 greater. Thus, the possibility that our violet compound might be ionic or saltlike, dissociating, for example, into ions,

$$[O_2ClF_2]^+ \text{ and } F^-$$

is excluded.

The stability of the O_2ClF_3 solution in anhydrous HF is much less than that of the pure compound. It shows a remarkable dependence on the partial pressure of O_2. At an O_2 pressure of 1.0 to 1.5 atm. and at 195° K. the concentrated solution can be kept for many hours; when the O_2 pressure is reduced to 50 to 20 mm. of Hg the deep violet solution decolorizes in a few minutes by decomposition to

$$O_2ClF_3 \xrightarrow{\text{HF}} O_2 + ClF_3$$

It is indicated that the easy decomposition is at least partly due to the formation of an intermediate complex:

$$ClF_3 + HF \rightleftharpoons H[ClF_4]$$

which weakens the bonds in the O_2ClF_3 molecule and promotes the liberation of O_2. Although the acidic complex itself is not known, the corresponding salts, such as $Cs[ClF_4]$ and $Rb[ClF_4]$, do exist.

Preparation of O_2ClF_3

Preparation by Direct Addition of Pure O_2F_2 to Pure ClF. In a typical example 1.130 grams of O_2F_2 were vacuum-distilled into a borosilicate glass reaction vessel (Kel-F test tubes may also be used) of about 100-cc. volume, melted, distributed evenly on the walls of the lower half of the reaction vessel by rotation, and frozen at 90° K. The stoichiometric amount (1:1 mole) or 0.880 gram of ClF (measured as a gas) was added in portions of $\simeq$ 100 mg. After each addition the reaction vessel was warmed up to 119° K. (melting point of ClF) and then slowly to 140° K. The violet compound, O_2ClF_3, is rapidly formed, by direct addition:

$$O_2F_2 + ClF \rightarrow O_2ClF_3 \tag{2}$$

while simultaneously the white solid ClF_3 is also formed, coupled with evolution of O_2 and small and varying amounts of F_2.

Assuming that the heat of formation of O_2ClF_3, as well as its heat of decomposition, is about half—i.e., 15 kcal. per mole—of the total heat of Reaction 1, one can readily understand that overheating can readily lead to the decomposition of O_2ClF_3, in line with Equation 3:

$$O_2ClF_3 \rightarrow O_2 + ClF_3 \tag{3}$$

The same overheating can also lead to a simple decomposition of O_2F_2, following Equation 4.

$$O_2F_2 \rightarrow O_2 + F_2 \tag{4}$$

The extent of each reaction can be determined by simple analysis (2, 3, 4) of the gases for O_2 and F_2, since only Reaction 4 leads to elementary fluorine and Reaction 2 takes place without evolution of O_2 or F_2.

After each addition the reaction vessel is again cooled to 90° K., O_2 and F_2 are evacuated (and collected if desired), a fresh portion of ClF is added, and the cycle is repeated.

In this example only negligible traces of F_2 were found, while the amount of O_2 evolved equaled 205.8 cc. (NTP) or 0.294 gram of O_2. Thus, all the oxygen liberated was due only to Reaction 3, corresponding to 56.9 weight % of the O_2F_2 used. The rest, or 43.1 weight %, combined, following Equation 2, with ClF. Thus, the yield was 43.15% of theory.

The over-all material balance is:

Reagents Used	G.	Products Formed	G.
O_2F_2	1.130	O_2ClF_3	0.869 by calculation (see above)
ClF	0.880	O_2	0.294 by gas analysis
Total	2.010	F_2	0.000 by gas analysis
		ClF_3	0.847 by difference
		Total	2.010

After decomposition of O_2ClF_3 the total amount of ClF_3 produced in the preparation equaled 1.493 grams, as determined by direct weighing.

Preparation from O_2F_2 and ClF in Presence of Solvent. The yield of O_2ClF_3 can be substantially increased by carrying out the reaction in the presence of an inert solvent. With perfluoropropane, C_3F_8 (m.p. 90° K., NBP 235° K.) the yield and concentration of O_2ClF_3 were increased to 81.0% of theory, as shown in the following preparation.

O_2F_2 (1.51 grams) and C_3F_8 (15.32 grams) were cooled in a borosilicate glass reaction vessel to 130° K. In a second tube the equivalent amount of ClF (1.17 grams) was dissolved in 13.58 grams of C_3F_8 (at 150° K. over 33 weight % ClF are soluble in it; at 160° K. it mixes homogeneously) and distilled into the reaction vessel. The ClF reacted immediately with the O_2F_2, forming O_2ClF_3, which being practically insoluble in C_3F_8, deposited on the walls of the reaction vessel. In all, 91.0 cc. of O_2 (NTP) were evolved, accompanying the formation of ClF_3, which contaminated the O_2ClF_3 to an extent of 19.0 weight %. Unfortunately, ClF_3 is insoluble in C_3F_8; at present no method is known for separating ClF_3 from O_2ClF_3. The solvent C_3F_8 can be readily pumped off, in a vacuum, preferably at 130° to 140° K.

[Freon 13, $CClF_3$, is a solvent for O_2F_2, but in its presence the thermal stability of O_2ClF_3 is markedly decreased. With Freon 12, CCl_2F_2, as a solvent no violet compound is formed, while with ClO_3F the yield was much smaller than with pure O_2F_2 and ClF.]

Formation of O_2ClF_3 in Reactions of O_2F_2 with Cl_2 and HCl. O_2ClF_3 is also formed if Cl_2 is added to O_2F_2. Here, the first step is the fluorination of Cl_2 to ClF, following the equation:

$$O_2F_2 + Cl_2 \rightarrow O_2 + 2 \; ClF \tag{5}$$

After ClF is formed it reacts, as described above, to form O_2ClF_3.

HCl reacts at 130° to 140° K. with O_2F_2, in accordance with the stoichiometric equation:

$$2 \; O_2F_2 + HCl \rightarrow O_2ClF_3 + HF + O_2 \tag{6}$$

The reaction steps probably first consist in the formation of Cl_2 and then ClF, in line with the equations:

$$O_2F_2 + HCl \rightarrow 2 \; HF + O_2 + Cl_2 \tag{7}$$

and

$$O_2F_2 + Cl_2 \rightarrow 2 \; ClF + O_2 \tag{8}$$

the ClF formed reacting in the usual manner to form O_2ClF_3.

Since the above fluorination reactions of both HCl and Cl_2 are exothermic, the yields of O_2ClF_3 are lower than with ClF as described above. The activation energies, however, may be less, particularly with HCl, and thus the reaction may be initiated at lower temperatures.

At 130° to 140° K. HCl is a solid (m.p. 158.9° K.), but has a vapor pressure of $\simeq$ 10 mm. of Hg at 140° K. Thus, the reaction takes place between gaseous HCl and gaseous or liquid O_2F_2. The violet compound partly deposits on the walls, but also dissolves in liquid O_2F_2. Solutions containing up to 8.5 weight % O_2ClF_3 in O_2F_2 were obtained.

At temperatures above 140° K. the reaction proceeds rapidly, with substantial amounts of O_2ClF_3 decomposing to O_2 and ClF_3.

Formation of O_2ClF_3 Directly from O_2 and ClF_3 under Influence of Ultraviolet Light

When pure liquid ClF_3 is placed in a quartz tube, and in a dry ice cavity— i.e., at a temperature of 195° K.—under a pressure of $\simeq$ 2 atm. of O_2 and irradiated with ultraviolet light, mainly at a wave length of 2537 A., and with an intensity of 7 mw. per sq. cm., a violet compound is produced in a few seconds, probably our O_2ClF_3, in line with the equation:

$$ClF_3 + O_2 \underset{\text{U.V.}}{\rightarrow} O_2ClF_3$$

The color of the ClF_3 solution increased appreciably with time. However, if the O_2 pressure equaled 15 mm. of Hg, no violet compound was formed. (A check experiment with pure ClF_3, in the absence of O_2, also failed to produce any violet compound.)

If ozone, O_3, was used instead of O_2, in the same experiment, no violet compound formed. Some O_3 decomposed, because of the irradiation, as observed from the increase in total pressure. The addition of O_2 to the system did not cause the formation of the violet compound. Evidently the heat of decomposition of ozone is sufficient to cause the decomposition of any violet compound formed.

Reactions of O_2ClF_3

The violet compound is a very strong oxidizer, even at low temperatures. In this respect it is similar to the highly reactive ozone, which, for example, reacts with NH_3 even at 150° K. (1). Usually no chemical reactions take place in a temperature range of 100° to 150° K. with the exception of free radicals or atoms, as has been strikingly demonstrated by H. Broida and his associates at the National Bureau of Standards.

A study was made of the reactions of O_2ClF_3 with NH_3, the hydrocarbons CH_4, C_2H_6, C_2H_4, and C_6H_6, H_2, and H_2O. In most cases fluorine has a preferential affinity for hydrogen and HF is usually formed.

Reaction with NH_3. When gaseous NH_3 is suddenly admitted to a reaction vessel containing O_2ClF_3 at 90° K., reaction takes place with a flash, forming white solids and some nitrogen-containing gases, while the violet color disappears.

If the ammonia is condensed first in the upper part of a reaction tube cooled to 90° K., the reaction proceeds slowly as the vessel is warmed to 150° to 160° K. Ammonia has a vapor pressure of about 1 mm. at 160° K. and reacts slowly as a gas with the solid O_2ClF_3. Under these conditions the reaction proceeds smoothly without any gas evolution, while the violet color disappears and a white solid is formed. Under the same conditions pure solid ClF_3 reacts much more slowly; this is to be expected, since, in any reaction with a fuel, the components formed from O_2ClF_3—i.e., O_2 and ClF_3—are activated by the endothermic heat of formation of O_2ClF_3 (ΔH_{298} assumed to be equal to $+ 15 \pm 10$ kcal. per mole).

Ammonium fluoride and other ammonium salts, HF, HCl, and the oxy-acids of chlorine (either free or as ammonium salts) were identified among the reaction products.

Hydrogen fluoride was identified by vacuum distillation, formation of NaF.HF, and titration. Hydrogen chloride was identified through formation of silver chloride. Ammonia was determined quantitatively by Kjeldahl's method. The oxynitrogen acids or oxychlorine acids were identified qualitatively by Lunge's reagent. Anions of the oxychlorine acids—i.e., chlorite, chlorate, or perchlorate—were identified by reduction with zinc to chloride ion.

In one experiment 0.25 gram of O_2ClF_3 was reacted with about 0.10 gram of ammonia; 52 mg. of NH_3 was found in the reaction product together with about 3 mg. of N_2 (gas). Thus, about one half of the ammonia added formed ammonium salts. (This mixture of ammonium salts and oxidizers is potentially dangerous and can detonate!)

Reactions with Hydrocarbons. WITH CH_4. O_2ClF_3 does not react with an excess of liquid methane at 90° K., or with gaseous methane at a pressure of 100 mm. of Hg at 150° K. During one hour there was neither a decrease in pressure nor a disappearance of the violet color.

WITH C_2H_6. Ethane, in contrast to methane, when admitted to the violet compound at a temperature of 140° K., reacts immediately. The violet color disappears and white solids are formed, but no gas is evolved—i.e., no formation of O_2, F_2, or CO is observed.

Hydrogen fluoride was also identified.

WITH CH_2:CH_2. The reaction vessel containing 1.39 grams of O_2ClF_3 was cooled to 120° K. and ethylene gas was introduced (ethylene has a vapor pressure of about 1.0 mm. of Hg at 120° K.) in portions of about 5 mg. at a rate of about 1 mg. per second. After an interruption of 1 to 2 minutes, new portions were added.

Under those conditions ethylene reacted immediately, causing decolorization of the violet compound and formation of the white solid products, while no measurable gas evolution—i.e., no formation of O_2, F_2, or CO—took place.

On one occasion when ethylene was added at a higher rate, the reaction proceeded with a flame which extinguished itself as soon as the ethylene flow was stopped. A total of 0.179 gram of ethylene was added to 1.3 grams of O_2ClF_3; the temperature of the bath after this addition was slowly raised at the rate of 1° to 15° per minute. No gas evolution was noticed up to 140° K. At 140° K. a violent explosion took place, shattering the reaction vessel and a large part of the reaction system. Evidently, intermediate or partly oxidized products were formed.

In all reactions of O_2ClF_3 with hydrogen-containing substances, HF is the most likely reaction product. Carbonyl fluoride, COF_2, and other intermediate oxyfluorides—for example, oxalyl fluoride, $C_2O_2F_2$—may be formed. In view of the violent explosion which took place, it is also likely that some C-H-containing compounds were present.

Reaction with Hydrogen. During one hour at 90° to 120° K. there was no noticeable reaction between O_2ClF_3 and hydrogen gas at a pressure of 100 mm. of Hg. Any reaction would be characterized by disappearance or change in the violet color or decrease in the pressure of hydrogen.

The nonreactivity of O_2ClF_3 with hydrogen and methane parallels the chemical properties of ozone. Pure (100%) ozone can be mixed at −78° C. and even at room temperature with hydrogen and methane without reaction (7, 8). (The mixture 1.5 CH_4 + 2 O_3, at 804 mm. of Hg, showed at +21° C. a pressure increase of 26 mm. of Hg on standing for 1.0 hour.)

From the present preliminary evidence it is likely that O_2ClF_3 will be more reactive than ozone at low temperatures.

Reaction with Benzene. The violet compound reacts violently with a solution of benzene in HF at 195° K. A few milligrams of C_6H_6, dissolved in HF, were distilled over into a Kel-F reaction vessel containing a 1 to 2% solution of O_2ClF_3 in HF, and frozen on the walls above the O_2ClF_3 solution. The tube was then warmed up to 195° K.; the melting HF began to run down, carrying the C_6H_6. Sparks were observed when the C_6H_6 came into contact with the O_2ClF_3 solution and the violet color disappeared rapidly.

Reaction with Water. To test the reactivity of O_2ClF_3 with H_2O, pulverized ice, cooled to 90° K., was added to the O_2ClF_3 contained in a tube and the tube was slowly warmed. A visible reaction started at about 130° K. with gas evolution and formation of a white solid. Oxygen was liberated and HF and ClOH (or ClO_2H) were formed. The reaction proceeded much faster at higher temperatures.

Conclusions

Further studies of this very interesting compound, as to both its physical properties and structure and its chemical reactivity, are indicated.

Literature Cited

(1) Grosse, A. V., Streng, A. G., Project 7-7968, Research Institute of Temple University, Tech. Note 4 (Aug. 1, 1957); Contract AF18(60)-1475.
(2) Grosse, A. V., Streng, A. G., Kirshenbaum, A. D., *J. Am. Chem. Soc.* **83**, 1004 (1961).
(3) Kirshenbaum, A. D., Grosse, A. V., *Ibid.*, **81**, 1277 (1959).
(4) Kirshenbaum, A. D., Grosse, A. V., Aston, J. G., *Ibid.*, **81**, 6398 (1959).
(5) Riehl, W. A., Perkins, H., Stokes, C. S., Kirshenbaum, A. D., *ARS Journal* **32**, 384–7 (1962).
(6) Streng, A. G., Grosse, A. V., "Addition and Substitution Products of Oxygen Fluorides," 1st and 2nd Annual Reports for Office of Naval Research, Contract Nonr 3085(01), Research Institute of Temple University, Jan. 3, 1961, and Jan. 19, 1962.
(7) Streng, A. G., Grosse, A. V., ADVAN. CHEM. SER., No. 20, 40 (1959).
(8) Streng, A. G., Grosse, A. V., *J. Am. Chem. Soc.* **79**, 3996 (1957).

RECEIVED May 16, 1962. Research sponsored by the Office of Naval Research, Contract Nonr 3085(01).

INDEX